PELI

THE ORIGIN

PHYSICAL SCIENCE · I

EDITED BY

D. L. HURD AND J. J. KIPLING

THE ORIGINS AND GROWTH OF PHYSICAL SCIENCE

I

EDITED BY
D. L. HURD AND J. J. KIPLING

BASED ON
'MOMENTS OF DISCOVERY'
EDITED BY GEORGE SCHWARTZ
AND PHILIP W. BISHOP

*

WITH EIGHT PLATES

PENGUIN BOOKS

Penguin Books Ltd, Harmondsworth, Middlesex
u.s.a.: Penguin Books Inc., 3300 Clipper Mill Road, Baltimore 11, Md
australia: Penguin Books Pty Ltd, 762 Whitehorse Road,
Mitcham, Victoria

—

Moments of Discovery first published in the U.S.A. 1958
The Origins and Growth of Physical Science · 1 first published in Pelican Books 1964

—

Copyright © Basic Books, Inc., 1958, and Penguin Books, 1964

—

Made and printed in Great Britain
by C. Nicholls & Company Ltd
Set in Monotype Baskerville

PUBLISHER'S NOTE

The Origins and Growth of Physical Science · 1
is one of three Pelican volumes, the other
two being *The Origins and Growth of Physical
Science · 2,* and *The Origins and Growth of
Biology* edited by Arthur Rook (Pelicans
A535 and A536), based on *Moments of Discovery,* edited by George Schwartz and Philip
W. Bishop, and published in America by
Basic Books in 1958. The extracts from
scientific writings in this volume are largely
the same as those used in the American
books, but the introductory material has
been extensively rewritten.

CONTENTS

III

THE MECHANISTIC UNIVERSE

IV

THE SCIENCE OF GASES

ACKNOWLEDGEMENTS

Acknowledgements are due to the following for the use of materials from the publications stated: Edward Arnold, *The Elder Pliny's Chapters of Chemical Subjects* (ed. and trans. K. C. Bailey), 1932: Cambridge University Press, Archimedes (trans. T. L. Heath), *Physical Treatises*, 1897, 1912, Aristotle (trans. W. C. Dampier-Whetham and M. D. Whetham), *On the Heavens*, from *Readings in the Literature of Science*, 1924, and also, for the latter, Harper & Brothers, New York, 1959; Columbia University Press, Copernicus (trans. Edward Rosen), *Three Copernican Treatises*, 1934, Evangelista Torricelli (trans. I. H. B. and A. G. H. Spiers), *The Physical Treatises of Pascal*, 1937; J. M. Dent, Eratosthenes, Ptolemy (trans. T. L. Heath), *Greek Astronomy*, 1932, Geber (trans. R. E. Russell, ed. E. J. Holmyard), *The Works of Geber*, 1928; Dover Publications, Agricola (trans. H. C. and L. H. Hoover), *De re metallica*, 1950; Harvard University Press, Robert Boyle (H. F. Magie), *A Sourcebook in Physics*, 1935 (first published by the McGraw-Hill Book Co.); Tycho Brahe (trans. J. H. Walden), Edmund Halley, Johann Kepler (trans. J. H. Walden), Pierre Simon Laplace (H. E. Howarth, trans. H. H. Harte), *A Source Book in Astronomy*, 1929, M. R. Cohen and I. E. Drabkin (Ptolemy), *A Source Book in Greek Science*, 1948 (first published by the McGraw-Hill Book Co.), H. M. Leicester and H. S. Klickstein (Georg Stahl), *A Source Book in Chemistry*, 1952; Northwestern University Press, Galileo Galilei (trans. Henry Crew and A. DeSalvio, *Dialogues Concerning Two New Sciences*, 1914; the Royal Society of Edinburgh, Alembic Club Reprints Nos. 1, 3, 7, 8 (Joseph Black, Henry Cavendish, Joseph Priestley, Carl Wilhelm Scheele); G. Bell & Sons, Carl Wilhelm Scheele (trans. Leonard Dobbin), *The Collected Papers of Carl Wilhelm Scheele*, 1931; University of California Press, Galileo Galilei (trans. Stillman Drake), *Dialogue Concerning Two Chief World Systems*, Isaac Newton (ed. Florian Cajori, trans. Andrew Motte), *Principia Mathematica*, 1934.

Acknowledgements are also due to the Burndy Library for permission to use illustrative material.

Joseph Priestley's *Experiments and Observations on Different Kinds of Air* published London 1775, not (see Plate 7) 1772.

INTRODUCTION:

THE ORIGINS OF PHYSICAL SCIENCE

MOST people in the highly developed countries of the world would probably claim nowadays to know what is meant by science. Not everyone could give a formal definition, but the scope of science is generally recognized and so, to some extent, are the methods by which scientists work. In the past, however, science has not so readily been seen as a subject in its own right; it grew from a number of roots in magic, folklore, primitive technology, religion, and philosophy.

The development of science, the way in which it came to have its present characteristics, can be told as a piece of history by men of our own time. In the two volumes of *The Origins and Growth of Physical Science*, however, it is described by the scientists who themselves contributed to that development and whose ideas shaped its characteristic features. This development has not come about automatically. Of political history, a modern historian (Alan Bullock) has recently emphasized that 'it is men who make history'. This is conspicuously true of the history of science. Each step forward has come from the creative thinking of an individual scientist, or from the cumulative effect of the work of several scientists. In many cases, the things they were thinking about depended on the kind of society they happened to be living in. What they made of their surroundings, however, depended on their individual perception, imagination, and creativity. Scientific theory advances only as fast as human limitations, no less than human genius, permit.

Modern textbooks of science are usually designed to give a clear picture of scientific theories as we now understand them. The more clearly a theory is presented, the more readily it is accepted. Sometimes acceptance of an idea is so ready that a modern reader would describe it as being 'obvious'. But when a scientist first puts forward a new idea, it has not until then been obvious even to the ablest of his contemporaries, or they would have advanced it themselves. It has not been obvious to him until he has expended a great deal of thought on it, and what he then produces may be only the beginning of an idea which has to be developed by others before it comes to have the significance attributed to it by later generations. Like a work of art, a scientific theory has to be fashioned as a new venture into the unknown; unlike any single work of art, however, it can be enlarged and improved by those who follow its creator.

These two volumes are an attempt to show how individual men (and, in one case, a woman) were thinking as they put forward ideas which have become landmarks in the history of the two main physical sciences. The quotations have been chosen to illustrate various periods from the early Greeks up to the end of the nineteenth century. The selection is to some extent arbitrary, and many well-known names are not represented. The aim has been to illustrate some of the more important developments in physical science, not to attempt the impossible task of providing a complete record. If, as is hoped, the reader is stimulated to inquire about some of the scientists who have not been included, he will find that many of them are cited in the source-books listed in the Acknowledgements.

*

It is only in comparatively recent times that science has become differentiated into the several subjects of mathematics, physics, chemistry, botany, zoology, geology, and so on which we know today. It is a matter of convenience that the scope of this volume is limited to the physical sciences; a better appreciation of early science is obtained by reading these two volumes in conjunction with the early sections of the companion volume on biology (*The Origins and Growth of Biology*).

The differentiation of chemistry from physics only became marked in the late eighteenth and early nineteenth centuries, as is shown in Volume 2. Volume 1 deals with physical science largely undifferentiated. Also, it is concerned with science and not technology. This again is a somewhat arbitrary distinction. Even today, when convenience has accustomed us to the terms pure and applied science, the boundaries between them are far from sharp. In the past they were often less deliberately drawn. The Charters of the Royal Society (1662 and 1663) specifically refer to 'further promoting by the authority of experiments the sciences of natural things *and of useful arts*'.

In the earliest records of man, technology is more evident than science, if the term 'technology' can be used in its widest sense. In twentieth-century industrial societies it is sometimes used synonymously with 'applied science', implying that scientific developments must precede any advance in industry or other 'useful arts'. Although much present-day industrial practice has developed from advances in the pure sciences, it is often overlooked that many phenomena can be usefully exploited before they are completely understood scientifically. The curative properties of penicillin were used in medicine, for example, before the chemical structure of the drug or its mode of action had been worked out. (More recently the scientific investigation of its chemical structure has paved the way for further technological progress, as so often happens.) Similarly lack of knowledge of the physics and chemistry of cotton, wool, and silk did not prevent the development of textile technology. The science of textiles which has followed has undoubtedly led to further technological progress in the use of these materials.

George Sarton, the American historian of science, has emphasized that the technical progress made by early man was concerned first with survival, and later with making life less burdensome and less hazardous. Man invented tools not only for hunting animals, but also for scraping the skins free of flesh so that they could be fashioned into clothing, to protect him from cold, rain, and excessive heat. Weaving fibres proved a better method of making garments. Early tools were made from stone or bones, but from the use of fire, perhaps for cooking, came the discovery and then the exploitation of metals. Shelter could also be provided by building, and this required the transport of heavy loads, an operation made possible by the invention of the lever, the pulley, and the wheel.

We should see, today, in these aspects of technical progress, plenty of material for scientific investigation. The records show that in the early civilizations, men were already exercising that curiosity about their surroundings which is one essential characteristic of science at all stages of its history. These records give only a partial view of the genesis of science. They mainly relate to the civilizations which influenced the present Western world, on which much more effort has been spent than in exploring more remote civilizations such as the Chinese.

The first steps were to observe regularities in man's environment. From the clay tablets of Babylonia and the papyri of Egypt it is clear that the movements of the sun and planets were seen to be regular and that they could be associated with the succession of the seasons of seed-time and harvest. The Phoenician mariners recognized that the regularity of the stars could be used in navigating the Mediterranean and even the Atlantic when they voyaged to Cornwall for tin. The Egyptian pyramids show that the early priests found ways of using the plumb-line, of constructing right angles, and of shaping stone with a mason's square.

A coherent written record begins with the Greeks, from whose writings our first extracts are taken. It shows a further development of the scientific process. For example, from the particular rules of practical measurement, which had been evolved in Egypt, the Ionian Colony produced the abstract generalizations of deductive geometry. Here is a science, which, although based on observations, is not primarily experimental. Deliberate experimentation as we now know it was not established, and with a scarcity of facts, science could strictly only be deductive; the time for induction came later.

The Greeks, however, had such an intense speculative interest in the nature of the cosmos that they jumped one stage ahead of induction. They would create, imaginatively, a conception of the universe implying certain general laws and then consider whether these laws might assist in the interpretation of the few available observations. The idea that all matter is composed of four 'elements' – earth, air, fire, and water – is a case in point. Plato was much concerned to discover whether observations conformed with a pre-conceived view of order, harmony, and beauty in the universe.

This method was not universally followed. Aristotle used the experimental technique of dissection to extend the range of his observation of animals, and produced conclusions which gave him great authority. (He was, however, less experimentally-minded in his approach to physics.) In the Middle Ages, unfortunately, more attention was paid to his conclusions than to the experimental methods by which he arrived at them.

The succeeding Roman civilization made use of Greek knowledge in farming, architecture, and engineering, in building roads, aqueducts, and stadia. By comparison with these achievements, however, the Romans added little to theoretical science, which was scarcely a live activity when their Empire declined in the fourth century A.D. Without the challenge of continued scientific searching, the tradition of Greek thought was incorporated extensively into early Christian theology and no major scientific advance was made in Europe for a period of many centuries.

Discovery was kept alive during this period by the Arabs and ultimately a knowledge of their culture filtered back into Europe, largely through Spain. Scholars then became familiar with the original Greek texts, especially those of Aristotle, which Thomas Aquinas in the thirteenth century A.D. sought to reconcile with Christian teaching in the *Summa theologiae*. His scholasticism was rational, in holding that human reason could give a description of the universe. In this sense it provided a basis for further scientific development, which is grounded on the assumption that nature is intelligible. Scholasticism, however, was ultimately based on authority, that of the Church, whereas science ultimately depends on the experience of observation and experiment.

One of the first to emphasize the need for experiment was Roger Bacon in the thirteenth century, though he had only limited opportunity to carry his principles into practice. He championed experience against four 'obstacles in grasping truth' – unworthy authority, custom, prejudice, and 'concealment of our own ignorance accompanied by ostentatious display of our knowledge'. From the point of view of science, these were followed by more substantial changes in the Renaissance of the second half of the fifteenth and the early sixteenth century. Bacon's ideas, though important later, were probably less effective at the time than the successive attacks on Scholasticism of philosophers such as Duns Scotus, William of Occam (or Ockham), and Cardinal Nicholas of Cusa in the fourteenth and fifteenth centuries.

Two factors seem to have stimulated the change in attitude. The capture of Constantinople by the Turks in 1453 led to the migration of scholars westwards with new manuscripts. Introduction to these encouraged the search for other collections hidden in monasteries for centuries. Moreover, the world suddenly became a larger place as Columbus discovered the New World (1492), Sebastian Cabot discovered Salvador in 1497, Vasco da Gama found the sea route to India (1497), and Magellan sailed round the world (1519).

A revolt against ecclesiastical authority was seen both in the development of science in which observations were no longer limited to supporting the doctrines of the Church, and in the growth of Protestantism seeking authority for its doctrines elsewhere than in the traditions of the Roman Catholic Church.

New theories of the Universe put forward by Copernicus and Kepler revived the scientific practice of reviewing previous thought if it no longer seemed entirely adequate.

Further discoveries, not only of new lands on the earth, but through Galileo's telescope, of new heavenly bodies, provided the basis for continuing the revival of theoretical discussion.

Francis Bacon, two and a half centuries later than Roger Bacon, lived in an age richer in observations and in the possibilities of accumulating them. In 1620 he described in *Novum Organum* his method of induction, that is of seeking by experiment all available facts, organizing the results in a systematic way, and observing the connexion between them so as to derive a general law. This was simultaneously part of the attack on scholasticism and the expounding of a further contribution to scientific method. Bacon also asserted the necessity of using instruments to extend the range of experimental observations. The production of such instruments as the telescope and the microscope during this period is itself evidence of a more deliberate attitude to experimentation.

The relative importance of induction and deduction in science gradually became established, Descartes advocating the value of the doubting mind (an important complement to curiosity in initiating new experiments) and Newton carefully avoiding metaphysical hypotheses about primary causes.

This volume takes us through the period dominated by Newton as far as the end of the eighteenth century. By that time scientific leadership was showing a pronounced drift from the Mediterranean to more northerly parts of Europe, to countries which had been enriched by the expansion of foreign trade and to some extent, as a modern historian of science (Stephen Mason) points out, to those in which the Protestant Reformation had had its strongest influence. In these trading countries it became very evident once more that science could influence commerce as well as philosophy; this is one of the themes of the Industrial Revolution which implicitly forms a background to much of the science described in Volume 2.

In scientific method the abundance of observations made

in the course of deliberate experimenting called forth further reflection, though conclusions came less mechanically than Francis Bacon implied. So many observations were made that, a little less than a century ago, Poincaré was writing of a 'hierarchy of facts' among which scientists have to choose. Once sufficient facts have been accumulated to establish a particular rule, 'the facts in full conformity with it are ere long without interest, since they no longer teach us anything new. It is then the exception which becomes important.' 'The more we can enlarge the number of anomalous facts and consequences the better it will be for the subject,' wrote Faraday, 'for they can only remain anomalies to us while we continue in error.'

The vast increase in the amount of observation at our disposal has not only allowed the nature of scientific method to develop, it has also changed the scientist's expectations. Periodically individuals foresaw the times when, after further experimenting, there would be a complete picture of the Universe. That dream has now been abandoned. In the twentieth century the scientist sees himself as a practical man with practical, that is, limited aims. 'He does not seek the ultimate but the proximate', in the words of G. N. Lewis. 'On the whole, he is satisfied with his work, for while science may never be wholly right, it certainly is never wholly wrong; and it seems to be improving from decade to decade.'

I

THE BEGINNINGS OF THE SCIENTIFIC APPROACH

IT is tempting to evaluate the importance of scientific inquiry in any society by reference to the scope and richness of the practical technology to which it has given rise. Certainly it would be short-sighted to ignore this feature of scientific activity. At the same time we must recognize that there are other motives which play an equally important part in shaping the outlook of the practising scientist, and give to science its special status. Foremost amongst these we recognize an urgency and passion which springs from a boundless curiosity, a spirit of inquiry which provides its own authority and satisfactions.

In searching the records of human activity for the earliest evidence of what we term the scientific approach we should, perhaps, not only note the gradual achievement of rudimentary practical skills, but also consider the part played in man's increasing mastery over his environment by patterns of thought which show the growth of speculative inquiry. Ritual and magic, primitive religions, crude as they seem to us today, surely directed attention away from the narrow confines of man's immediate environment and towards an appreciation of the forms and patterns of the world of his comprehension.

With the growth of Greek civilization we reach a stage at which we clearly recognize preoccupations and attitudes which we share today. It would be wrong to discount the achievements of earlier civilizations, but a wealth of documentation has revealed to us a picture of Greek thought and behaviour that is not only of interest to the historian, but which is the source of modes of thought surviving to the present day, and it is from the Greeks that our first extracts are taken.

In the discussion of Greek thought it is very difficult to draw a sharp distinction between science and philosophy. Yet there is no lack of achievement which we should unhesitatingly call scientific. As a good example we might point to the prediction, by Thales (c.640–546 B.C.), of the eclipse of the sun in 585 B.C. Such an achievement clearly indicates the comparative sophistication that scientific inquiry had reached, and points to the part played by earlier civilizations.

Pythagoras (582–507 B.C.) founded a brotherhood in Southern Italy whose principal concern was the discovery of harmonies and symmetries in the physical world, and their expression as numerical ratios. Much of their work was surrounded in mysticism, but there were contributions to mathematics and physics of undoubted importance. The influence of Pythagoras is to be found in the work of many Greek thinkers, and much cosmological speculation of later centuries shows a preoccupation with geometrical shapes and patterns strongly reminiscent of the Pythagorean approach to science.

This is no place to attempt to assess the enormous importance of such great philosophers as Socrates (470–399 B.C.) and Plato (427–347 B.C.). Their influence on the development of human thought has been immense, and while neither was a scientist in the accepted sense of the word, speculative and analytical modes of thought in all fields show something of the stamp of their achievement.

A philosopher of comparable stature, and one whose contribution to science was more direct, was Aristotle, from whose works the first extract is taken. A student of Plato in his early life, Aristotle developed a wide range of interests, which carried him beyond the bounds of pure philosophy. Two of his works are of special interest to the history of science, *Physics* and *On The Heavens*, and it is from the latter that the extract comes. What gives such interest to Aristotle's views, on cosmology as on many other topics, is the enormous influence he exerted on later thought. Reverence for the authority of Aristotle was to play a part in the survival of Greek thought throughout the Dark Ages that were to follow, and yet, such was the degree of reverence in which he was held, that his influence had a stultifying effect on creative thought. The freeing of scientific thought from its Aristotelean bonds was to prove an immensely difficult task for scientists over many hundreds of years.

We come much closer to the spirit of modern science in the work of Archimedes. Both as scientist and mathematician his great genius played a vital role in the establishment of the physical sciences and much of his work shows an appreciation of scientific method that is characteristic of the more highly developed approach of later centuries. Of the growing bond between mathematics and natural philosophy the extract from Eratosthenes provides an interesting example.

The final extract in this section reveals a fascinating link between Greek thought on the nature of matter and that which prevails today. The atomic picture of matter on which modern physics is based is a theory of great subtlety and precision, while the atomic picture of matter conveyed by Lucretius is crude by comparison. And yet for there to be such similarities at all over a period of two thousand years is a startling comment on the continuity of speculation in man's growing understanding of the world about him.

Lacking the accepted aims and methods of scientific inquiry which guide the scientist today, Greek science presents a picture of scattered contributions, often of great brilliance, of which but few aspects can be illustrated here. But from this scene there emerges with growing clarity the beginnings of the scientific outlook which has played so monumental a part in the shaping of the modern world.

———

ARISTOTLE
384–322 B.C.

ON COSMOLOGY

OF Aristotle's position as one of the very greatest of Greek thinkers there can be no doubt, and yet his place in the history of science is one of paradox. As has already been mentioned in the Introduction, the assessment of Aristotle's achievement, however favourable when viewed against the work of his predecessors, must take into account the crippling influence of his authority on later thought. In regard to his contribution towards the founding of an acceptable approach to the investigation of physical problems, a similar situation is to be found. In his biological studies he can be seen as a pioneer of the scientific method in that he stressed the importance of careful observation. And yet, in his studies in physics, Aristotle adopted an approach in which speculation reigned unchallenged and observation played a negligible role.

At the age of seventeen Aristotle became a pupil of Plato at the Academy in Athens, and remained there for twenty years, until the death of his teacher. This early training in the idealistic philosophy of the Platonic school is evident in much of Aristotle's later thought, and to this influence one may trace the source of those conflicting trends which characterize his scientific thinking. The insistence on observation, which played so important a part in Aristotle's biological work, was in sharp conflict with the teachings of Plato.

In formulating his conception of the nature of matter Aristotle rejected the atomic ideas of Democritus in favour of an older tradition in which matter was compounded of four 'elements' – earth, water, air, and fire. It was a scheme which provided attractive material for philosophical speculation, but the absence of any appeal to careful observation prevented a critical appraisal of the theory in scientific terms.

27

In his cosmological writings, from which the present extract is taken, we find once more the powerful influence of philosophical traditions. The heavens are perfectly spherical, and the stars and planets move in circular orbits about the earth. The heavenly bodies are composed of a fifth 'element', and not of the materials from which the earth is formed. The divine nature of the heavens is contrasted with the gross and imperfect nature of earthly things. Not only do such theories lack observational support, but in pointing such a contrast between the heavens and the earth, the divine and eternal nature of the first and the ephemeral and corruptible nature of the second, Aristotle goes far towards discouraging the use of observation in the study of the stars and planets. To the medieval Churchmen, whose picture of the universe was based on Aristotle's ideas, the astronomer's attempt to probe and question the divine order of the heavens must have appeared as sacrilege. Not until the time of Galileo was the authority of science sufficiently strong to challenge, and defeat, the Aristotelian conception of the universe.

The reading that follows is taken from Aristotle's cosmological work *On The Heavens*, and appears in *Readings in the Literature of Science*, by W. C. Dampier and M. Dampier (Cambridge University Press). The translation is based on that of Thomas Taylor (1807).

―――――――

All men believe that there are gods, and all men, both barbarians and Greeks, assign the highest place in heaven to the divine nature. ... For, according to tradition, in the whole of past time no change has taken place either in the heaven as a whole or in any of its parts. Moreover, the name by which we call it appears to have been handed down in succession from the ancients, who held the same opinion about its divine nature which lasts to the present time.

For such reasons, then, we believe that the heaven was neither created nor is it corruptible, but that it is one and everlasting, unchanged through infinite time. Hence we may well persuade ourselves that ancient assertions, especially those of our own ancestors, are true, and see that one kind of motion is immortal and divine, having no end, but being itself the end of other motions. Now motion in a circle is perfect, having neither beginning nor end, nor ceasing in infinite time.

As the ancients attributed heaven and the space above it to the gods, so our reasoning shows that it is incorruptible and uncreated and untouched by mortal troubles. No force is needed to keep the heaven moving, or to prevent it moving in another manner; . . . nor need we suppose that its stability depends on its support by a certain giant Atlas, as in the ancient fable: as though forsooth all bodies on high possessed gravity and an earthly nature. Not thus has it been preserved for so long, nor yet, as Empedocles asserts, by whirling round faster than its natural motion downwards. Nor is it reasonable to think that it remains unchanged by the compulsion of a soul, untiring and sleepless, unlike the soul of mortal animals, for it would need the fate of some Ixion (bound for ever to a fiery wheel) to keep it in motion. . . .

The heaven, moreover, must be a sphere, for this is the only form worthy of its essence, as it holds the first place in nature. . . . Every plane figure is contained by straight lines or by a circumference. The right-lined figure is bounded by many lines, but the circle by but one. But as the one is prior to the many and the simple to the composite, so the circle is the first of plane figures. . . . Again, to a straight line an addition can always be made, but to a circular line never. Thus once more the line which traces a circle is perfect. Hence if the perfect is prior to the imperfect, the circle again will be the first of figures. In like manner also the sphere will be the first of solids; for this alone is contained by one superficies, while flat-sided figures are contained by many. As a circle is in planes, so is a sphere in solids. . . .

Further still, since it seems clear and we assume that the universe revolves in a circle, and since beyond the uttermost sky is neither body nor space nor vacuum, once more it

follows that the universe is spherical. For, if it were rectilinear, there must be space beyond it: a rectilinear body as it
revolves will never occupy the same place: where it formerly
was it is not now, and where it is not now it will be again,
because the corners project. . . .

It remains to discuss the earth – where it is situated,
whether it is at rest or moves, and what is its form. With
regard to its position, all philosophers have not the same
opinion. Most of those who assert that the heaven is finite
say that the earth lies at the centre, while those in Italy
who are called Pythagoreans hold the contrary. For they
say that at the centre of the universe is fire, and that the
earth being one of the stars moves in a circle about that
centre and thus causes day and night. They also invent
opposite to our earth another earth, which they call counter-
earth: not investigating theories and causes to explain the
facts, but adjusting the facts to fit certain opinions and
theories of their own. To many others also it seems that a
central place should not be assigned to the earth for reasons
not based on facts but on opinions. For they fancy that the
most honourable place belongs to the most honourable
nature: that fire is more honourable than earth and the
boundaries of a space than the region within. But the circumference and the centre they say are boundaries. So that,
thus reasoning, they think not the earth but fire holds place
in the centre of the sphere. Further still, the Pythagoreans
hold that the chief place should be best guarded, and call the
centre the altar of Zeus, and thus again assign this place to
fire, as if the centre of a mathematical figure and the middle
of a thing or the natural centre were of the same kind. . . .
Such as assert that the earth is not situated in the middle of
the universe are of opinion that it and the counter-earth also
move round the centre in a circle. And to some it appears
that many such bodies may move round the centre though
invisible to us by the intervention of the earth. Hence they
say there are more eclipses of the moon than of the sun, for
each of the moving bodies, and not the earth only, can
obstruct the light of the moon . . . But some say that the

earth, being situated in the centre, rolls round the pole which is extended through the universe, as it is written in the *Timaeus*.

In a similar way there is doubt about the shape of the earth. To some it seems to be spherical, but to others flat, in the form of a drum. To support this opinion they urge that, when the sun rises and sets, he appears to make a straight and not a circular occultation, as should be if the earth were spherical. These men do not realize the distance of the sun from the earth and the magnitude of the circumference, nor do they consider that, when seen cutting a small circle, a part of the large circle appears at a distance as a straight line. Because of this appearance, therefore, they ought not to deny that the earth is round. ... It is indeed irrational not to wonder how it is that a small fragment of earth if dropt from a high place moves downward and a larger fragment more swiftly downward, while the whole earth does not tend downward and its great bulk is at rest. For if, while fragments of earth are falling, some one could take away the whole earth before they reached it, they would nevertheless move downward if nothing opposed them. Hence this question is of general philosophic interest, its consequences seeming no less difficult than the problem. For some on this account hold that the part of the earth below us must be infinite, as Xenophanes of Colophon says, rooted to infinity. ... Hence the rebuke of Empedocles when he writes:

> The boundless depths of earth, the aether vast,
> In vain the tongues of multitudes extol
> Who see but little of the mighty all.

But others say the earth floats upon water. This view we consider the most ancient: it is ascribed to Thales the Milesian. It regards the earth as upheld in its place because it floats like a piece of wood or anything else of the same kind. ... But water itself cannot remain suspended on high, but must be upheld in its turn by something. Further, as air is lighter than water, so water is lighter than earth. How then can they fancy that what is lighter lies below and supports what is heavier? Again, were the whole earth able to float upon water, this would also be the case with its fragments. But this seems not so, for any piece of earth sinks to the bottom of water, and larger fragments sink more swiftly.

ARCHIMEDES
287–212 B.C.

THE LAW OF THE LEVER IS
DEVELOPED AND SOME APPLICATIONS
OF THIS PRINCIPLE ARE SET FORTH

THERE was an implicit conflict between Plato and Aristotle
that derived from the deductive methods of the one and the
experimental, or inductive, methods of the other. In Archimedes we find a synthesis. Combining mathematics with
experiment, he was able to set up hypotheses with respect to
limited aspects of the problem, to make deductions there-
from, and, finally, to test the results against further observation. As he was clearly a pioneer in the modern scientific
method, so he was a leader in applying science to contemporary problems. His life is surrounded with legend; but
much of it accords with the capacity of this great mathematician and inventor.

Archimedes was born and died in Syracuse, on the island
of Sicily. He may have been a relative of its king, Hiero. He
may have studied in Alexandria; if not, he had close contacts
with the scholars there and made use of its publishing faci-
lities. Many of his practical discoveries are associated with
King Hiero; for him he invented the water screw, which,
turning in a tightly fitting cylinder, would raise water from
the hold of a ship or, as in Egypt, from the river Nile.

When Hiero suspected that his craftsmen had stolen some
of the gold intended for his crown and had alloyed the remainder with silver in order to cover the theft, he called on
Archimedes to examine the case. The incident supposedly
led to the observations from which Archimedes evolved the
concept of relative density of bodies. It is said that Archimedes noticed, when he entered his bath, that he displaced
a volume of water equal to that of his own body. From this
he went on to show, by experiment, that when a body is

immersed in a liquid, its weight is diminished by the weight of the water displaced; when a body floats, its weight is equal to the weight of the liquid displaced. Archimedes was able to exonerate the craftsmen from Hiero's charge and went on to demonstrate some general principles, which he deducted mathematically, as to the nature of fluids. From these came laws of hydrostatics and the means of making hydrometers, used today for measuring the density of liquids. Archimedes's skills were also applied to the arts of war; for example, he invented a catapult which was used in defending Syracuse for three years against the besieging Romans. When the city was finally stormed, Archimedes was slain by a soldier who came upon him while he was studying a geometrical problem he had drawn in the sand.

From Archimedes's original work in mathematics, we obtained our everyday value of the term π for determining the area of a circle, πr^2. His work on the measurement of the sphere and the cylinder was so significant to his contemporaries that these figures were cut into his tombstone.

The reading included here is from his *Physical Treatises* (from the translation by T. L. Heath, published by the Cambridge University Press). It shows his analysis of the equilibrium of planes and the centre of gravity, from which he established the law of the lever. Here we see Archimedes as an inventor, demonstrating that geometry had a practical application. In this he is to be contrasted with his predecessor, Euclid, who contented himself with summarizing the accumulated knowledge of geometry.

¶ *On the Equilibrium of Planes or the Centres of Gravity of Planes*

I postulate the following:

1. Equal weights at equal distances are in equilibrium, and equal weights at unequal distances are not in equilibrium but incline towards the weight which is at the greater distance.

2. If, when weights at certain distances are in equilibrium, something be added to one of the weights, they are not in equilibrium but incline towards that weight to which the addition was made.

3. Similarly, if anything be taken away from one of the weights, they are not in equilibrium but incline towards the weight from which nothing was taken.

4. When equal and similar plane figures coincide if applied to one another, their centres of gravity similarly coincide.

5. In figures which are unequal but similar the centres of gravity will be similarly situated. By points similarly situated in relation to similar figures I mean points such that, if straight lines be drawn from them to the equal angles, they make equal angles with the corresponding sides.

6. If magnitudes at certain distances be in equilibrium, (other) magnitudes equal to them will also be in equilibrium at the same distances.

7. In any figure whose perimeter is concave in (one and) the same direction the centre of gravity must be within the figure.

§ PROPOSITION 1 *Weights which balance at equal distances are equal.*

For, if they are unequal, take away from the greater the difference between the two. The remainders will then not balance [*Post. 3*]; which is absurd.

Therefore the weights cannot be unequal.

§ PROPOSITION 2 *Unequal weights at equal distances will not balance but will incline towards the greater weight.*

For take away from the greater the difference between the two. The equal remainders will therefore balance [*Post. 1*]. Hence, if we add the difference again, the weights will not balance but incline towards the greater [*Post. 2*].

§ PROPOSITION 3 *Unequal weights will balance at unequal distances, the greater weight being at the lesser distance.*

Let A, B be two unequal weights (of which A is the greater) balancing about C at distances AC, BC respectively.

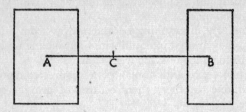

Then shall AC be less than BC. For, if not, take away from A the weight $(A - B)$. The remainders will then incline towards B [*Post. 3*]. But this is impossible, for (1) if $AC = CB$, the equal remainders will balance, or (2) if $AC > CB$, they will incline towards A at the greater distance [*Post. 1*].

Hence $AC < CB$.

Conversely, if the weights balance, and $AC < CB$, then $A > B$.

§ PROPOSITION 4 *If two equal weights have not the same centre of gravity, the centre of gravity of both taken together is at the middle point of the line joining their centres of gravity.*

§ PROPOSITION 5 *If three equal magnitudes have their centres of gravity on a straight line at equal distances, the centre of gravity of the system will coincide with that of the middle magnitude.* [This follows immediately from Prop. 4.]

Cor. 1. *The same is true of any odd number of magnitudes if those which are at equal distances from the middle one are equal, while the distances between their centres of gravity are equal.*

Cor. 2. *If there be an even number of magnitudes with their centres of gravity situated at equal distances on one straight line, and if the two middle ones be equal, while those which are equidistant from them (on each side) are equal respectively, the centre of gravity of the system is the middle point of the line joining the centres of gravity of the two middle ones.*

§ PROPOSITION 6, 7 *Two magnitudes, whether commensurable*

[Prop. 6] *or incommensurable* [Prop. 7], *balance at distances reciprocally proportional to the magnitudes.*

I. Suppose the magnitudes A, B to be commensurable, and the points A, B to be their centres of gravity. Let DE be a straight line so divided at C that.

$$A : B = DC : CE.$$

We have then to prove that, if A be placed at E and B at D, C is the centre of gravity of the two taken together.

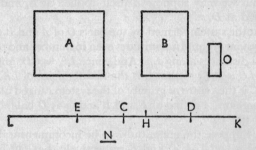

Since A, B are commensurable, so are DC, CE. Let N be a common measure of DC, CE. Make DH, DK each equal to CE, and EL (on CE produced) equal to CD. Then $EH = CD$, since $DH = CE$. Therefore LH is bisected at E, as HK is bisected at D.

Thus LH, HK must each contain N an even number of times.

Take a magnitude O such that O is contained as many times in A as N is contained in LH, whence

$$A : O = LH : N.$$

But

$$B : A = CE : DC$$
$$= HK : LH.$$

Hence, *ex aequali*, $B : O = HK : N$, or O is contained in B as many times as N is contained in HK.

Thus O is a common measure of A, B.

Divide LH, HK into parts each equal to N, and A, B into parts each equal to O. The parts of A will therefore be equal in number to those of LH, and the parts of B equal in number to those of HK. Place one of the parts of A at the middle point of each of the parts N of LH, and one of the parts of B at the middle point of each of the parts N of HK.

Then the centre of gravity of the parts of A placed at equal distances on LH will be at E, the middle point of LH [Prop. 5, Cor. 2], and the centre of gravity of the parts of B placed at equal distances along HK will be at D, the middle point of HK.

Thus we may suppose A itself applied at E, and B itself applied at D.

But the system formed by the parts O of A and B together is a system of equal magnitudes even in number and placed at equal distances along LK. And, since $LE = CD$, and $EC = DK$, $LC = CK$, so that C is the middle point of LK. Therefore C is the centre of gravity of the system ranged along LK.

Therefore A acting at E and B acting at D balance about the point C.

II. Suppose the magnitudes to be incommensurable, and let them be $(A + a)$ and B respectively. Let DE be a line divided at C so that

$$(A + a) : B = DC : CE.$$

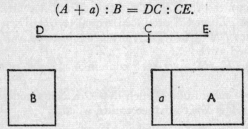

Then, if $(A + a)$ placed at E and B placed at D do not balance about C, $(A + a)$ is either too great to balance B, or not great enough.

Suppose, if possible, that $(A + a)$ is too great to balance B. Take from $(A + a)$ a magnitude a smaller than the deduction which would make the remainder balance B, but such that the remainder A and the magnitude B are commensurable.

Then, since A, B are commensurable, and
$$A : B < DC : CE,$$
A and B will not balance [Prop. 6], but D will be depressed.

But this is impossible, since the deduction a was an insufficient deduction from $(A + a)$ to produce equilibrium, so that E was still depressed.

Therefore $(A + a)$ is not too great to balance B; and similarly it may be proved that B is not too great to balance $(A + a)$.

Hence $(A + a)$, B taken together have their centre of gravity at C.

§ PROPOSITION 8 *If AB be a magnitude whose centre of gravity is C, and AD a part of it whose centre of gravity is F, then the centre of gravity of the remaining part will be a point G on FC produced such that*
$$GC : CF = (AD) : (DE).$$

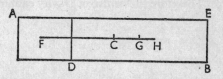

For, if the centre of gravity of the remainder (DE) be not G, let it be a point H. Then an absurdity follows at once from Props. 6, 7.

§ PROPOSITION 9 *The centre of gravity of any parallelogram lies on the straight line joining the middle points of opposite sides.*

Let $ABCD$ be a parallelogram, and let EF join the middle points of the opposite sides AD, BC.

If the centre of gravity does not lie on EF, suppose it to be H, and draw HK parallel to AD or BC meeting EF in K.

Then it is possible, by bisecting ED, then bisecting the halves, and so on continually, to arrive at a length EL less than KH. Divide both AE and ED into parts each equal to EL, and through the points of division draw parallels to AB or CD.

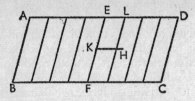

We have then a number of equal and similar parallelograms, and, if any one be applied to any other, their centres of gravity coincide [*Post.* 4]. Thus we have an even number of equal magnitudes whose centres of gravity lie at equal distances along a straight line. Hence the centre of gravity of the whole parallelogram will lie on the line joining the centres of gravity of the two middle parallelograms [Prop. 5, Cor. 2].

But this is impossible, for *H* is outside the middle parallelograms. Therefore the centre of gravity cannot but lie on *EF*.

ERATOSTHENES

c. 275–195 B.C.

A METHOD IS DESCRIBED FOR MEASURING
THE CIRCUMFERENCE OF THE EARTH

DURING the third century B.C. the Egyptian city of
Alexandria, founded by Alexander the Great, became one of
the most important centres of Greek thought. Favourably
placed for commerce, and separated from the Greek main-
land where the Hellenistic culture was beginning to break
up under the strain of political problems, the city attracted
many of the leading thinkers of the time. The librarian
appointed in the year 235 B.C. was Eratosthenes, who
proved to be the first great geographer and the founder of
the science of geography. He made maps, conceived the
idea of projections (by means of which the map surface on a
globe may be presented on a plane surface), and compiled a
general treatise on geography. He is best known for his
highly successful attempt to measure the circumference of
the globe, which is described in the reading that follows.
This comes not from his own account, which has disappeared, but from that of a Greek astronomer, Cleomedes,
writing a hundred years or so later.

It should be noted that Eratosthenes exposed himself to
error by making two basic assumptions: first, that Alexandria and Syene were on the same meridian, and second, that
Syene was on the Tropic of Cancer. He was slightly incorrect in both assumptions; but this does not invalidate the
essential accuracy of his discovery that the angle between
Alexandria and Syene, as measured by the angle of the noon
sun on midsummer day, was exactly one-fiftieth of the 360°
circle. We do not know the modern equivalent of Eratosthenes's unit of linear measurement, the *stade*. If, as
George Sarton says, it is ·157 miles, Eratosthenes measured
the circumference of the earth as 24,662 miles, with a

corresponding diameter of 7,850 miles, or only fifty miles less than the actual diameter at the poles. The technique of measurement depended on two other propositions, remarkable for the period when they were made: that the earth was a sphere and that the rays of the sun, when they strike the earth, are, for all practical purposes, parallel.

Eratosthenes is said to have relied mostly on data in books for his studies, and this often led him to inaccurate conclusions. His reputation seems to be justified, however, by the conclusions he reached when he had accurate data with which to work.

The reading is from the T. L. Heath translation from Cleomedes, in *Greek Astronomy*, published by Dent (1932).

¶ *The Measurement of the Circumference of the Earth*

About the size of the earth the physicists, or natural philosophers, have held different views, but those of Posidonius and Eratosthenes are preferable to the rest. The latter shows the size of the earth by a geometrical method; the method of Posidonius is simpler. Both lay down certain hypotheses, and, by successive inferences from the hypotheses, arrive at their demonstrations.

*

The method of Eratosthenes depends on a geometrical argument and gives the impression of being slightly more difficult to follow. But his statement will be made clear if we premise the following. Let us suppose, in this case too, first, that Syene and Alexandria lie under the same meridian circle; secondly, that the distance between the two cities is 5,000 stades; and thirdly, that the rays sent down from different parts of the sun on different parts of the earth are parallel; for this is the hypothesis on which geometers proceed. Fourthly, let us assume that, as proved by the geometers, straight lines falling on parallel straight lines make the alternate angles equal, and fifthly, that the arcs standing on [i.e. subtended by] equal angles are similar that is, have the same proportion and the same ratio to their proper circles – this, too, being a fact proved by the geometers. Whenever, therefore, arcs of circles stand on equal angles, if any one of these is [say] one-tenth of its proper circle, all the other arcs will be tenth parts of their proper circles.

Anyone who has grasped these facts will have no difficulty in understanding the method of Eratosthenes, which is this. Syene and Alexandria lie, he says, under the same meridian circle. Since meridian circles are great circles in the universe, the circles of the earth which lie under them are necessarily also great circles. Thus, of whatever size this method shows the circle on the earth passing through Syene and Alexandria to be, this will be the size of the great circle of the earth. Now Eratosthenes asserts, and it is the fact, that Syene lies under the summer tropic. Whenever, therefore, the sun, being in the Crab at the summer solstice, is exactly in the middle of the heaven, the gnomons [pointers] of sundials necessarily throw no shadows, the position of the sun above them being exactly vertical; and it is said that this is true throughout a space three hundred stades in diameter. But in Alexandria, at the same hour, the pointers of sundials throw shadows, because Alexandria lies further to the north than Syene. The two cities lying under the same meridian great circle, if we draw an arc from the extremity of the shadow to the base of the pointer of the sundial in Alexandria, the arc will be a segment of a great circle in the [hemispherical] bowl of the sundial, since the bowl of the sundial lies under the great circle [of the meridian]. If now we conceive straight lines produced from each of the pointers through the earth, they will meet at the centre of the earth. Since then the sundial at Syene is vertically under the sun, if we conceive a straight line coming from the sun to the top of the pointer of the sundial, the line reaching from the sun to the centre of the earth will be one straight line. If now we conceive another straight line drawn upwards from the extremity of the shadow of the pointer of the sundial in Alexandria, through the top of the pointer to the sun, this straight line and the aforesaid straight line will be parallel, since they are straight lines coming through from different parts of the sun to different parts of the earth. On these straight lines, therefore, which are parallel, there falls the straight line drawn from the centre of the earth to the pointer at Alexandria, so that the alternate angles which it makes are equal. One of these angles is that formed at the centre of the earth, at the intersection of the straight lines which were drawn from the sundials to the centre of the earth; the other is at the point of intersection of the top of the pointer at Alexandria and the straight line drawn from the extremity of its shadow to the sun through the point [the top] where it meets the pointer. Now on this latter angle stands the arc carried round from the extremity of the shadow of the pointer to its base, while on the angle at the centre of the earth stands the arc reaching from Syene to Alexandria. But the arcs are similar, since they stand on equal angles. Whatever ratio, therefore, the arc in the bowl of the sundial has to its proper circle, the arc reaching from Syene to Alexandria has that ratio to *its* proper circle. But the arc in the bowl is found to be one-fiftieth of its proper circle. Therefore the distance from Syene to Alexandria must necessarily be one-fiftieth part of the great circle of the earth. And the said distance is 5,000 stades; therefore the complete great circle measures 250,000 stades. Such is Eratosthenes' method.

LUCRETIUS

c. 95–55 B.C.

THE ATOMIC THEORY OF THE NATURE
OF THINGS ACCORDING TO THE IDEAS OF
DEMOCRITUS AND EPICURUS

ONE of the most obvious subjects for speculation is the composition of matter, which means the composition of everything in the physical world. *De rerum natura* is an early result of such speculation. Although written by a Roman it is based on the views of two Greek philosophers, Democritus (or Demokritos, 470–400 B.C.) and Epicurus (341–270 B.C.), whose lives overlapped that of Aristotle at either end. It is evidence of two features of the time: that Greek scientific thinking was taken over by the Romans, and that little development of thought on this subject took place in the three centuries following Democritus.

Democritus tried to explain the origin of matter in terms other than those of the senses. For him to describe a thing as sweet or bitter was to describe only an attribute. Its essential being could be accounted for by the concept of 'atoms', the word being used less specifically than it is today, but nevertheless referring to indivisible, indestructible particles which could combine in various ways to form objects with differing properties. The universe consisted of atoms and a vacuum.

Aristotle rejected this atomic theory and, in particular, the possibility of a vacuum. The theory was revived by Epicurus and, though containing only a primitive idea, it comes closer to modern views of the structure of matter than any other concept of the Greek or later thinkers. Something of this is seen by reading the extract from John Dalton in Volume 2.

Lucretius was a contemporary of Cicero and Julius Caesar. His ideas are written in a form unusual for a collection of readings in science, though in no way lacking in clarity or logical expression. George Sarton has described *De rerum natura* as the greatest philosophical poem of all time. Some English translations present it in blank verse. For present purposes, however, it seemed appropriate to use, for the following selection, the modern translation by Ronald Latham, *The Nature of the Universe*, in the Penguin Classics edition (1951).

———

To pick up the thread of my discourse, all nature as it is in itself consists of two things – bodies and the vacant space in which the bodies are situated and through which they move in different directions. The existence of bodies is vouched for by the agreement of the senses. If a belief resting directly on this foundation is not valid, there will be no standard to which we can refer any doubt on obscure questions for rational confirmation. If there were no place and space, which we call vacuity, these bodies could not be situated anywhere or move in any direction whatever. This I have just demonstrated. It remains to show that nothing exists that is distinct both from body and from vacuity and could be ranked with the others as a third substance. For whatever is must also be something. If it offers resistance to touch, however light and slight, it will increase the mass of body by such amount, great or small, as it may amount to, and will rank with it. If, on the other hand, it is intangible, so that it offers no resistance whatever to anything passing through it, then it will be that empty space which we call vacuity. Besides, whatever it may be in itself, either it will act in some way, or react to other things acting upon it, or else it will be such that things can be and happen in it. But without body nothing can act or react; and nothing can afford a place except emptiness and vacancy. Therefore, besides matter and vacuity, we cannot include in the number of things any third substance that can either affect our senses at any time or be grasped by the reasoning of our minds.

You will find that anything that can be named is either

a property or an accident of these two. A property is something that cannot be detached or separated from a thing without destroying it, as weight is a property of rocks, heat of fire, fluidity of water, tangibility of all bodies, intangibility of vacuum. On the other hand, servitude and liberty, poverty and riches, war and peace, and all other things whose advent or departure leaves the essence of a thing intact, all these it is our practice to call by their appropriate name, accidents.

Similarly, time by itself does not exist; but from things themselves there results a sense of what has already taken place, what is now going on and what is to ensue. It must not be claimed that anyone can sense time by itself apart from the movement of things or their restful immobility.

Again, when men say it is a fact that Helen was ravished, or the Trojans were conquered, do not let anyone drive you to the admission that any such event *is* independently of any object, on the ground that the generations of men of whom these events were accidents have been swept away by the irrevocable lapse of time. For we could put it that whatever has taken place is an accident of a particular tract of earth or of the space it occupied. If there had been no matter and no space or place in which things could happen, no spark of love kindled by the beauty of Tyndareus' daughter would ever have stolen into the breast of Phrygian Paris to light that dazzling blaze of pitiless war; no Wooden Horse, unmarked by the sons of Troy, would have set the towers of Ilium aflame through the midnight issue of Greeks from its womb. So you may see that events cannot be said to be by themselves like matter or in the same sense as space. Rather you should describe them as accidents of matter, or of the place in which things happen.

Material objects are of two kinds, atoms and compounds of atoms. The atoms themselves cannot be swamped by any force, for they are preserved indefinitely by their absolute solidity. Admittedly, it is hard to believe that anything can exist that is absolutely solid. The lightning stroke from the sky penetrates closed buildings, as do shouts and other

47

noises. Iron glows molten in the fire, and hot rocks are cracked by untempered scorching. Hard gold is softened and melted by heat; and bronze, ice-like, is liquefied by flame. Both heat and piercing cold seep through silver, since we feel both alike when a cooling shower of water is poured into a goblet that we hold ceremonially in our hands. All these facts point to the conclusion that nothing is really solid. But sound reasoning and nature itself drive us to the opposite conclusion. Pay attention, therefore, while I demonstrate in a few lines that there exist certain bodies that are absolutely solid and indestructible, namely those atoms which according to our teaching are the seeds or prime units of things from which the whole universe is built up.

In the first place, we have found that nature is twofold, consisting of two totally different things, matter and the space in which things happen. Hence each of these must exist by itself without admixture of the other. For, where there is empty space (what we call vacuity), there matter is not; where matter exists, there cannot be a vacuum. Therefore the prime units of matter are solid and free from vacuity.

Again, since composite things contain some vacuum, the surrounding matter must be solid. For you cannot reasonably maintain that anything can hide vacuity and hold it within its body unless you allow that the container itself is solid. And what contains the vacuum in things can only be an accumulation of matter. Hence matter, which possesses absolute solidity, can be everlasting when other things are decomposed.

Again, if there were no empty space, everything would be one solid mass; if there were no material objects with the property of filling the space they occupy, all existing space would be utterly void. It is clear, then, that there is an alternation of matter and vacuity, mutually distinct, since the whole is neither completely full nor completely empty. There are therefore solid bodies, causing the distinction between empty space and full. And these, as I have just shown, can be neither decomposed by blows from without nor invaded and unknit from within nor destroyed by any other form of assault. For it seems that a thing without vacuum can be neither knocked to bits nor snapped nor chopped in two by cutting; nor can it let in moisture or seeping cold or piercing fire, the universal agents of destruction. The more vacuum a thing contains within it, the more readily it yields to these assailants. Hence, if the units of matter are solid and without vacuity, as I have shown, they must be everlasting.

Yet again, if the matter in things had not been everlasting, everything by now would have gone back to nothing, and the things we see would be the product of rebirth out of nothing. But, since I have already shown that nothing can be created out of nothing nor any existing thing be summoned back to nothing, the atoms must be made of imperishable stuff into which everything can be resolved in the end, so that there may be a stock of matter for building the world anew. The atoms, therefore, are absolutely solid and unalloyed. In no other way could they have survived throughout infinite time to keep the world in being.

Furthermore, if nature had set no limit to the breaking of things, the particles of matter in the course of ages would have been ground so small that nothing could be generated from them so as to attain in the fullness of time to the summit of its growth. For we see that anything can be more speedily disintegrated than put together again. Hence, what the long day of time, the bygone eternity, has already shaken and loosened to fragments could never in the residue of time be reconstructed. As it is, there is evidently a limit set to breaking, since we see that everything is renewed and each according to its kind has a fixed period in which to grow to its prime.

Here is a further argument. Granted that the particles of matter are absolutely solid, we can still explain the composition and behaviour of soft things – air, water, earth, fire – by their intermixture with empty space. On the other hand, supposing the atoms to be soft, we cannot account for the origin of hard flint and iron. For there would be no foundation for nature to build on. Therefore there must be bodies strong in their unalloyed solidity by whose closer clustering things can be knit together and display unyielding toughness.

If we suppose that there is no limit set to the breaking of matter, we must still admit that material objects consist of particles which throughout eternity have resisted the forces of destruction. To say that these are breakable does not square with the fact that they have survived throughout eternity under a perpetual bombardment of innumerable blows.

Again, there is laid down for each thing a specific limit to its growth and its tenure of life, and the laws of nature ordain what each can do and what it cannot. No species is ever changed, but each remains so much itself that every kind of bird displays on its body its own specific markings. This is a further proof that their bodies are composed of changeless matter. For, if the atoms could yield in any way to change, there would be no certainty as to what could arise and what could not, at what point the power of everything was limited by an immovable frontier-post; nor could successive generations so regularly repeat the nature, behaviour, habits, and movements of their parents.

To proceed with our argument, there is an ultimate point in visible objects which represents the smallest thing that can be seen. So also there must be an ultimate point in objects that lie below the limit of perception by our senses. This point is without parts and is the smallest thing that can exist. It never has been and never will be able to exist by itself, but only as one primary part of something else. It is with a mass of such parts, solidly jammed together in order, that matter is filled up. Since they cannot exist by themselves, they must needs stick together in a mass from which they cannot by any means be prised loose. The atoms therefore are absolutely solid and unalloyed, consisting of a mass of least parts tightly packed together. They are not compounds formed by the coalescence of their parts, but bodies of absolute and everlasting solidity. To these nature allows no loss or diminution, but guards them as seeds for things. If

there are no such least parts, even the smallest bodies will
consist of an infinite number of parts, since they can always
be halved and their halves halved again without limit. On
this showing, what difference will there be between the whole
universe and the very least of things? None at all. For, however endlessly infinite the universe may be, yet the smallest
things will equally consist of an infinite number of parts.
Since true reason cries out against this and denies that the
mind can believe it, you must needs give in and admit that
there are least parts which themselves are partless. Granted
that these parts exist, you must needs admit that the atoms
they compose are also solid and everlasting. But, if all
things were compelled by all-creating nature to be broken
up into these least parts, nature would lack the power to
rebuild anything out of them. For partless objects cannot
have the essential properties of generative matter – those
varieties of attachment, weight, impetus, impact, and movement on which everything depends.

———

II

FROM CLASSICAL TIMES TO
THE RENAISSANCE

A LONG period in time, which included the Dark Ages, separated the decline of the Greco–Roman civilization from the revival of learning and scientific inquiry, often regarded as dating from the birth of Leonardo da Vinci. Discovery appears to have been at a low ebb in Europe, though the available records of much of the period are far from complete. Intellectual activity did not, however, die out. Information was collected, treatises were compiled, and much discussion centred round the efforts of the schoolmen to reconcile Greek science with the teachings of the Church. Sarton's summary of these activities in the fourteenth century extends to over a thousand pages. By such means the gap was bridged, a line of intellectual communication was maintained from the Greek and Roman scientists to those of the Renaissance.

The illustrations in this section are taken from the fields of cosmology and the composition of matter, which are developed extensively in later sections. The extracts from Pliny and Ptolemy belong to the last phase of the Greco–Roman period and are included to show the kind of foundation on which the medieval scholar worked. Stahl represents a transition between the medieval and modern approach to chemistry, which occurred, in this aspect, much later than the corresponding transition in physics.

Ptolemy's systematic account of the universe was later superseded by the more workable model of Copernicus. He did, however, evolve a workable structure by which the heavenly phenomena could be explained in terms acceptable for contemporary needs. The medieval scholars thought more of perfecting his compilations than criticizing them. Re-examination came much later when further exploration of the oceans gave rise to the need for better aids to navigation.

By contrast, the emphasis in the extract from Pliny is on observation. He records that the metal gold is malleable, of high melting point, and chemically inert. The last he regarded as more significant than the aesthetic qualities for which it was held in esteem. Indeed in his emphasis on its purity and its resistance to reaction with charcoal we can see the early hints of one of the criteria which later came to characterize the chemical elements.

Stahl, like Ptolemy, was seeking a universal theory to explain the phenomena of chemical reactions as known in his time. The phlogiston theory, like the Ptolemaic system, was successful in unifying the available observations. It stimulated further experiment, and most of the eighteenth-century chemists found it a satisfactory basis for interpreting their results throughout their lives. Although much of modern chemistry could still be explained in phlogistic terms, the theory was replaced by Lavoisier's ideas which experience showed to give simpler and more direct explanations.

The extract from Agricola is included as a reminder that technological progress continued during this period; it should not be ignored because it now appears overshadowed by the greater developments of the Industrial Revolution. Changes in intellectual climate did not obviate the need to attend to practical matters – to manufacture clothing, to fabricate armour, to build ships, to shoe and saddle horses, to till fields and harvest crops, even (as throughout history) to produce jewellery for the adornment of womankind. Without an adequate scientific background, progress was made towards better methods of mining and metallurgy. Agricola codifies much precise observation obtained in the craft tradition on a quite empirical basis.

The remaining extract represents a second and quite different link between the two periods. In Alexandria, an essentially Greek city on the frontiers of the Arab world, the translation of Greek texts into Arabic was the starting-point for Arabic work in medicine, alchemy, astronomy, and geometry. Ultimately Arabian influence was felt in Europe, beginning in Moorish Spain. Not only were Arabic ideas transmitted in this way, but Arabic translations from the Greek were retranslated into Latin long before the original Greek manuscripts were rediscovered. The writings of Geber show the alchemists' admixture of experiment and something approaching mysticism (the latter is notably absent from Agricola); but the interest in the composition of matter is again insistent.

PLINY THE ELDER

A.D. 23-79

THE PROPERTIES OF GOLD

NOT far from Naples is the crater of Vesuvius, the great
volcano whose erupting ash overwhelmed the cities of
Pompeii and Herculaneum in A.D. 79. In that ash lies the
body of Pliny the Elder, quite possibly preserved, as were
many others discovered during recent excavations. Pliny
died a victim of his own curiosity, two years after publishing,
in thirty-nine books, a remarkable encyclopedia containing
all that was known about science in his day. As a good
scholar should, he cited all his authorities, 150 of them
Roman and more than 300 Greek. He was concerned mainly
with nature – that is, with human beings, animals, and birds,
with metals, and with the whole range of country activities:
farming, wine-making, forestry. He wrote a history of art
and touched on chemistry, medicine, and astronomy. Some
of his information is based on facts; some on legend and
superstition. Pliny's *Historia naturalis* has been described
as 'an old curiosity shop – precious early information
side by side with all the rubbish'. The unicorn was included, for example, without any question as to its actual
existence.

The importance of Pliny's work lies in the fact that it
provided the early medieval scholars with a convenient
primer of Greek science. Indeed, as early as the end of the
seventh century we find an Anglo-Saxon monk, Bede,
making use of the *Natural History* for his own summary of
Western European knowledge. It is said, too, that some of
the medieval bestiaries drew imaginatively on some of
Pliny's descriptions.

Pliny had views on the nature of the earth's structure: he
thought for example, that people lived in the antipodes.
He realized, too, that light travels faster than sound.

Pliny's description of the properties of gold is extraordinarily similar to those found in modern textbooks.

This selection is from the K. C. Bailey translation, *The Elder Pliny's Chapters of Chemical Subjects*, published by E. Arnold and Co. (1932).

¶ *Gold and its Properties*

I think that pride of place is given to this substance [gold], not by reason of its colour, for silver is brighter and more like sun-light (that is why it is more commonly used for military standards, since its gleaming is visible at a greater distance), and those who think it is the star-like hue of gold that charms are clearly mistaken, since no special importance is attached to such a colour in gems and other things; nor again is it preferred to the other metals by reason of its heaviness or its malleability, for in both it is surpassed by lead, but because it alone of all substances loses nothing on heating, and survives even conflagrations and the funeral pyre. In fact, the oftener it is heated the better it becomes, and ignition is the test for gold, that on heating till red hot it should still keep its colour. The test is called *obrussa*.

But the best proof of purity is a high melting-point. It is strange too that a substance unsubdued by charcoal, made from the most fiercely-burning wood, is swiftly heated by chaff, and that it is fused with lead to purify it.

Another and more important reason for holding gold in esteem is that it is least worn away by use. On the other hand, lines can be drawn with silver, copper, and lead, and the hands become soiled by the material that wears off. Again, nothing can be beaten into thinner leaves nor divided more finely, for an ounce of it is hammered out into seven hundred and fifty, or even more, gold-leaves measuring four fingers each way. The thickest of gold-leaves are called 'leaf of Praeneste', where the image of Fortune, gilded most faithfully, still helps to maintain the name. The next type of leaf is called 'quaestorian'. In Spain, nuggets of gold are called *striges*.

Above all, it alone is found in nuggets or fine dust. The other metals, after discovery in the mines, have to be perfected by roasting, but gold is gold straight off. Its substance is perfect when found in this way, for the gold in this case is pure; in the other cases which we shall describe it has to be extracted. Finally, neither rust nor verdigris nor anything else can waste its excellence or diminish its weight.

Again, brine and vinegar, the conquerors of matter, make no impression on it, and, more than any other metal, it is spun and woven like wool – even without wool.

According to Verrius, Tarquinius Priscus triumphed in a golden tunic, and we ourselves have seen Agrippina, wife of the Emperor Claudius, sitting beside him when he was exhibiting a mimic sea-fight, clad in a cloak woven of gold without other material. Indeed the method of weaving gold into Attalic cloth is old, and was invented by the kings of Asia.

On marble and other objects which cannot be heated white-hot, gold is laid on with white of egg; on wood with a glue called *leucophorum*, made in accordance with a certain formula. Its composition and preparation will be described in its proper place.

It was legal to gild copper by means of quicksilver or at least hydrargyrum, in place of which a fraudulent substitute has been devised, as we shall relate when we are describing their properties.

The copper is first subjected to the violence of fire; then when red-hot, quenched with brine, vinegar, or alum. The brightness of the surface is then used as a test whether the heating has been sufficiently prolonged, and the copper is dried again by heat so that, after polishing with a mixture of pumice and alum, it is fit to receive the gold-leaf laid on with mercury. Alum has purifying properties [in the case of copper] comparable to those already attributed to lead [in the case of gold].

PTOLEMY
(CLAUDIUS PTOLEMAEUS)
Second century

THE HYPOTHESES OF THE GEOCENTRIC
UNIVERSE ARE SET DOWN

NOT much is known about Claudius Ptolemaeus as a man
except that he was probably born in Egypt and most certainly played an important part in the life of the great
museum and library of Alexandria. Ptolemy, the astronomer,
geographer, and mathematician, neglected to leave records
of his own life, and no one seems to have taken the trouble
to record the exact date of his death. Had his students known
what was to be the extent of Ptolemy's influence on the
Western world, they might have left a little more information about him. We do not know either how much of the
writings credited to him were actually his own. Scholars
agree, however, that whatever the source of his material,
Ptolemy's presentation is so skilful that he is entitled to full
credit.

Ptolemy cites enough references to show that his main
inspiration in the field of mathematics and astronomy was
Hipparchus; in geography, Marinus of Tyre. Hipparchus
may have been still living while Ptolemy was a child, but
there was no personal connexion between them. Hipparchus
appears to have provided one of the links between Babylonian science and that of Greece, as is shown, for example,
by his adoption of the Babylonian system of dividing the
circumference of the circle into 360°. He was using, or
perhaps actually invented, a number of the instruments
subsequently discussed by Ptolemy. He constructed a
celestial globe – the first we know of – and founded trigonometry.

Marinus of Tyre left no writings of his own, but the results
of his work are included in Ptolemy's *Geographical Treatise*.

Both of these men were of the generation preceding Ptolemy's, and they became his involuntary collaborators – not without advantage to the world of science.

Ptolemy's work fell into two major divisions: the *Mathematical Treatise*, which has become known as the *Almagest*, and the *Geographical Treatise* already mentioned. Not enough is known about his work on optics, although it should be mentioned that Sarton regards it as 'the most remarkable experimental research of antiquity'. Ptolemy's astronomical work is included in both *Treatises*, the Geography containing mostly the latitudes and longitudes of the important places of the ancient world – slightly inaccurate, it is true, because of his reliance on incorrect estimates of the size of the globe. It is the *Almagest* with which we are principally concerned and from which the reading is selected.

The name *Almagest* is probably derived from an Arabic mispronunciation of a Greek word, *megali,* meaning 'great', preceded by the Arabic article *al* – from the idea of the 'great work' as opposed to the lesser work through which the students were introduced to the subject. The full title is translated as *The Mathematical Treatise* or *The Great Treatise of Astronomy*. It is, in fact, an encyclopedia of astronomy, containing eleven books covering all the known knowledge on the subject. Our selection is taken from the introductory propositions, translated by T. L. Heath in *Greek Astronomy*. The work goes on to explain the motion of the planets and to deal with trigonometry as a tool of the astronomer, providing one of the earliest examples of work in applied mathematics. Ptolemy's catalogue of stars (he lists 1022), which he expanded from an earlier list of Hipparchus, is considered the most ancient accurate description of the heavens and the last one to be made for three hundred years.

The basic features of the Ptolemaic model of the universe follow the picture put forward by Aristotle. The earth is at the centre of the universe and the stars and planets revolve in circular orbits about the earth. To this older and simpler picture astronomical observations demanded certain modifications. The fact that the velocities of the sun and planets were not uniform had to be overcome by the suggestion that the circular paths did not have their centres directly at the centre of the earth. It was further necessary to suppose that the planets, in addition to circling the earth, rotated in an epicycle, a secondary, smaller circle, and that this latter motion was superimposed upon the principal form of motion.

With this more complex scheme it became possible to predict the behaviour of the planets and to test such predictions against observation. It is a tribute to the Ptolemaic system that it survived for so many centuries before the accumulation of errors was sufficient to indicate the need for a radically new picture of the structure of the solar system.

Ptolemy's insistence on the absolute immobility of the earth and its position as the centre of the universe proved to be strongly attractive to the medieval theologians, for whom man and his world were the sole object of creation. Thomas Aquinas qualified his acceptance of Ptolemy's theory by recognizing it as a working hypothesis only, but the Schoolmen made the theory a part of their general philosophy. Even after Copernicus published his theory in 1530, the Ptolemaic idea persisted. The principal factor in building up a case against Ptolemy proved to be the great maritime expeditions of the fifteenth century.

¶ *On the Order of the Theorems*

2. The work which we have projected commences with a consideration of the general relation between the earth as a whole and the heavens as a whole. Of the special treatments that follow, the first part deals with the position of the ecliptic, the places inhabited by the human race, and the differences among the successive places, in each separate horizon, along the curvature of the earth's surface. The preliminary study of these relations makes easier the examination of the subsequent questions. The second part gives an account of the motion of the sun and the moon and of the

phenomena that depend on these motions. For without the previous understanding of these matters it would be impossible to set forth a complete theory of the stars. Since the theory of the stars is contained, in accordance with the general plan, in the concluding portion of this essay, the investigation of the sphere of the so-called fixed stars would properly find its place there, and the material on the five so-called planets would follow. We shall try to set forth all this material using as the basic foundations for knowledge the manifest phenomena themselves and those recorded observations of the ancients and the moderns about which there is no dispute; and we shall seek to fit the propositions together by geometrical proofs.

With respect to the general portion of the treatise the following preliminary assumptions are to be made: (1) that the heaven is spherical in form and rotates as a sphere; (2) that the earth, too, viewed as a complete whole, is spherical in form; (3) that it is situated in the middle of the whole heaven, like a centre; (4) that by reason of its size and its distance from the sphere of fixed stars the earth bears to this sphere the relation of a point; (5) that the earth does not participate in any locomotion. We shall say a few words by way of commentary on each of these propositions.

¶ *That the Heaven Rotates as a Sphere*

3. It is reasonable to assume that the first ideas on these matters came to the ancients from observation such as the following. They saw the sun and the moon and the other stars moving from east to west in circles always parallel to each other; they saw the bodies begin to rise from below, as if from the earth itself, and gradually to rise to their highest point, and then, with a correspondingly gradual decline, to trace a downward course until they finally disappeared, apparently sinking into the earth. And then they saw these stars, once more, after remaining invisible for a time, make a fresh start and in rising and setting repeat the same periods

of time and the same places of rising and setting with regularity and virtual similarity.

They were, however, led to the view of a spherical heaven chiefly by the observed circular motion described about one and the same centre by those stars that are always above the horizon. For this point was, necessarily, the pole of the heavenly sphere, since the stars that are nearer this pole revolve in smaller circles, whereas those further away make larger circles, proportionately to their distance, until the distance reaches that of the stars not always visible. And of these latter they observed that those stars nearer the stars that are always visible remained invisible for a shorter time while those farther away remained invisible for a correspondingly longer time. And so, from these phenomena alone they first conceived the aforesaid idea, and then from the consideration of its consequences they adopted the other ideas that follow from it, since all the phenomena without qualification refuted the alternative hypotheses.

For example, if one should suppose, as some have, that the motion of the stars proceeds by a straight line without limit, how could one explain the fact that the daily motion of each star is always seen to begin from the same point? How could the stars in their unlimited motion turn back? And if they did turn back, how could this escape observation? Or how could they fail eventually to become altogether invisible, since they would appear ever smaller and smaller? In point of fact, however, they appear larger when near the region where they disappear, and are only gradually occulted and, as it were, cut off by the surface of the earth.

Again, the suggestion that the stars are kindled when they rise from the earth and again are snuffed out when they return to the earth is quite contrary to reason. For even if one should grant that the arrangement, size, and number of the stars, and their distances and intervals in space and time could have been the fulfilment of mere random and accidental procedure and that one part of the earth [the eastern part] had throughout it a kindling force, while the other [the western part] had an extinguishing force, or rather that the same part acted as a kindler from the point of view of some and as an extinguisher from the point of view of others, and that of the stars the very same ones were already kindled or extinguished, as the case might be, for some observers, but not yet for others – if, I repeat, one should grant all this, absurd as it is, what of the stars always visible, those that neither rise nor set? Why should the stars that are kindled and extinguished not rise and set everywhere? Why should those not subject to such kindling and extinguishing always be above the horizon in all latitudes? For surely the stars which for some observers are always kindled and extinguished cannot be the same as those which for other observers are never kindled and extinguished. [Yet the proponents of the hypothesis of kindling would have to assume that they are the same] for it is quite evident that the same stars rise and set for some observers [i.e., those further south] whereas they neither rise nor set for others [i.e., those further north].

In a word, if one should suppose any other form of motion of the heavens save the spherical, the distances from the earth to the heavenly bodies would necessarily be unequal, however and wherever the earth itself might be supposed to lie situate. Consequently the sizes of the stars and their distances from one another would have to appear unequal to the same observers at each return, since the distances from the observers would sometimes be greater and at other times smaller. But this is not seen to be the case. For what makes the apparent size of a heavenly body greater when it is near the horizon is not its smaller distance but the vaporous moisture surrounding the earth between our eye and the heavenly body. It is the same as when objects immersed in water appear larger, and in fact the more deeply immersed the larger.

The hypothesis of spherical motion finds support also in the fact that on any other hypothesis save this one alone it is impossible that the instruments for measuring hours should be correct. There is also support in the following fact. Just as the motion of the heavenly bodies is completely without hindrance and the smoothest of all motions, and the most easily moved of all shapes is the circular for plane figures and the spherical for solids, so also since the polygon with the greater number of sides is the larger of regular polygons having equal perimeters, it follows that in the case of plane figures the circle is greater than any polygon of equal perimeter, and in the case of solid figures the sphere is greater. And the heaven is greater than all other bodies.

Various physical considerations, too, lead to the same conclusion. Thus the aether consists of finer and more homogeneous parts than does any other body. Now surfaces of bodies of homogeneous parts are themselves of homogeneous parts, and the circular surface in the case of plane figures and the spherical surface in the case of solid figures are the only surfaces that consist of homogeneous parts. The aether not being a plane surface but a solid may therefore be inferred to be of spherical form. A similar inference may be made from the fact that nature has constructed all earthly and destructible bodies entirely of circular forms but forms not having homogeneous parts, while she has constructed the divine bodies in the aether of spherical form having homogeneous parts. For if these bodies were flat or quoit-shaped their form would not appear circular to all observers at the same time from different places of the earth. Hence it is reasonable to infer that the aether which encloses the heavenly bodies, being of the same nature, is of spherical form, and, because of its composition out of homogeneous parts, moves with uniform circular motion.

¶ *The Absolute Immobility of the Earth*

In the same way as before it can be proved that the earth cannot make any movement whatever in the aforesaid oblique direction, or ever change its position at all from its place at the centre; for the same results would, in that case, have followed as if it had happened to be placed elsewhere than at the centre. So I, for one, think it is gratuitous for any one to inquire into the causes of the motion towards the centre when once the fact that the earth occupies the middle place in the universe, and that all weights move towards it, is made so patent by the observed phenomena themselves. The ground for this conviction which is readiest to hand, seeing that the earth has been proved to be spherical and situated in the middle of the universe, is this simple fact: in all parts of the earth without exception the tendencies and the motions of bodies which have weight – I mean their own proper motions – always and everywhere operate at right angles to the (tangent) plane drawn evenly through the point of contact where the object falls. That this is so makes it also clear that, if the objects were not stopped by the surface of the earth, they would absolutely reach the centre itself, since the straight line leading to the centre is always at right angles to the tangent-plane to the sphere drawn through the intersection at the point of contact.

All who think it strange that such an immense mass as that of the earth should neither move itself nor be carried somewhere seem to me to look to their own personal experience, and not to the special character of the universe, and to go wrong through regarding the two things as analogous. They would not, I fancy, think the fact in question to be strange if they could realize that the earth, great as it is, is nevertheless, when compared with the enclosing body, in the relation of a point to that body. For in this way it will seem to be quite possible that a body relatively so small should be dominated and pressed upon with equal and similarly directed force on all sides by the absolutely greatest body formed of like constituents, there being no up and down in the universe any more than one would think of such things in an ordinary sphere. So far as the composite objects in the universe, and their motion on their own account and in their own nature are concerned, those objects which are light, being composed of fine particles, fly towards the outside, that is, towards the circumference, though their impulse seems to be towards what is for individuals 'up', because with all of us what is over our heads, and is also called 'up', points towards the bounding surface; but all things which are heavy, being composed of denser particles, are carried towards the middle, that is, to the centre, though they seem to fall 'down', because, again, with all of us the place at our feet, called 'down', itself points towards the centre of the earth, and they naturally settle in a position about the centre, under the action of mutual resistance and pressure which is equal and similar from all directions. Thus it is easy to conceive that the whole solid mass of the earth is of huge size in comparison with the things that are carried down to it, and that the earth remains unaffected by the impact of the quite small weights (falling on it), seeing that these fall from all sides alike, and the earth welcomes, as it were, what falls and joins it. But, of course, if as a whole it had had a common motion, one and the same with that of the weights, it would, as it was carried down, have got ahead of every other falling body, in virtue of its enormous excess of size, and the animals and all separate weights would have been left behind floating on the air, while the earth, for its part, at its great speed, would have fallen completely out of the universe itself. But indeed this sort of suggestion has only to be thought of in order to be seen to be utterly ridiculous.

Certain thinkers, though they have nothing to oppose to the above arguments, have concocted a scheme which they consider more acceptable, and they think that no evidence can be brought against them if they suggest for the sake of argument that the heaven is motionless, but that the earth rotates about one and the same axis from west to east, completing one revolution approximately every day, or alternatively that both the heaven and the earth have a rotation of a certain amount, whatever it is, about the same axis, as we said, but such as to maintain their *relative* situations.

These persons forget however that, while, so far as appearances in the stellar world are concerned, there might, perhaps, be no objection to this theory in the simpler form, yet, to judge by the conditions affecting ourselves and those in the air about us, such a hypothesis must be seen to be quite ridiculous. Suppose we could concede to them such an unnatural thing as that the most rarefied and lightest things either do not move at all or do not move differently from those of the opposite character – when it is clear as day that things in the air and less rarefied have swifter motions than any bodies of more earthy character – and that (we could further concede that) the densest and heaviest things could have a movement of their own so swift and uniform – when earthy bodies admittedly sometimes do not readily respond even to motion communicated to them by other things – yet they must admit that the rotation of the earth would be more violent than any whatever of the movements which take place about it, if it made in such a short time such a colossal turn back to the same position again, that everything not actually standing on the earth must have seemed to make one and the same movement always in the contrary sense to the earth, and clouds, and any of the things that fly or can be thrown could never be seen travelling towards the east, because the earth would always be anticipating them all and forestalling their motion towards the east, insomuch that everything else would seem to recede towards the west and the parts which the earth would be leaving behind it.

For, even if they should maintain that the air is carried round with the earth in the same way and at the same speed, nevertheless the solid bodies in it would always have appeared to be left behind in the motion of the earth and air together, or, even if the solid bodies themselves were, so to speak, attached to the air and carried round with it, they could no longer have appeared either to move forwards or to be left behind, but would always have seemed to stand still, and never, even when flying or being thrown, to make any excursion or change their position, although we so clearly see all these things happening, just as if no slowness or swiftness whatever accrued to them in consequence of the earth not being stationary.

JABIR IBN HAYYAN
(GEBER)

THE AIMS AND SOME OF THE METHODS OF
THE ALCHEMISTS ARE INDICATED

DURING the thirteenth or fourteenth century, there appeared, in Latin, some alchemical texts over the name of 'Geber'. This was at one time thought to be a latinized form of the name of Jabir ibn Hayyan, a noted Arabic alchemist who had lived five centuries previously. Except for two minor works, however, the Latin texts do not correspond to any Arabic originals, and it is still uncertain how 'Geber's' writings originated. They may be the work of a Latin writer who assembled and translated various Arabic works, not necessarily those of Jabir only. More recently it has been suggested that they are connected with encyclopedias written by a Muslim sect, 'The Brethren of Purity', devoted to educational activities.

'Geber' stands here for the transmission of chemical and alchemical knowledge of the Arabs to the medieval European alchemists. The writings show an interest in chemical manipulation – evaporation, distillation,* filtration, melting – and discuss the manufacture of steel, the dyeing of cloth, and methods of preparing such chemicals as sulphuric and nitric acids and *aqua regia* (which dissolves gold). *Argentvive* means mercury (quicksilver). The alchemists regarded metals as being composed of the two principles, sulphur and mercury. These could be released from the base metals by the art of the alchemist and, if they were sufficiently pure, could be recombined to make silver (if the sulphur were white) and gold (if the sulphur were red).

The selection is taken from R. Russell's translation of *The Works of Geber* (re-edited in 1928 by E. J. Holmyard and published by J. M. Dent and Sons Ltd). It consists of a short homily on the nature of the alchemist's work in his

*Plate 1 shows one kind of distillation furnace used by alchemists.

searching for the philosopher's stone, the substance which would transmute base metals into gold. The alchemists wrote in a mystical language (which contrasts strongly with the direct expression of Agricola in the following passage). It is, indeed, difficult to assess how much genuine scientific work accompanied the quest, but there is no doubt that some did.

¶ CHAPTER II *Of the Stone of Philosophers, that it is one only, for the White, and for the Red, and from what Things it is extracted. And of the Possibility and Way of Perfection.*

We find Modern Artists to describe to us one only *Stone*, both for the *White* and for the *Red*; which we grant to be true: for in every *Elixir*, that is prepared, *White* or *Red*, there is no other Thing than *Argentvive* and *Sulphur*, of which, one cannot act, nor be, without the other: Therefore it is called, by *Philosophers*, one *Stone*, although it is extracted from many Bodies or Things. For it would be a foolish and vain thing to think to extract the same from a Thing, in which it is not, as some infatuated Men have conceited; for it never was the Intention of *Philosophers*: yet they speak many things by similitude. And because all *Metallick* Bodies are compounded of *Argentvive* and *Sulphur*, pure or impure, by accident, and not innate in their first Nature; therefore, by convenient *Preparation*, 'tis possible to take away such Impurity. For the *Expoliation of Accidents* is not impossible: therefore, the end of *Preparation* is, to take away *Superfluity*, and supply the *Deficiency* in Perfect Bodies. But *Preparation* is diversified according to the *Diversity* of things indigent. For experience hath taught us diverse ways of acting, *viz. Calcination, Sublimation, Descension, Solution, Distillation, Coagulation, Fixation,* and *Inceration*: All which we sufficiently declare in the *Sum of the Perfection of the Magistery*. For these are Works helpful in *Preparation*.

¶ CHAPTER V *The Conclusion of this First Part, containing the Qualifications of the Artificer*

Therefore, from what is abovesaid, we conclude, that the *Artificer* of this *Work* ought to be well skilled, and perfect in the *Sciences* of *Natural Philosophy*: because, how much *Money* soever he hath, and although he be endowed with a naturally profound *Wit* and *Desire* in this *Artifice*, yet he cannot attain his *End*, unless he hath by *Learning* acquired *Natural Philosophy*. For the defect of that which is not acquired by *Natural Ingenuity*, must be supplied by *Learning*. Therefore the *Artificer* must be helped by most deep *Search* and *Natural Industry*. For, by reason of his *Learning* only, how much soever of *Science* he hath acquired, unless he be also helped by *Natural Industry*, he will not be invited to so precious a *Banquet*. By his *Industry*, he must amend his *Errour* in the point, to which he will be ignorant how to apply a *Remedy*, if he rely only upon his *Learning*: so likewise, he may remedy his *Errour* in the *Point*, from his Knowledg acquired by *Natural Learning*, which by *Industry* only he cannot avoid; because *Art* is helped by *Ingenuity*, and *Ingenuity* by *Art* likewise.

Also it is necessary for him to be of a constant Will in his *Work*, that he may not presume to attempt this now, and that another time: because our *Art* consists not, nor is perfected in a Multitude of *Things*. For there is one *Stone*, one *Medicine*, in which the *Magistery* consists, to which we add not any extraneous *Thing*, nor remove we ought; except that in *Preparation* we take away *Superfluities*.

Also he must be diligent in the *Work*, persisting to the final *Consummation* thereof, that he leave not off abruptly; because he can acquire neither Knowledge nor Profit from a diminished *Work*; but shall rather reap *Desperation* and *Dammage*. It is also expedient he should know the *Principles* and Principal *Radixes* of this *Art*, which are essential to the *Work*: because, he that is ignorant of the *Beginnings*, cannot find the *End*. And we show you all those *Principles* in a Discourse compleat, and sufficiently clear and manifest to wise Men, according to the exigency of this our *Art*. It is likewise expedient, the *Artist* should be temperate and slow to *Anger*, least he suddenly (through the force of *Rage*) spoil and destroy his *Works* begun.

Likewise also, he must keep his *Money*, and not presumptuously distribute it vainly, least he happen not to find the *Art*, and be left in *Misery*, and in the *Desperation* of *Poverty*; or at least, when (by his Diligent Endeavour) he is come near to the *End* of his *Magistery*, his *Money* being all spent, he be forced to leave the *End* (miserable Man as he is) uncompleated. For they, who in the *Beginning* prodigally waste their whole *Treasure*, when they draw nigh to the *End*, have not wherewith to Labour. Whence such Men are twofoldly overwhelmed with Grief, *viz.* because they spent their *Money* in Things unprofitable, and because they lose the most noble *Science* which they were in quest of. For you need not to consume your *Goods*, seeing you may come to the compleatment of the *Magistery* for a small price, if you be not ignorant of the *Principles* of *Art*, and rightly understand what we have declared to you. Therefore, if you waste your *Money*, not minding our Admonitions plain and manifest, written in this Little Book, inveigh not against Us; but impute what you suffer to your own *Ignorance* and *Presumption*. For this *Science* agrees not well with a *Man* poor and indigent, but is rather inimical and adverse to him.

Nor should the *Artist* endeavour to find the *Sophistical* end of his *Work*, but be intent on the true *Compleatment* only; because our *Art* is reserved in the *Divine Will* of God, and is given to, or with-held from, whom he will; who is *Glorious*, *Sublime*, and full of all *Justice* and *Goodness*. And perhaps, for the punishment of your *Sophistical Work*, he denies you the *Art*, and lamentably thrusts you into the *By-Path* of *Error*, and from your *Error* into perpetual *Infelicity* and *Misery*: because he is most miserable and unhappy, to whom (after the *End* of his *Work* and *Labour*) GOD denies the sight of *Truth*. For such a *Man* is constituted in perpetual *Labour*, beset with all *Misfortune* and *Infelicity*, loseth the *Consolation*, *Joy*, and *Delight* of his whole *Time*, and consumes his Life in Grief without Profit. Likewise, the *Artist*, when he shall be in his *Work*, should study to impress in his *Mind*, all *Signs* that appear in every *Decoction*, and to search out their *Causes*.

These are the *Things* necessary for an *Artificer* fit for our *Art*; but if any of these We have declared be wanting in him, he should not approach to our *Art*.

¶ CHAPTER VIII *Of Sol, or Gold*

We have already given you, in a *General Chapter*, the *Sum* of the *Intention* of *Metals*; and here we now intend to make a special *Declaration* of each one. And first of *Gold*. We say, *Gold* is a *Metallick Body, Citrine,* ponderous, mute, fulgid, equally digested in the *Bowels* of the *Earth*, and very long washed with *Mineral Water*; under the *Hammer* extensible, fusible, and sustaining the Tryal of the *Cupel,* and *Cement*. According to this Definition, you may conclude, that nothing is true *Gold*, unless it hath all the *Causes* and *Differences* of the Definition of *Gold*. Yet, whatsoever *Metal* is radically Citrine, and brings to *Equality*, and cleanseth, it makes *Gold* of every kind of *Metals*. Therefore, we consider by the *Work* of *Nature*, and discern, that *Copper* may be changed into *Gold* by *Artifice*. For we see in *Copper Mines*, a certain *Water* which flows out, and carries with it thin *Scales* of *Copper*, which (by a continual and long continued Course) it washeth and cleanseth. But after such *Water* ceaseth to flow, we find these thin *Scales* with the dry *Sand*, in three years time to be digested with the *Heat* of the *Sun*; and among these *Scales* the purest *Gold* is found. Therefore, We judg, those *Scales* were cleansed by the benefit of the *Water*, but were equally digested by heat of the *Sun*, in the *Dryness* of the *Sand*, and so brought to *Equality*. Wherefore, imitating *Nature*, as far as we can, we likewise alter; yet in this we cannot follow *Nature*.

Also *Gold* is of *Metals* the most precious, and it is the *Tincture* of *Redness*; because it tingeth and transforms every *Body*. It is calcined and dissolved without profit, and is a *Medicine* rejoycing, and conserving the *Body* in *Youth*. It is most easily broken with *Mercury*, and by the *Odour* of *Lead*. There is not any *Body* that in act more agrees with it in *Substance* than *Jupiter* and *Luna*; but in *Weight, Deafeness*, and *Putrescibility, Saturn*, in *Colour Venus*; in *Potency* indeed *Venus* is more next *Luna* than *Jupiter*, and then *Saturn*: but lastly *Mars*. And this one of the *Secrets* of *Nature*. Likewise *Spirits* are commixed with it, and by it fixed, but not without very great *Ingenuity*, which comes not to an *Artificer* of a stiff neck.

¶ CHAPTER IX *Of Luna, or Silver*

Having premised the *Chapter* of *Sol*, We come now to speak of *Luna*, by a common name called *Silver*. Therefore, We say, *Silver* is a *Metallick Body*, White with pure Whiteness, Clean, Hard, Sounding, very durable in the *Cupel*, extensible under the *Hammer*, and fusible. And it is the *Tincture* of *Whiteness*, and hardens *Tin* by *Artifice*, and converts it to it self; and it is mixed with *Sol*, and breaks not; but in the *Examination* it perseveres not without *Artifice*. He who knows how more to subtiliate it, and after subtiliation, to inspissate and fix it associated with *Gold*; it remains with it in the *Test*, and will in no wise forsake it. Being put over the fume of acute Things, as of *Vinegar, Salarmoniac*, etc. it will be of a wonderful *Celestine Colour*. And it is a noble *Body*, but wants of the *Nobility* of *Gold*; and its *Minera* is found determinate: but it often hath a *Minera* confused with other *Bodies*, and that *Silver* is not so noble. It is likewise dissolved, and calcined with great *Labour*, and no *Profit*.

¶ CHAPTER X *Of Saturn, or Lead*

Of *Lead* we likewise treat, and say, *Lead* is a *Metallick Body*, livid, earthy, ponderous, mute, partaking of a little *Whiteness*, with much paleness, refusing the *Cineritium* and *Cement*, easily in all its dimensions with small *Compression extensible*, and readily fusible, without *Ignition*. Yet some foolish Men conceit, and say, that *Lead* in its own *Nature* is much approximated to *Gold*. But because they are stiff-necked, and void of all *Reason*, they cannot conceive of the *Truth* of Things most subtile, as it is in it self, but judg of them according to sense. And because they see it ponderous, and mute, and not to putrifie, they believe it to be much nigh in *Property* to *Sol*; but this is wholly erroneous, as by the following shall be by us manifestly proved at large. Also *Lead* hath much of an *Earthy Substance*, therefore it is washed, and by a *Lavament* turned into *Tin*. Hence it is manifest that *Tin* is more assimilated to the *Perfect*. *Lead* is in like manner burnt, and made *Minium;* and it is put over the *Vapours* of *Vinegar*, and made *Ceruss*. And although it is not much approximate to *Perfection*, yet of it, by our *Artifice*, we easily make *Silver*; and it keeps not its proper weight in *Transmutation*, but is changed into a new weight: All this it acquires in our *Magistery*. *Lead* also is the *Tryal* of *Silver* in the *Cupel*, the *Causes* of which We give.

¶ CHAPTER XI *Of Jupiter, or Tin*

Therefore, not omitting to discourse of *Jupiter*, We signifie to the *Sons* of *Learning*, that *Tin* is a *Metallick Body*, white, not pure, livid, and sounding little, partaking of little *Earthiness;* possessing in its *Root Harshness*, *Softness*, and swiftness of *Liquefaction*, without *Ignition*, and not abiding the *Cupel*, or *Cement*, but Extensible under the *Hammer*. Therefore, *Jupiter*, among *Bodies* diminished from *Perfection*, is in the *Radix* of its Nature of Affinity to the more Perfect, *viz.* to *Sol* and *Luna*; more to *Luna*, but less to *Sol*, as shall be clearly declared in the following. *Jupiter*, because it receives much *Whiteness* from the *Radix* of its *Generation*, therefore it whitens all *Bodies* not White; yet its vice is, that it breaks every *Body*, but *Saturn*, and most pure *Sol*. And *Jupiter* adheres much to *Sol* and *Luna*, and therefore doth not easily recede from them, by *Examen* (or *Tryal* of *Cupel*). In the *Magistery* of this *Art*, it receives a *Tincture* of *Redness*, and that shines in it with inestimable *Brightness*. It is hardned and cleansed more easily than *Saturn*. And he who knows how to take away its *Vice* of breaking, will suddenly reap the fruit of his Labour with joy. For it agrees with *Sol* and *Luna*, and will never be separated from them.

AGRICOLA
(GEORG BAUER)
1490–1555

THE FORMATION OF METALS IN
THE EARTH IS DISCUSSED

In contrast to the alchemists, such men as Biringuccio (fl. 1540) and Agricola were forerunners of a new period in chemical investigation; abandoning the dark mysteries of transmutation, they studied and described natural (and especially geological) phenomena, the preparation of metals from ores, and the various mechanical procedures available in their times. Agricola, whose writings are chosen to represent this new phase, was a Latin scholar and a physician. Under the name of Georg Bauer (George the Farmer), he lived in mining towns in Bohemia and Saxony, where he observed the mining of the ores of gold, silver, iron, copper, tin, and lead and described the various methods of separation of the ore, of smelting, and of the transformation of raw materials into usable products. He demonstrated, also, how gold and silver were separated from base metals.

The beauty of Agricola's work lies in his use of illustrations. The woodcuts are clear enough to enable a modern builder to recreate models of the machines Agricola describes; thus we have, for the first time, a definite picture of metallurgical art in the early days of the Renaissance.

This kind of observation, which brought out much information about chemical processes, was a prelude to a new period in the history of chemistry. The mystical assumptions of the alchemists were supplanted by accurate observation – a method which was to be ably demonstrated later by Robert Boyle and his contemporaries.

Agricola's theories of the origins of metals described in the present selection show the influence of Aristotle, who had posited that the elements of earth and water were combined into a juice and solidified by cold into a metal.

These two passages are from *De ortu et causis subterraneorum,* and are included in H. C. Hoover and L. H. Hoover's translation of *De re metallica,* published originally in 1912, and reprinted by Dover Publications in 1950.

¶ *How Metals are Produced*

I now come to the *canales* in the earth. These are veins, veinlets, and what are called 'seams in the rock'. These serve as vessels or receptacles for the material from which minerals (*res fossiles*) are formed. The term *vena* is most frequently given to what is contained in the *canales,* but likewise the same name is applied to the *canales* themselves. The term vein is borrowed from that used for animals, for just as their veins are distributed through all parts of the body, and just as by means of the veins blood is diffused from the liver throughout the whole body, so also the veins traverse the whole globe, and more particularly the mountainous districts; and water runs and flows through them. With regard to veinlets or stringers and 'seams in the rocks', which are the thinnest stringers, the following is the mode of their arrangement. Veins in the earth, just like the veins of an animal, have certain veinlets of their own, but in a contrary way. For the larger veins of animals pour blood into the veinlets, while in the earth the humours are usually poured from the veinlets into the larger veins, and rarely flow from the larger into the smaller ones. As for the seams in the rocks (*commissurae saxorum*) we consider that they are produced by two methods: by the first, which is peculiar to themselves, they are formed at the same time as the rocks, for the heat bakes the refractory material into stone and the non-refractory material similarly heated exhales its humours and is made into 'earth', generally friable. The other method is common also to veins and veinlets, when water is collected into one place it softens the rock by its liquid nature, and by its weight and pressure breaks and divides it. Now, if the rock is hard, it makes seams in the rocks and veinlets, and if it is not too hard it makes veins.

However, if the rocks are not hard, seams and veinlets are created as well as veins. If these do not carry a very large quantity of water, or if they are pressed by a great volume of it, they soon discharge themselves into the nearest veins. . . .

. . . I must explain what it really is from which metals are produced. The best proof that there is water in their materials is the fact that they flow when melted, whereas they are again solidified by the cold of air or water. This, however, must be understood in the sense that there is more water in them and less 'earth'; for it is not simply water that is their substance but water mixed with 'earth'. And such a proportion of 'earth' is in the mixture as may obscure the transparency of the water, but not remove the brilliance which is frequently in unpolished things. Again, the purer the mixture, the more precious the metal which is made from it, and the greater its resistance to fire. But what proportion of 'earth' is in each liquid from which a metal is made no mortal can ever ascertain, or still less explain, but the one God has known it, Who has given certain sure and fixed laws to nature for mixing and blending things together. It is a juice (*succus*) then, from which metals are formed; and this juice is created by various operations. Of these operations the first is a flow of water which softens the 'earth' or carries the 'earth' along with it, thus there is a mixture of 'earth' and water, then the power of heat works upon the mixtures so as to produce that kind of a juice.

We have spoken of the substance of metals; we must now speak of their efficient cause. . . . We do not deny the statement of Albertus Magnus that the mixture of 'earth' and water is baked by subterranean heat to a certain denseness, but it is our opinion that the juice so obtained is afterwards solidified by a cold so as to become a metal. . . . We grant, indeed, that heat is the efficient cause of a good mixture of elements, and also cooks this same mixture into a juice, but until this juice is solidified by cold it is not a metal. This view of Aristotle is the true one. For metals melt through the heat and somehow become softened; but those which have become softened through heat are again solidified by the influence of cold, and, on the contrary, those which become softened by moisture are solidified by heat.

¶ *Construction and Destruction of Mountains*

Hills and mountains are produced by two forces, one of which is the power of water, and the other the strength of the wind. There are three forces which loosen and demolish the mountains, for in this case, to the power of the water and the strength of the wind we must add the fire in the interior of the earth. Now we can plainly see that a great abundance of water produces mountains, for the torrents first of all wash out the soft earth, next carry away the harder earth, and then roll down the rocks, and thus in a few years they excavate the plains or slopes to a considerable depth; this may be noticed in mountainous regions even by unskilled observers. By such excavation to a great depth through many ages, there rises an immense eminence on each side. When an eminence has thus arisen, the earth rolls down, loosened by constant rain and split away by frost, and the rocks, unless they are exceedingly firm, since their seams are similarly softened by the damp, roll down into the excavations below. This continues until the steep eminence is changed into a slope. Each side of the excavation is said to be a mountain, just as the bottom is called a valley. Moreover, streams, and to a far greater extent rivers, effect the same results by their rushing and washing; for this reason they are frequently seen flowing either between very high mountains which they have created, or close by the shore which borders them. . . .

Nor did the hollow places which now contain the seas all formerly exist, nor yet the mountains which check and break their advance, but in many parts there was a level plain, until the force of winds let loose upon it a tumultuous sea and a scathing tide. By a similar process the impact of water entirely overthrows and flattens out hills and mountains. But these changes of local conditions, numerous and important as they are, are not noticed by the common people to be taking place at the very moment when they are happening, because, through their antiquity, the time, place, and manner in which they began is far prior to human memory.

The wind produces hills and mountains in two ways: either when set loose and free from bonds, it violently moves and agitates the sand; or else when, after having been driven into the hidden recesses of the earth by cold, as into a prison, it struggles with a great effort to burst out. For hills and mountains are created in hot countries, whether they are situated by the sea coasts or in districts remote from the sea, by the force of winds; these no longer held in check by the valleys, but set free, heap up the sand and dust, which they gather from all sides, to one spot, and a mass arises and grows together. If time and space allow, it grows together and hardens, but if it be not allowed (and in truth this is more often the case), the same force again scatters the sand far and wide. . . .

Then, on the other hand, an earthquake either rends and tears away part of a mountain, or engulfs and devours the whole mountain in some fearful chasm. In this way it is recorded the Cybotus was destroyed, and it is believed that within the memory of man an island under the rule of Denmark disappeared. Historians tell us that Taygetus suffered a loss in this way, and that Therasia was swallowed up with the island of Thera. Thus it is clear that water and the powerful winds produce mountains, and also scatter and destroy them. Fire only consumes them, and does not produce at all, for part of the mountains – usually the inner part – takes fire.

GEORG ERNST STAHL
1660–1734

PHLOGISTON

THE scholastic approach remained far longer in chemistry than in physics. Men continued to explain chemical phenomena in terms of 'principles'. The iatrochemists saw the three 'principles', sulphur, mercury, and salt, not so much as a chemist regards elements today, but as representing respectively inflammability, volatility, and inertness. These ideas were somewhat modified in 1669 by Becher, a professor of medicine, and were set out more specifically by his pupil, Stahl, a German professor of medicine and chemistry.

Stahl renamed the inflammable principle 'phlogiston'. Combustible substances were regarded as consisting of two parts: the calx, or ash, and phlogiston. On combustion, the phlogiston escaped and the calx remained. Different substances contained different calces, but phlogiston was common to all those which could be burned. The air could take up a certain amount of phlogiston but when completely 'phlogisticated' would neither sustain combustion nor support animal life.

In some ways it is remarkable that the phlogiston theory was put forward at the time when Robert Boyle and others were beginning to understand the chemical significance of gases and Boyle himself was defining the term 'element'. Yet many modern descriptions of chemical reactions could be described in terms of the phlogiston theory if 'evolution of phlogiston' is replaced by 'uptake of oxygen' and vice versa. This makes it easier to understand the continued use of the theory for another century. It was self-consistent in most respects and proved an adequate basis for explaining the results of the very important chemical investigations carried out especially by Black, Priestley, Scheele, and Cavendish.

It is interesting that, thirty years before Stahl's birth,

Jean Rey showed that tin and lead actually gained weight when calcined. This merely produced an addition to the phlogiston theory that phlogiston possessed the property of levity; it buoyed up the metal, which therefore gained weight when freed of its phlogiston on combustion. A more considered judgement, based on a greater attention to weighing solids and measuring the volumes of gases, led Lavoisier to the alternative interpretation which we use today.

The reading that follows has been taken from translations in *A Source Book in Chemistry* by H. M. Leicester and H. S. Klickstein (Harvard, 1952). The first passage is from *Zymotechnia fundamentalis,* first published in 1697, and the second from a later book on sulphur, published in 1718.

¶ *Definition of Phlogiston*

The same thing works very well with sulphur, when certainly two parts, or better, three parts of alkali salt and one of pulverized sulphur are successively poured into and fused in a crucible. There is formed liver of sulphur. This, in the space of a quarter of an hour more or less, by fire alone, without any addition, can be converted to such a salt as is obtained from oil of sulphur *per campanum* [H_2SO_4] and salt of tartar, that which is commonly called *vitriolated tartar*. There is no more trace of sulphur or alkali salt, and in place of the red colour of the liver, this salt is most white; in place of the very evil taste of the·liver, this salt is very bitter; in place of the easy solution, nay, the spontaneous deliquescence of the liver, by reason of its alkali salt, this salt is the most difficult of all salts except tartar of wine to be dissolved; in place of the impossibility of crystallizing the liver, this is very prone to form almost octahedral crystals; in place of the fusibility of the liver, this is devoid of all fusion.

If this new salt, from the acid of sulphur and alkaline salt formed as stated above when the phlogiston has been used up, is treated with charcoal, in the space of a quarter of an hour the original liver of sulphur reappears, and this can be so converted a hundred times. ...

I can indeed show by various other experiments how phlogiston from fatty substances and charcoal enters very promptly into metals themselves and regenerates them from the burned calx into their own *fusible, malleable,* and *amalgamable* state.

*

Now the first thing to consider concerning the principle of sulphur is its properties, as follows:

1. Behaviour towards fire
2. Display of colours
3. Subtle and intimate mixing with other metal substances
4. Behaviour towards water and humidity
5. Its own great and wonderful subtlety
6. Its own form in the dry or fluid state
7. Where it can be found or occurs.

According to these conditions and intentions, I now have demonstrable grounds to say, first,

Toward fire, this sulphur principle behaves in such a manner that it is not only suitable for the movement of fire but is also one and the same being, yes, even created and designed for it.

But also, according to a reasonable manner of speaking, it is the corporeal fire, the essential fire material, the true basis of fire movement in all inflammable compounds.

However, except in compounds, no fire at all occurs, but it dissipates and volatilizes in invisible particles, or at least, develops and forms a finely divided and invisible fire, namely, heat.

On the other hand, it is very important to note that this fire material, of and by itself and apart from other things, especially air and water, is not found united and active, either as a liquid or in an attenuated state. But if once by the movement of fire, with the addition of free air, it is attenuated and volatilized, then by this in all such conditions it is lost through unrecognizable subtlety and immeasurable attenuation, so that from this point on no science known to man, no human art, can collect it together or bring it into narrow limits, especially if this occurred rapidly and in quantity.

But how enormously attenuated and subtle material becomes through the movement of fire is shown by experience, which furnishes a field for thought and which also delights us.

From all these various conditions, therefore, I have believed that it should be given a name, as the first, unique, basic, inflammable principle. But since it cannot, until this hour, be found by itself, outside of all compounds and unions with other materials, and so there are no grounds or basis for giving a descriptive name based on properties, I have felt that it is most fitting to name it from its general action, which it customarily shows in all its compounds. And therefore I have chosen the Greek name phlogiston, in German, *brennlich* [inflammable]. . . .

The seventh and last consideration was where it could be found or occurred. The answer to this is now also in part easy to give from the discussion already presented, and from consideration that all corporeal compounded things have more or less of this substance, in all the so-called 'kingdoms': vegetable, animal, and mineral. As then in the first two kingdoms there is contained a great amount of this principle, and all their parts are intimately penetrated and combined with it (except the watery parts which occur in them, but which still are not entirely free from it as long as they are in the body), then it is chiefly found in the fatty materials of both kingdoms.

In the mineral kingdom there is nothing but water, common salt, pure vitriolic salts, and light sand and stones in which the substance is little or not at all found. On the other hand, coal and bitumen are full of it; sulphur, not indeed in weight, but in the number of its finest particles, is completely possessed with it. Not less is it found in all inflammable, incomplete, and so-called 'unripe' metals.

III

THE MECHANISTIC UNIVERSE

THE textbooks of physics and chemistry which we consult today present a picture of our knowledge of the physical world of such enormous range and depth as to outreach the comprehension of a single mind. The gradual building up of this great body of knowledge, the succession of theory upon theory, experiment upon experiment, has been the work of many men and of hundreds of years. Indeed, the extracts in this book span a period of well over two thousand years. And yet, physical science as we know it today is characterized by techniques of investigation and an underlying outlook which is of more recent origin. It will not have escaped the reader that in the writings of the earlier sections there is to be found evidence for preoccupations and attitudes of mind which the scientist of today would consider irrelevant, if not actually confusing, to the development of scientific thought.

The history of the physical sciences in the seventeenth and eighteenth centuries is remarkable not only for the rapidly expanding scope and intensity of physical inquiry but also for the founding of a radically new viewpoint towards these studies, a movement evidenced by the introduction of modes of thought of greater penetration and precision, which gave to science an authority of its own and set it free from the frequently hampering strictures of other kinds of thought. Earlier insights into what we should now call 'the scientific method' coalesced into a programme of activities which provided the framework and the inspiration for the continually progressing inquiry into the nature of the physical world with which we are familiar today.

The extracts of this section illustrate just one aspect of the great developments of these times, but it is an aspect which concerns a field of investigation – the nature and motions of the stars and planets – that had been a challenge to the scientist from the earliest times and was to play a crucial part in the revolutionary developments to come. Such cosmological speculation has been the subject of some of the earlier extracts and comparison with the writings quoted in this section will serve to illustrate the immense advances which took place.

The same comparison serves to introduce a cautionary note. In sketching out the triumphant progress of these times it must not be forgotten that our distant viewpoint lends a simplifying clarity to a scene by no means so free from confusion when looked at in the light of personal contributions. In the work of many whose thought played an essential part in the establishment of the new outlook is to be found clear evidence for the survival of those older preoccupations which they themselves helped to overthrow.

The section begins with an extract from Copernicus, whose famous hypothesis, that the planets revolve about the sun and not about the earth, was a decisive step, not only in the history of cosmological speculation, but for the history of physics as a whole. The essential correctness of his view, despite the occasionally dubious nature of his reasoning, was to lay a foundation for later achievements.

The intimate relation between theory and observation which is so characteristic of mature scientific inquiry was increasingly employed in such astronomical studies. The gradual accumulation of observational data, with its resulting restrictions on the scope of pure speculation, is well represented by the labours of such men as Tycho Brahe and Johann Kepler, whose observational skills played no less an essential role than the more dramatic achievements of the theoreticians. Kepler himself, in fact, was far from averse to such speculation, but his attempts in this field are more in sympathy with the cosmological models of the Greeks, and it is with his laws of planetary motions, based on the results of dedicated observation, that he played such a vital role in the development of new theories.

The two extracts from Galileo Galilei serve not only as an acknowledgement to one whose contribution to the founding of the modern scientific outlook is almost without equal, but further demonstrates the twin theme of theory and experiment. The part played by Galileo in the invention of the telescope has been questioned, but of his development and use of that instrument there is no doubt. The importance of such a development to astronomical observation is self-evident. Galileo's careful and comprehensive studies of the sun, the moon, and the stars were to provide a wealth of information which far transcended earlier achievements, and provided a powerful stimulus to further research. That such a sudden extension of the boundaries of human knowledge should have provoked the censure of those whose horizons were more rigidly confined is not altogether surprising. Of this clash between Church and Science there may be much to lament, and yet from such conflict the scientist emerged with a clearer conception of the aims of his subject and of the sources of the authority which supported his conclusions.

The second extract from the work of Galileo takes us right to the heart of the revolutionary developments that gave to the physical sciences the form we know today. Every physical theory necessarily employs such fundamental concepts as velocity and acceleration, force and mass. Concepts such as these, to which might be added the even more basic notions of space and time, must undergo rigorous examination and definition if they are to play their essential role in a physical theory without giving rise to confusion. In addition to such a 'vocabulary' of concepts the physicist requires 'laws of motion', general laws which provide a basis for the description of the manner in which a physical system changes with time. Such laws do not refer to any specific physical situation involving special kinds of forces, but are capable of application to all such problems. Concepts and laws together provide a theory of mechanics. We might, perhaps, think of the theory of mechanics as providing a basic language, with a vocabulary of concepts and a grammar whose structure is represented by the laws of motion, in terms of which the theories of physics are written.

The first decisive steps in the foundation of such a mechanics we owe to Galileo. Not only did he establish the patterns of thought which were to lead to the established theory presented by Newton, but he anticipated the Englishman by formulating two out of the three fundamental laws. In reading Newton's account of his mechanics, the 'Mathematical Principles of Natural Philosophy' as he called them, one cannot but be impressed by the manner of presentation, a manner so appropriate to the far-reaching importance of the subject matter. The care and precision with which each concept is introduced and defined, the statement of the laws themselves as axioms, reminding the reader that the consequences are to be logically deduced, and the labelling of the consequences as corollaries, all is reminiscent of the account of geometry presented by Euclid, and this indeed is the point at which the physical sciences attained something of the clarity and rigour of that older discipline. That later commentators should question the logical basis of Newton's scheme, and that the revolutions of the twentieth century should call in question, and condemn, the foundations of the laws, in no way detracts from the immensity of his achievement.

This achievement was all the greater in that, in association with his theory of mechanics, Newton produced a theory of gravitation which, in conjunction with his laws of motion, was able to provide a satisfactory account of the planetary motions, and in so doing demonstrate the origins of Kepler's laws. The theory of gravitation was to remain unchallenged for two centuries and provided an exemplary model for theories in other branches of physics. The tremendous impetus which astronomy received from this achievement is well illustrated by the extract from Newton's contemporary Edmund Halley, where the ability of the theory to correlate astronomical observation over long periods of time, and, what is more important, to predict future happenings with confidence, is a clear indication of the power of the theory. The full flowering of the classical theory of planetary motions came in the following century with the work of Pierre Simon Laplace, and the final extract represents his attempt to account for the origin of the solar system. Modern cosmology has as its basis the newer conceptual approaches which were to arrive with the twentieth century, yet the classical theories remain as a magnificent vindication of the attitudes and techniques that were to grow out of the scientific revolution.

COPERNICUS
1473–1543

THE REJECTION OF THE
PTOLEMAIC UNIVERSE

NIKLAS KOPPERNIGK (called in Latin, Copernicus), born in Torun, in Poland, student at Cracow, Bologna, Ferrara, and Padua, and, thereafter and until his death, canon of the Cathedral at Frauenburg, was a splendid example of the medieval scholar. His genius was universal, and his reading ranged from economics and medicine to mathematics and astronomy. Such breadth of interest reflected a high intelligence and imaginative instructors. One of the latter, Domenico Novaro, Professor of Mathematics and Astronomy at Bologna, was a Pythagorean in that he believed in the essential simplicity and harmony of the universe, and he criticized the complexities of the Ptolemaic system. Copernicus was thus encouraged to study the classics in order to discover the objections to the concept that the earth was fixed and immovable and the centre of the universe. He found that Hicetas, for example, who lived in the fifth century before Christ, had taught that the earth rotated on its own axis in twenty-four hours. Aristarchus, two hundred years after Hicetas, taught the same idea and added that the sun was the centre of an immeasurably great universe. These views had been discussed by Bishop Oresme (1330?–82) and others whose works were included in Copernicus's curriculum.

Copernicus's system was, in the main, a reconstruction of Ptolemy's, which by the end of the fifteenth century had grown extremely complex and cumbersome, consisting of more than eighty spheres but still inadequate to explain celestial movements. Copernicus was able to simplify the celestial model by reducing the number of spheres to thirty-four. By assuming that the earth moved and that the sun was at the centre of the universe, he was able, in some thirty years of effort, to devise a new scheme of the universe which was much simpler and explained more. He recalculated the tables which had been developed out of the Ptolemaic system, but in doing this he had to rely on the basic observations made by his predecessors, even those of Ptolemy himself. He represented the symmetry and order of the sun-centred system by a combination of a few uniform circular paths, retaining a few of the epicycles of Ptolemy to 'save the phenomena' and account for observed details of motion.

Copernicus was an eminently modest and gentle man, not over-eager to publicize the results of his work. There is no evidence that he himself feared the reactions of the Church to his assertion that the earth moved; he was more concerned with the possibility of ridicule and once said, 'The contempt which I had to fear because of the novelty and apparent absurdity of my view nearly induced me to abandon utterly the work I had begun.' Three years before Copernicus's death, one Rheticus published a summary of his book under the title *De libris revolutionum narratio prima*, apparently with the permission of Church officials who had read some of Copernicus's drafts during the long period of its preparation. His definitive work, *De revolutionibus orbium coelestium*, was published shortly before he died. The book contained a preface, afterwards found to have been written by a Lutheran minister named Osiander, intended to placate the Protestants and describing the work as a mathematical exercise rather than an astronomical treatise. This preface may have been the reason why the Copernican ideas failed to have an immediate revolutionary effect; in fact, the Ptolemaic system and the new Copernican model were taught as alternative explanations until the eighteenth century.

The Church took no positive action against the Copernican view until the teachings of Giordano Bruno (1548?–1600) drew attention to its consequences on Church doctrine. Thus, almost a century after Copernicus's death, his work became the centre of a violent intellectual controversy by undermining the unity of the medieval system of thought. Bruno accepted the Copernican scheme and went one step further by denying the necessity for a finite universe. If the Deity were infinite, why should his creations be finite? The effect was to abolish the idea of that final sphere which, Ptolemy and his followers held, contained the fixed stars. Since the Church had located Heaven beyond this last sphere and Bruno had now removed the boundaries of the physical universe, the way was open to the idea that creation might extend beyond the world described in the book of *Genesis*. Bruno was burned at the stake for thus upsetting the Church's teaching that man was God's principal concern. Copernicus's work was banned and remained in the Church's disfavour until 1822.

Thus the full impact of the Copernican hypothesis on the world of science was not to be felt until Galileo's telescope had brought observational support and Newton's theories had revealed the logical basis of the model.

The reading that follows has been taken from Edward Rosen's translation of *Three Copernican Treatises*, Columbia University Press (1934). See also Plate 2.

¶ CHAPTER I *That the Universe Is Spherical*

First of all we assert that the universe is spherical; partly because this form, being a complete whole, needing no joints, is the most perfect of all; partly because it constitutes the most spacious form, which is thus best suited to contain and retain all things, or also because all discrete parts of the world, I mean the sun, the moon, and the planets, appear as spheres; or because all things tend to assume the spherical shape, a fact which appears in a drop of water and in other fluid bodies when they seek of their own accord to limit themselves. Therefore no one will doubt that this form is natural for the heavenly bodies.

¶ CHAPTER II *That the Earth Is Likewise Spherical*

That the earth is likewise spherical is beyond doubt, because it presses from all sides to its centre. Although a perfect sphere is not immediately recognized because of the great height of the mountains and the depression of the valleys, yet this in no wise invalidates the general spherical form of the earth. This becomes clear in the following manner: To people who travel from any place to the North, the north pole of the daily revolution rises gradually, while the south pole sinks a like amount. Most of the stars in the neighbourhood of the Great Bear appear not to set, and in the South some stars appear no longer to rise. Thus Italy does not see Canopus, which is visible to the Egyptians. And Italy sees the outermost star of the River, which is unknown to us of a colder zone. On the other hand, to people who travel towards the South, these stars rise higher in the heavens, while those stars which are higher to us become lower. Therefore, it is plain that the earth is included between the poles and is spherical. Let us add that the inhabitants of the East do not see the solar and lunar eclipses that occur in the evening, and people who live in the West do not see eclipses that occur in the morning, while those living in between see the former later, and the latter earlier.

That even the water has the same shape is observed on ships, in that the land which can not be seen from the ships can be spied from the tip of the mast. And, conversely, when a light is put on the tip of the mast, it appears to observers on land gradually to drop as the ship recedes until the light disappears, seeming to sink in the water. It is clear that the water, too, in accordance with its fluid nature, is drawn downwards, just as is the earth, and its level at the shore is no higher than its convexity allows. The land therefore projects everywhere only as far above the ocean as the land accidentally happens to be higher. . . .

❡ CHAPTER IV *That the Motions of the Heavenly Bodies are Uniform, Circular, Uninterrupted, or Are Made Up of Combined Circular Motions*

Hereupon, we note that the motions of the heavenly bodies are circular. When a sphere is in motion it rotates, expressing, through this activity, its form as that of the simplest of bodies, in which there is to be found neither a beginning nor an end; nor can the beginning be distinguished from the end, as the sphere achieves, through the same intermediate points, its original position. Because of the multiplicity of circles there are, however, numerous possible motions. The best known of all is the daily revolution which the Greeks call Nychthemeron, i.e., the period of day and night. To achieve this motion, it is believed the whole universe with the exception of the earth, turns from east to west. It is recognized as the common measure of all motions, since time itself is measured chiefly by the number of days. In addition, we see progressing other revolutions which are apparently retrograde, i.e., from west to east; namely those of the sun, the moon, and the five planets.

By means of this motion the sun measures for us the year, the moon, the month, as the most common units of time. And thus each of the other five planets completes its orbit. Yet they are peculiar in many ways. First, in that they do not revolve about the same poles around which the first motion takes place, progressing instead in the oblique path of the Zodiac; second, in that they do not seem to move uniformly in their own orbits, for the sun and the moon are discovered moving now with a slower, now a faster motion. The remaining five planets, moreover, we also see at times going backwards and, in the transition, standing still. And while the sun moves along always in its direct path, the planets wander in various ways, roaming, now to the South, now to the North. Wherefore they are designated 'planets'. They have the added peculiarity that they at times come nearer to the earth, where they are called at perigee, then again they recede from it, where they are called at apogee.

Nevertheless, it must be admitted that the motions are circular, or are built up of many circles; for thus such irregularities would occur according to a reliable law and a fixed p eriod, which could not be the case if they were not circular. For the circle alone can bring back the past, as the sun, so to speak, brings back to us, through its motion made up of circles, the irregularities of the days and nights and the four seasons; in which several motions are recognized because it cannot happen that the simple heavenly bodies move irregularly in a single circle. For this would either have to be caused by an inconstancy in the nature of the moving force – whether the inconstancy be brought about by a cause from without or within – or would have to originate in an irregularity of the moving body. But as reason rebels against both, and as it is unworthy to assume such a thing concerning that which is arranged in the best of order, so one must admit that the regular motions seem irregular to us, either because the various circles have different poles, or because the earth is not situated in the centre of the circles in which the planets move; and that to us who observe the motions of the stars from the earth, the planets, because of the varying distances, appear larger when near us than when they are in paths more remote; that can be proved in optics. In this way the motions which take place in equal times through equal arcs, seem to us unequal due to different distances. Therefore, I consider it above all things necessary that we investigate carefully what relation the earth has to the heavens, so that we, when we wish to investigate the most noble things in nature, do not leave out of consideration the nearest, and erroneously attribute to the heavenly bodies what belongs to the earth.

¶ CHAPTER V *Whether the Earth Has a Circular Motion, and Concerning the Location of the Earth*

Since it has already been proved that the earth has the shape of a sphere, I insist that we must investigate whether from its form can be deduced a motion, and what place the earth occupies in the universe. Without this knowledge no certain computation can be made for the phenomena occurring in the heavens. To be sure, the great majority of writers agree that the earth is at rest in the centre of the universe, so that they consider it unbelievable and even ridiculous to suppose the contrary. Yet, when one weighs the matter carefully, he will see that this question is not yet disposed of, and for that reason is by no means to be considered unimportant. Every change of position which is observed is due either to the motion of the observed object or of the observer, or to motions, naturally in different directions, of both; for when the observed object and the observer move in the same manner and in the same direction, then no motion is observed. Now the earth is the place from which we observe the revolution of the heavens and where it is displayed to our eyes. Therefore, if the earth should possess any motion, the latter would be noticeable in everything that is situated outside of it, but in the opposite direction, just as if everything were travelling past the earth. And of this nature is, above all, the daily revolution. For this motion seems to embrace the whole world, in fact, everything that is outside of the earth, with the single exception of the earth itself. But if one should admit that the heavens possess none of this motion, but that the earth rotates from west to east; and if one should consider this seriously with respect to the seeming rising and setting of the sun, of the moon, and stars; then one would find that it is actually true. Since the heavens which contain and retain all things are the common home of all things, it is not at once comprehensible why a motion is not rather ascribed to the thing contained than to the containing, to the located rather than to the locating. This opinion was actually held by the Pythagoreans Heraklid and Ekphantus and the Syracusean Nicetas (as told by Cicero), in that they assumed the earth to be rotating in the centre of the universe. They were indeed of the opinion that the stars set due to the intervening of the earth, and rose due to its receding.

From this assumption follows the other not less important doubt concerning the position of the earth, though it is assumed and believed by almost everyone that the earth occupies the centre of the universe. If, therefore, one should maintain that the earth is not in the centre of the universe, but that the discrepancy between the two is not great enough to be measurable on the sphere of the fixed stars, but on the other hand noticeable and recognizable in the orbits of the sun and the planets; and if further he were of the opinion that the motions of the latter for this reason appear irregular, just as if they were oriented with respect to another centre than that of the earth – such a person might, perhaps, have assigned the true reason for the apparently irregular motions. For since the planets appear now nearer, now more distant from the earth, this betrays necessarily that the centre of the earth is not the centre of those circular orbits. And yet it is not determined whether the earth decreases and increases its distance from them or they their distance from the earth.

It would thus not be strange if someone should ascribe to the earth, in addition to its daily rotation, also another motion. However, it is said that the Pythagorean Philolaus, a not ordinary mathematician, believed that the earth rotates, that it moves along in space with various motions, and that it belongs to the planets; wherefore, Plato did not delay journeying to Italy to interview him, as is told by those who have described Plato's life. Many, on the other hand, believed that it could be proved by mathematical calculation that the earth is situated in the centre of the universe, and since, compared with the enormous size of the heavens, it can be considered as a point, it occupies the central point and is for this reason immovable; because if the universe moves, its central point must remain motionless, and that which is nearest the central point must move most slowly.

¶ CHAPTER VII *Why the Ancients Believed that the Earth Rests in the Middle of the Universe, as Its Central Point*

Thus for certain other reasons the ancient philosophers sought to prove that the earth is in the centre of the universe. As chief cause, however, they cite weight and imponderability. The element earth is, to be sure, the heaviest of all, and everything ponderable tends to move, governed by its impulse, towards the innermost centre of the earth. Now since the earth is spherical – the earth, on to the surface of which heavy bodies from all sides fall perpendicularly, due to their own nature – the falling bodies would meet at its centre if they were not held back on the surface; because, indeed, a straight line which is perpendicular to the tangent plane at its point of tangency leads to the centre. As to those bodies which move towards the centre, it seems to follow that they would come to rest at the centre. All the more would the whole earth be at rest in the centre, and no matter what it might accumulate in the way of falling bodies, it would remain motionless due to its own weight.

In a similar manner the ancients support their proofs with the cause of motion and its nature. Aristotle says, for example, that a simple body has a simple motion; of possible simple motions, however, one is motion in a straight line, the other is circular motion. Of simple motions in a straight line, one is upwards, and the other is downwards. Therefore, every simple motion would be either towards the centre, i.e. downward, or away from the centre, i.e., upwards, or around the centre, and this would be the circular motion or revolution. Only the earth and the water, which are considered heavy, move downwards, that is, tend to move towards the centre. Air, however, and fire, which are endowed with imponderability, move upwards and away from the centre. It seems clear that one must admit motion in a straight line for these four elements; as regards the heavenly bodies, however, one must admit motion in a circle around the centre. Thus says Aristotle. 'If, therefore,' says the Alexandrian Ptolemy, 'the earth turns, at least in daily rotation, the opposite of all that is said above must take place; that is to say the motion which traverses throughout the whole circumference of the earth in twenty-four hours would have to be the most violent of all and its velocity would have to be transcendent. But matter which is set in violent rotation does not seem at all fit to be massed together, but rather to be dispersed, if the component parts are not held together with some firmness. And long before now,' he says, 'the disintegrated earth would have been dissipated over the heavens themselves, which is very ridiculous; and much less would the living beings and other separated masses in any way have remained unannihilated. But also the bodies falling in straight lines would not arrive on the places destined for them, as these spots would in the meantime have moved from under which such great velocity. We would also see the clouds and whatever else is floating in the air always moving towards the west.'

¶ CHAPTER VIII *Refutation of the Arguments, and Their Insufficiency*

From these and similar reasons it is claimed that the earth is at rest in the centre of the universe and that this is undoubtedly true. But one who believes that the earth rotates will also certainly be of the opinion that this motion is natural and not violent. Whatever is in accordance with nature produces effects which are the opposite of what happens through violence. Things upon which violence or an external force is exerted must become annihilated and cannot long exist. But whatever happens in the course of nature remains in good condition and in its best arrangement. Without cause, therefore, Ptolemy feared that the earth and all earthly things if set in rotation would be dissolved by the action of nature, for the functioning of nature is something entirely different from artifice, or from that which could be contrived by the human mind. But why did he not fear the same and indeed in much higher degree, for the universe, whose motion would have to be as much more rapid as the heavens are larger than the earth? Or have the heavens become infinite just because they have been removed from the centre by the inexpressible force of the motion; while otherwise, if they were at rest, they would collapse? Certainly if this argument were true the extent of the heavens would become infinite. For the more they were driven aloft by the outward impulse of the motion, the more rapid would the motion become because of the ever increasing circle which it would have to describe in the space of twenty-four hours; and, conversely, if the motion increased, the immensity of the heavens would also increase. Thus velocity would augment size into infinity, and size, velocity. But according to the physical law that the infinite can neither be traversed, nor can it for any reason have motion, the heavens would, however, of necessity be at rest.

But it is said that outside of the heavens there is no body, nor place, nor empty space, in fact, that nothing at all exists, and that, therefore, there is no space in which the heavens could expand; then it is really strange that something could be enclosed by nothing. If, however, the heavens were infinite and were bounded only by their inner concavity, then we have, perhaps, even better confirmation that there is nothing outside of the heavens, because everything, whatever its size, is within them; but then the heavens would remain motionless. The most important argument, on which depends the proof of the finiteness of the universe, is motion. Now, whether the world is finite or infinite, we will leave to the quarrels of the natural philosophers; for us remains the certainty that the earth, contained between poles, is bounded by a spherical surface. Why should we hesitate to grant it a motion, natural and corresponding to its form; rather than assume that the whole world, whose boundary is not known and cannot be known, moves? And why are we not willing to acknowledge that the appearance of a daily revolution belongs to the heavens, its actuality to the earth? The relation is similar to that of which Virgil's Aeneas says: 'We sail out of the harbour, and the countries and cities recede.' For when a ship is sailing along quietly, everything which is outside of it will appear to those on board to have a motion corresponding to the movement of the ship, and the voyagers are of the erroneous opinion that they with all that they have with them are at rest. This can without doubt also apply to the motion of the earth, and it may appear as if the whole universe were revolving.

Now what shall we say about the clouds and whatever else is somehow floating, falling or rising in the air? Except that not only does the earth move with its attached watery element, but it also carries with it no small part of the air and whatever else is thus joined with the earth. It may be that the air lying nearest the earth, mixed with earthy and watery material, obeys the same nature as the earth; it may be that the motion has been communicated to the air, the atmosphere partaking of this motion because of the contact with the earth and the resistance during the constant rotation. Again, an equally astonishing claim, namely, that the highest region of the air obeys the heavenly motion, is said to be supported by those suddenly-appearing stellar objects which are called by the Greeks comets or bearded stars, the origin of which one assigns to just that region, and which, like other constellations, rise and set. It may be said that that part of the air, due to its great remoteness from the earth, has remained immune from the earthly motion. Therefore, the air which lies nearest the earth will appear at rest, as well as those objects floating in it, when they are not driven hither and yon by the wind or by some other external force, as may happen by chance; for what is the wind in the air other than the waves in the sea? We must admit that the motion of falling and rising objects is, with respect to the universe, a double one, compounded always of rectilinear and circular motions. Since that which, due to its weight, is attracted downwards is essentially earthy, there is no doubt that these parts obey the same law as their whole – namely, the earth; and for the same reason such objects as belong to the fire class are drawn aloft with violence. Earthly fire is fed principally with earthy materials, and it is said that a

flame is only burning smoke. The peculiarity of fire, however, consists in expanding that which it has taken hold of;
and it achieves this with such violence that it can be hindered by no method or machine from breaking down the
barriers and fulfilling its work. But the expanding motion is
directed from the centre to the periphery. Therefore, when
anything composed of earthy parts is ignited, it moves from
the centre upwards.

Thus, as has been claimed, a simple body has a simple
motion and this proves to be preferably a circular motion as
long as the simple body remains in its natural position and
retains its unity. In this position its motion is merely the
circular motion which, being entirely within the body, makes
it seem to be at rest. Rectilinear motion, however, attacks
bodies which have left or have been left or have been forced
from their natural positions, or have in some manner
become displaced. Nothing militates so against the order
and form of the whole world as 'being-out-of-its-place'.
Thus motion in a straight line enters only when things are
not in their proper relations and are not completely as they
should be, having been separated from their whole and
having lost their unity. Moreover, such bodies which are
driven upwards or downwards, disregarding the circular
motion, do not describe simple uniform and constant
motion, for they cannot orient themselves by their lightness
or the pressure of their weight; and if at the beginning of
their plunge they have a slower motion, they increase their
velocity in falling. While on the other hand we see that
earthly fire (and we know of no other kind) when driven
aloft at once becomes inert, as if it showed by this means
the origin of the earthy materials. Circular motion, on the
other hand, is always uniform because it has a cause that
does not slacken. The other motions, however, diminish
during their progress, when the bodies have reached their
natural position they cease to be either imponderable or
heavy, and, therefore, their motion ceases. If, therefore,
the universe possesses circular motion and its parts possess
also rectilinear motion, then we might say that circular

motion is compatible with rectilinear motion, just as the animal with disease. If Aristotle divided simple motions into three kinds, away from the centre, towards the centre, and around the centre, that seems to be only an intellectual exercise, just as we distinguish between a line, a point, and a surface, even though one of these cannot exist without the others, and none of them without matter. Moreover, the condition of rest is considered as nobler and more divine than that of change and inconstancy, so the latter would, therefore, be more suited to the earth than to the universe. And I add to this that it seems irrational to ascribe a motion to that which contains and locates and not to that which is contained and is located, namely the earth. Finally, since the planets clearly are now nearer, now farther from the earth, the motion of one and the same body about the centre (which is said to be the centre of the earth), is also directed away from and towards this centre. It is, therefore, necessary to have a more general conception of motion about a centre, and it should be sufficient if each single motion has its own centre. It is clear, therefore, from all this, that motion of the earth is more probable than rest, especially in relation to the daily rotation, which is most characteristic of the earth.

¶ CHAPTER IX *Whether the Earth Can Be Assigned Several Motions; and Concerning the Centre of the Universe*

Since nothing stands in the way of the movability of the earth, I believe we must now investigate whether it also has several motions, so that it can be considered one of the planets. That it is not the centre of all the revolutions is proved by the irregular motions of the planets, and their varying distances from the earth, which cannot be explained as concentric circles with the earth at the centre. Therefore, since there are several central points, no one will without cause be uncertain whether the centre of the universe is the centre of gravity of the earth or some other central point. I, at least, am of the opinion that gravity is nothing else than a natural force planted by the divine providence of the Master of the World into its parts, by means of which they, assuming a spherical shape, form a unity and a whole. And it is to be assumed that the impulse is also inherent in the sun and the moon and the other planets, and that by the operation of this force they remain in the spherical shape in which they appear; while they, nevertheless, complete their revolutions in diverse ways. If then the earth, too, possesses other motions besides that around its centre, then they must be of such a character as to become apparent in many ways and in appropriate manners; and among such possible effects we recognize the yearly revolution. If one admits the motionlessness of the sun, and transfers the annual revolution from the sun to the earth, there would result, in the same manner as actually observed, the rising and setting of the constellations and the fixed stars, by means of which they become morning and evening stars; and it will thus become apparent that also the haltings and the backward and forward motion of the planets are not motions of these but of the earth, which lends them the appearance of being actual planetary motions. Finally, one will be convinced that the sun itself occupies the centre of the universe. And all this is taught us by the law of sequence in which things follow one upon another and the harmony of the universe; that is, if we only (so to speak) look at the matter with both eyes.

TYCHO BRAHE
1546–1601

A NEW STAR IS REPORTED

COPERNICUS, the contemplative scholar, was first opposed
by an aggressive, practical astronomer, Tycho Brahe. Brahe
– a Dane who had studied mathematics and astronomy in
German and Swiss universities – came to the conclusion that
Copernicus's assumption that the earth moved in space
defied the scriptures and violated the principles of physics;
and so he set out to rehabilitate Ptolemaic astronomy. Brahe
succeeded in restating Ptolemy's system by showing that the
sun revolved around the earth and the planets turned
around the sun in epicycles. He made no great effort, however, to promote his theories, finding himself much more
interested in making observations of the stars.

With the encouragement of royal patrons, Brahe worked
at Uraniborg (near Hamlet's Elsinore) in Denmark until
1597 and then, for the few years until his death, at Prague.
With instruments based mainly on the astrolabe but improved and enlarged by him, Brahe attained an accuracy
that could hardly be improved upon without lenses. Moreover, he refined the methods of his predecessors, who had
relied on what they believed to be the best possible observations. With a group of assistants, Brahe maintained systematic series of observations of the planets and stars, averaging
the results so as to minimize errors. His data were regularly
recorded, and his catalogue of the stars – listing 777 when
he published it in 1592 – became a standard reference,
especially as enlarged by his pupil Kepler. Brahe's detailed
records provided data that upset the long-held proposition
that the heavenly orbits were perfectly circular.

Brahe's instruments merely guided his naked eye; they
did not supplement its powers. Yet he was able to record
measurements of stellar positions with an error of less than

one-sixtieth of a degree of arc – an achievement that testifies to the persistence as well as the accuracy of his researches. His data long retained their value, establishing Brahe as one of the most successful astronomical observers of all time. His return to Ptolemaic theory was, perhaps, the result of his cantankerousness; he was a natural objector to other people's ideas who nevertheless served science by expanding its horizons and adding to its store of accumulated verified fact.

Brahe's observation of a new star in 1572, recorded in the following selection, was a direct challenge to the Aristotelian concept that the universe was confined by a sphere containing an unalterable number of stars.

The reading that follows has been taken from the J. H. Walden translation of *De nova stella* in *A Source Book of Astronomy*, Harvard (1929).

¶ *On a New Star, Not Previously Seen Within the Memory of Any Age Since the Beginning of the World*

Its First Appearance in 1572. Last year (1572), in the month of November, on the eleventh day of that month, in the evening, after sunset, when, according to my habit, I was contemplating the stars in a clear sky, I noticed that a new and unusual star, surpassing the other stars in brilliancy, was shining almost directly above my head; and since I had, almost from boyhood, known all the stars of the heavens perfectly (there is no great difficulty in attaining that knowledge), it was quite evident to me that there had never before been any star in that place in the sky, even the smallest, to say nothing of a star so conspicuously bright as this. I was so astonished at this sight that I was not ashamed to doubt the trustworthiness of my own eyes. But when I observed that others, too, on having the place pointed out to them, could see that there was really a star there, I had no further doubts. A miracle indeed, either the greatest of all that have occurred in the whole range of nature since the beginning of the world, or one certainly that is to be classed with those attested by the Holy Oracles, the staying of the Sun in its course in answer to the prayers of Joshua, and the darkening of the Sun's face at the time of the Crucifixion. For all philosophers agree, and facts clearly prove it to be the case, that in the ethereal region of the celestial world no change, in the way either of generation or of corruption, takes place; but that the heavens and the celestial bodies in the heavens are without increase or diminution, and that they undergo no alteration, either in number or in size or in light or in any other respect; that they always remain the same, like unto themselves in all respects, no years wearing them away. Furthermore, the observations of all founders of the science, made some thousands of years ago, testify that all the stars have always retained the same number, position, order, motion, and size as they are found, by careful observation on the part of those who take delight in heavenly phenomena, to preserve even in our own day. Nor do we read that it was ever before noted by any one of the founders that a new star had appeared in the celestial world, except only by Hipparchus, if we are to believe Pliny. For Hipparchus, according to Pliny (Book II of his Natural History), noticed a star different from all others previously seen, one born in his own age. . . .

Its Position with Reference to the Diameter of the World and its Distance from the Earth, the Centre of the Universe. It is a difficult matter, and one that requires a subtle mind, to try to determine the distances of the stars from us, because they are so incredibly far removed from the earth; nor can it be done in any way more conveniently and with greater certainty than by the measure of the parallax (diurnal), if a star have one. For if a star that is near the horizon is seen in a different place than when it is at its highest point and near the vertex, it is necessarily found in some orbit with respect to which the Earth has a sensible size. How far distant the said orbit is, the size of the parallax compared with the semidiameter of the Earth will make clear. If, however, a (circumpolar) star, that is as near to the horizon (at lower culmination) as to the vertex (at upper culmination), is seen at the same point of the Primum Mobile, there is no doubt that it is situated either in the eighth sphere or not far below it, in an orbit with respect to which the whole Earth is as a point.

In order, therefore, that I might find out in this way whether this star was in the region of the Element or among the celestial orbits, and what its distance was from the Earth itself, I tried to determine whether it had a parallax, and, if so, how great a one; and this I did in the following way: I observed the distance between this star and Schedir of Cassiopeia (for the latter and the new star were both nearly on the meridian), when the star was at its nearest point to the vertex, being only 6 degrees removed from the zenith itself (and for that reason, though it were near the Earth, would produce no parallax in that place, the visual position of the star and the real position then uniting in one point, since the line from the centre of the Earth and that from the surface nearly coincide). I made the same observation when the star was farthest from the zenith and at its nearest point to the horizon, and in each case I found that the distance from the above-mentioned fixed star was exactly the same, without the variation of a minute: namely 7 degrees and 55 minutes. Then I went through the same process, making numerous observations with other stars. Whence I conclude that this new star has no diversity of aspect, even when it is near the horizon. For otherwise in its least altitude it would have been farther away from the above-mentioned star in the breast of Cassiopeia than when in its greatest altitude. Therefore, we shall find it necessary to place this star, not in the region of the Element, below the Moon, but far above, in an orbit with respect to which the Earth has no sensible size. For if it were in the highest region of the air, below the hollow region of the Lunar sphere, it would, when nearest the horizon, have produced on the circle a sensible variation of altitude from that which it held when near the vertex.

To make the proof clearer, let a circle be drawn representing the meridian, or some other vertical circle of the Primum

Mobile, in which the places of all the stars are held to be, and let this circle be *CBDE*, with its centre *A*. Let the diameter *BE* indicate the vertex, and *CD* the horizon. Furthermore, let there be described with the same centre a circle *MKL*, which shall indicate the circumference of the Earth. Between these let there be drawn another circle *GHFI*, to represent the lowest circle of the Lunar sphere and the one nearest the Earth, in which we are to imagine this star to be. And let it first be in its greatest altitude, near the point *G*: it is clear that it is entirely without diversity of aspect; for the two lines, one drawn from the centre of the Earth, and the other drawn from the eye placed on the sur-

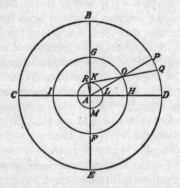

face of the Earth, unite in one and the same point of the circle of the Primum Mobile *CBDE*, that is, in the point *B*, or near it if the star is not exactly at *G*. For this star is removed 6 degrees from the vertex, when it is for us at its highest point; which distance, however, produces no sensible variation from the vertex itself. But let this star be placed in the same circle *GHFI* at its lowest altitude, which is the point *O*, and, if the eye is placed at *K* on the surface of the Earth, the star will necessarily be seen in another place on the outermost circle from what it will if the eye is at *A*, the centre of the earth. For, if lines are drawn from *K* on the surface, and *A*, the centre of the Earth, through *O*, which is the position of the star, to the outermost orbit *BDEC*, the line from A through O will fall in P, while the line from K through the same point O will fall in Q. PQ, therefore, is the arc of the Primum Mobile showing the diversity of aspect of the star.

I will try to determine, therefore, the length of the arc PQ, so that we may learn how great is the diversity of aspect which this star has when it is at its nearest point to the horizon, if it is placed in the circle $IGHF$, immediately below the orbit of the Moon, at the point O. That this may be done more conveniently, let the line QOK be produced until another line drawn from the centre A meets it perpendicularly, and let the point of meeting be R. Since the angle BKO is known by observation – for it is the complement of the least altitude of the star itself, namely 62 degrees, 5 minutes – its vertical angle RKA will be known, being its equal. Furthermore, the angle KRA is by hypothesis a right angle; and the side KA is known by some measurement or other, for it is the semidiameter of the Earth itself. AR will be found by Proposition 29 of Regiomontanus concerning plane triangles. If, therefore, we give to the semi-diameter of the earth, KA, as being the whole sine, since it is the side opposite the right angle R the length of 100,000 units, the side AR proves to be 88,363 units. Now at last I form my concept of the triangle ROA, two sides of which, RA and AO, are known. For AO is the distance from the centre of the Earth to the lowest surface of the orbit of the Moon, which distance, with Copernicus, I have set at 5,200,000 of the same units in which the semidiameter of the Earth, AK, was reckoned as 100,000 (for I find it best to make use of larger numbers in this computation, that the calculation may be carried on more conveniently and the result be given more exactly); and since in the aforementioned triangle the angle ORA is by hypothesis a right angle, the angle ROA will be found by the 27th Proposition of Regiomontanus on plane triangles. For by multiplying the side AR in to the whole sine, we get 8,836,300,000, which number, being divided by the side AO, gives 1699 units, the sine, namely, of the angle ROA, whose arc is 0 degrees, $58\frac{1}{2}$ minutes; and this number

determines the size of the required angle. To this angle,
ROA, the angle *POQ* is equal, since it is its vertical angle,
as is manifest from the principles of geometry. Therefore,
the arc *PQ*, which is the measure of this angle (for, owing to
the immense distance between the Lunar sphere and
Primum Mobile, the arc *PQ* does not differ sensibly from
the arc of the circle intercepted by the same lines at the
distance *OP*) and indicates the parallax of the star, will be
$58\frac{1}{2}$ minutes, which was what we had to find. So great,
therefore, would have been the diversity of aspect of this
star in the position *O*, as between that place which it held
near the vertex and that in which it was seen when nearest
the horizon. But after making many careful observations, as
I said above, with a most delicate and accurate instrument,
I found that this was not the case. Whence I conclude that
this star which has recently become visible is not in the
circle *IGHF*, in the uppermost region, that is, of the air,
immediately below the orbit of the Moon, nor in any place
yet nearer the Earth – for in the latter case the arc *PQ* would
have produced a greater length, and the diversity of aspect
would be greater – but that it is situated far above the
Lunar sphere, in the heaven itself, and in fact in some orbit
so far removed from the Earth that the line *KA*, the semidiameter of the Earth, has no sensible size in respect to it,
but that the whole Earth, when compared to it, is observed
to be no more than a point; and this has been found by the
founders of the science to be in the eighth sphere or not far
from it in the higher orbits of the three superior planets.
Whence this star will be placed in the heavens themselves,
either in the eighth orbit with the other fixed stars or in the
spheres which are immediately beneath it. That it is not in the
orbit of Saturn, however, or in that of Jupiter, or in that of
Mars, or in that of any one of the other planets, is clear from
this fact: after the lapse of six months it had not advanced
by its own motion a single minute from that place in which
I first saw it; and this it must have done if it were in some
planetary orbit. For, unlike the Primum Mobile, it would be
moved by the peculiar motion of the orbit itself, unless it

were at rest at one or the other pole of the orbits of the Secundum Mobile; from which, however, as I have shown above, it is removed 28 degrees. For the entire orbits, revolving on their own poles, carry along their own stars, or (as I see Pliny and some others hold) are carried along by them; unless, indeed, one would deny the belief accepted by philosophers and mathematicians, and assert (what is absurd) that the stars alone revolve, while the orbits are fixed. Therefore, if this star were placed in some one of the orbits of the seven wandering stars, it would necessarily be carried around with the orbit itself to which it were affixed, in the opposite direction to the daily revolution. And, furthermore, this motion, even in the case of the orbit which moves the slowest, that of Saturn, would, after such a length of time, be noticed, though one were to make his observation without any instrument at all.

Therefore, this new star is neither in the region of the Element, below the Moon, nor among the orbits of the seven wandering stars, but it is in the eighth sphere, among the other fixed stars, which was what we had to prove. Hence it follows that it is not some peculiar kind of comet or some other kind of fiery meteor become visible. For none of these are generated in the heavens themselves, but they are below the Moon, in the upper region of the air, as all philosophers testify; unless one would believe with Albategnius that comets are produced, not in the air, but in the heavens. For he believes that he has observed a comet above the Moon, in the sphere of Venus. That this can be the case, is not yet clear to me. But, please God, sometime, if a comet shows itself in our age, I will investigate the truth of the matter. Even should we assume that it can happen (which I, in company with other philosophers, can hardly admit), still it does not follow that this star is a kind of comet; first, by reason of its very form, which is the same as the form of the real stars and different from the form of all the comets hitherto seen, and then because, in such a length of time, it advances neither latitudinally nor longitudinally by any motion of its own, as comets have been observed to do. For although these sometimes seem to remain in one place several days, still, when the observation is made carefully by exact instruments, they are seen not to keep the same position for so very long or so very exactly. I conclude, therefore, that this star is not some kind of comet or a fiery meteor, whether these be generated beneath the Moon or above the Moon, but that it is a star shining in the firmament itself – one that has never previously been seen before our time, in any age since the beginning of the world.

JOHANN KEPLER
1571–1630

ON THE MOTION OF THE PLANETS

SHORTLY before his death, Tycho Brahe appointed as his assistant a young German, Johann Kepler – a protégé of the Holy Roman Emperor and already a convinced follower of Copernicus. Kepler took over Brahe's records and edited and extended them by his own observations, adding another 228 stars to Brahe's catalogue. He did more than this; he established, inductively, laws of the planetary orbits which were later to serve as the foundation of Newton's astronomy.

Before joining Brahe in Prague, Kepler had published, in 1596, his *Mysterium cosmographicum*, in which he had defended Copernicus and, at the same time, presented his own ideas as to the shape of the universe. This concept, based on his preoccupation with the mysticism of numbers, involved the use of various polygons as well as spheres and resulted in a model whose attributes appeared to be verifiable against observation. Brahe's examination of Copernican doctrines with the use of his observed data left him with certain errors. Kepler, in investigating these errors, found himself obliged to question a fundamental assumption – that heavenly movements were limited to the circular or to curves derived from a circle. Basing his work on the observation of Mars, he came to the conclusion that the shape of the planetary orbit was elliptical. From this hypothesis, Kepler established his three laws of planetary motion. Although it has since been shown that Kepler's laws are not absolutely precise, they stood the test of observation for two hundred years before any error was detected.

Kepler succeeded in presenting a workable explanation of the movement of the planets, but he left a gap to be filled by others. Since the old, spherical conception assumed the circle as the divinely perfect form, the question of what kept the planets moving in their orbits had been taken for granted. Now a new kind of orbit was suggested – but why an ellipse and not some other curve? Kepler's explanations were not satisfactory, relying on a vague application of the ideas of magnetism, just then receiving the attention of the scientists, and of a motive force emanating from the sun.

It is perhaps one of the accidents of the history of science that Kepler and Galileo did not collaborate with each other. It was to be the task of Newton to synthesize the work of these two great contemporaries.

The following reading from *The Laws of Planetary Motion* has been taken from the J. H. Walden translation in *A Source Book in Astronomy*. See also Plate 3.

¶ *The Discovery of the Laws of Planetary Motion*

In the beginning let my readers understand this: that the old astronomical hypotheses of Ptolemy, as they are set forth in the *Theoriae* of Purbach and the writings of the other epitomizers, are to be kept far from the present inquiry and banished wholly from the mind; for they fail to give a true account either of the arrangement of the heavenly bodies or of the laws governing their motions.

In their place I cannot do otherwise than substitute simply Copernicus's theory of the universe, and (were it possible) convince all men of its truth; but, since among the mass of students the idea is still unfamiliar, and the theory that the Earth is one of the planets and moves among the stars about the Sun, which is stationary, sounds to the most of them quite absurd, let those who are offended by the strangeness of this doctrine know that these harmonic speculations hold a place even among the hypotheses of Tycho Brahe. While that author agrees with Copernicus in regard to everything else which concerns the arrangement of the heavenly bodies and the laws governing their motions, the annual motion of the Earth alone, as held by Copernicus, he transfers to the whole system of the planetary orbits and to the Sun, which, according to both authors, is the centre of the system. For from this transference, motion results just the same, so that, if not in that utterly vast and immense space of the sphere of the fixed stars, at least in the system of the planetary world, the Earth holds at any one time the same place according to Brahe as is given to it by Copernicus. Furthermore, just as he who draws a circle on paper moves the writing foot of the compass around, while he who fastens the paper or a board to a revolving wheel keeps the foot of the compass or the style stationary and draws the same circle on the moving board, so also in the present case; for Copernicus, the Earth measures out its orbit, between the outer circle of Mars and the inner circle of Venus, by the real motion of its own body, while for Tycho Brahe the whole planetary system (in which among the other orbits are also those of Mars and Venus) turns around like the board on the wheel and brings to the stationary Earth, as to the style of the turner, the space between the orbits of Mars and Venus; and from this motion of the system it results that the Earth, itself remaining stationary, marks on space the same course around the Sun, between Mars and Venus, which, according to Copernicus, it marks by the real motion of its own body with the system at rest. Since, then, the harmonic speculation considers the eccentric motions of the planets, as seen from the Sun, one can easily understand that, if an observer were on the Sun, however great the Sun's motion; the Earth, although it were at rest (to grant this for the moment to Brahe), would, nevertheless, seem to him to run its annual course in the space between the planets, and also in a time between the planets' times. Although, therefore, a man may be weak in faith and so unable to conceive of the motion of the Earth among the stars, he may still find it possible to take pleasure in the exalted contemplation of this most divine mechanism; he needs but to apply whatever he hears about the daily motions of the Earth in its eccentric to the appearance of those motions on the Sun, as even Tycho Brahe presents it with the Earth at rest.

The true followers of the Samian philosophy, however, have no just cause for envying such men this participation in a most delightful speculation, for if they accept also the immovability of the Sun and the motion of the Earth, their pleasure will be more exquisite in many ways, since it will be derived from the very consummated perfection of contemplation.

In the first place, therefore, let my readers understand that at the present day among all astronomers it is held to be a well-established fact that all the planets except the Moon, which alone has the Earth as its centre, revolve around the Sun; the Moon's orbit or course, be it said, is not large enough to enable it to be drawn on this chart in proper relation to the other orbits. To the other five planets, therefore, is added the Earth as sixth, which either by its own motion, with the Sun stationary, or, itself being at rest while the whole planetary system is in revolution, describes, it too, its orbit, the sixth, about the Sun.

Secondly, the following fact is also established: that all the planets revolve in eccentric orbits; that is, they alter their distances from the Sun, so that in one part of the orbit they are very remote from the Sun, while in the opposite part they come very near the Sun. In the appended scheme there have been made for each planet three circles, no one of which indicates the real eccentric path of the planet; the middle one, however, as, for instance, in the case of Mars, BE, has a diameter equal to the longer diameter of the eccentric orbit; the orbit itself, as AD, touches AF, the highest of the three, in the one quarter, A, and CD the lowest, in the other quarter, D.

The orbit, GH, represented by points and drawn through the centre of the Sun, indicates the path of the Sun according to Tycho Brahe. If the Sun travels this path, every point of the planetary system here depicted advances in a like path, each in its own; and if one point of it, that is the centre of the Sun, stands in one part of its orbit, as here in the lowest part, all parts of the system will stand, each in the lowest part of its own orbit. Owing to the narrowness of the space, the three circles of Venus have run into one, contrary to my intention.

Thirdly, let the reader recall from my *Mysterium cosmographicum*, which I published twenty-two years ago, that the number of the planets, or orbits about the Sun, was derived by the most wise Creator from the five solid figures, about which Euclid so many centuries ago wrote the book which, since it is made up of a series of propositions, is called *Elementa*. That there cannot be more regular bodies, that regular plane figures, that is, cannot unite into a solid in more than five ways, was made clear in the second book of the present work.

Fourthly, as regards the relations of the planetary orbits, the relation between two neighbouring orbits is always such that, as will easily be seen, each one of the orbits approximates one of the terms of the ratio which exists between the orbits of one of the five solid bodies; the ratio, that is, of the orbit circumscribed about the figure to the orbit inscribed. For when, following the observations of Brahe, I had completed the demonstration of the distances, I discovered this fact: if the angles of the cube are applied to the innermost circle of Saturn, the centres of the planes nearly touch the middle circle of Jupiter, and if the angles of the tetrahedron rest on the innermost circle of Jupiter, the centres of the planes of the tetrahedron nearly touch the outermost circle of Mars; also, if the angles of the octahedron rise from any one of the circles of Venus (for all three are reduced to a very narrow space), the centres of the planes of the octahedron enter and descend below the outermost circle of Mercury; finally, coming to the ratios which exist between the orbits of the dodecahedron and the orbits of the icosahedron, which ratios are equal to each other, we find that the nearest of all to these are the ratios or distances between the circles of Mars and the Earth and between those of the Earth and Venus, and these ratios also, if we reckon from the innermost circle of Mars to the middle circle of the Earth and from the middle circle of the Earth to the middle circle of Venus, are similarly equal to each other; for the

middle distance of the Earth is the mean proportional between the smallest distance of Mars and the middle distance of Venus; but these two ratios between the circles of the planets are still larger than are the ratios of those two sets of orbits in the figures, so that the centres of the planes of the dodecahedron do not touch the outermost circle of the Earth, nor do the centres of the planes of the icosahedron touch the outermost circle of Venus; and this hiatus is not filled up by the semidiameter of the orbit of the Moon, added to the greatest distance of the Earth and taken away from the smallest distance. But there is a certain other relation connected with a figure that I notice: if an enlarged dodecahedron to which I have given the name *echinus* (hedgehog) as being formed of twelve five-cornered stars and thereby being very near to the five regular bodies, if, I say, this dodecahedron should place its twelve points on the innermost circle of Mars, then the sides of the pentagons, which are, respectively, the bases of the different radii or points, touch the middle circle of Venus.

Briefly: the cube and the octahedron enter somewhat their conjugate planetary orbits, the dodecahedron and the icosahedron do not quite reach their conjugate orbits, the tetrahedron just touches both orbits; in the first case there is a deficiency, in the second case an excess, in the last case an equality, in the distances of the planets.

From these considerations it is apparent that the exact relations of the planetary distances were not derived from the regular figures alone; for the Creator, the very fountain-head of geometry, who, as Plato says, practises geometry eternally, does not deviate from his archetype. And indeed this fact might be gathered from the consideration that all the planets change their distances through definite periods of time; so that each one has two notable distances from the Sun, the maximum and minimum; and there may be made between every two planets a fourfold comparison of their distances from the Sun, comparisons of their maximum and of their minimum distances, and comparisons of their mutually opposed distances, those that are farthest apart and those that are nearest together; thus, of all the combinations of two neighbouring planets, the comparisons are twenty in number, while on the other hand the solid figures are but five. It is reasonable to believe, however, that the Creator, if he paid attention to the relation of the orbits in their general aspect, paid attention also to the relation of the varying distances of the individual orbits in detail, and that these acts of attention were the same in both cases and were connected with each other. When we duly consider this fact, we shall certainly arrive at the conclusion that for establishing the diameters and the eccentricities of the orbits there are required several principles in combination, besides the principle of the five regular bodies.

Fifthly, to come to the motions, among which are established the harmonies, I again impress upon the reader the fact that it has been shown by me in my *Commentaries on Mars*, from the exceedingly accurate observations of Brahe, that equal diurnal arcs on one and the same eccentric are not traversed with equal velocities, but that these different times in equal parts of the eccentric are to each other as the distances from the Sun, the source of the motion; and, on the other hand, that, the times being supposed equal, as, for instance, one natural day in each case, the true diurnal arcs corresponding to them in a single eccentric orbit are inversely proportional to the two distances from the Sun. It has likewise been shown by me that the orbit of a planet is elliptical, and the Sun, the source of motion, is in one of the foci of this ellipse, and so it results that the planet, when it has completed a quarter of the entire circuit, beginning at the aphelion, is at a distance from the Sun exactly half way between the maximum distance in aphelion and the minimum distance in perihelion. From these two axioms it results that the mean diurnal motion of the planet in its eccentric is the same as the real diurnal arc of that eccentric at the moments at which the planet is at the end of the quarter eccentric reckoned from the aphelion, although that true quadrant as yet appears smaller than the exact quadrant. It follows, further, that any two perfectly exact diurnal arcs of the eccentric, at exactly the same distance, the one from the aphelion, the other from the perihelion, are together equal to two median diurnal arcs; and consequently, that, since circumferences are to each other as diameters, one mean diurnal arc is to the sum of all the mean arcs, which are equal to each other, as many as there are in the whole circumference, as one mean diurnal arc is to the sum of all the real eccentric arcs, the same in number but unequal to each other. And these truths concerning the real diurnal arcs of the eccentric and the real motions must be known beforehand, that now from these we may understand the apparent motions as they are when observed from the Sun.

Sixthly, as regards the apparent arcs as seen from the Sun, it is known even from the ancient astronomy that of real motions, even when they are equal to each other, that which is farther from the centre of the universe (as one that is in aphelion) appears to the eye looking at it from that centre to be less, and that which is nearer (as one that is in perihelion) seems to be greater. Since, therefore, in addition, the real diurnal arcs which are in proximity are greater still on account of the greater velocity, and the real arcs in the remote aphelion are smaller still on account of the retardation, it results, as I have shown in my *Commentaries on Mars,* that the apparent diurnal arcs of one eccentric are almost exactly inversely proportional to the square of their distances from the Sun. As, for instance, if a planet in one of its days when it is in aphelion is distant from the Sun ten units, in any measure whatsoever, and in its opposite day, when it is in perihelion, is distant nine units of exactly the same kind, it is certain that, as seen from the Sun, its apparent progress in aphelion will be to its apparent progress in perihelion as 81 is to 100.

Now this is true with these reservations; first, that the arcs of the eccentric be not large, that they may not have different distances varying greatly, that is, that they may not cause a sensible variation in the distances of their ends from the apsides; secondly, that the eccentricity be not very great, for the greater the eccentricity, that is the greater the arc, the greater is the increase of the angle of that appearance in comparison with its own advance towards the Sun, according to Theorem 8 of the *Optics* of Euclid. But there is another reason why I give this warning. The arcs of the eccentric about the middle of the anomalies are observed obliquely from the centre of the Sun, and this obliquity diminishes the size of their appearance, while, on the other hand, the arcs round the apsides are presented to the sight, which is supposed to be on the Sun, from directly in front. When, therefore, the eccentricity is very great, the relation of the motions is sensibly disarranged if we apply the mean diurnal motion without diminution to the mean distance, as if it appeared from the mean distance as large as it is; and this will appear below in the case of Mercury. All this matter is treated at greater length in *Epitome Astronomiae Copernicae*, Book V, but it had to be given here because it concerns the very terms themselves of the celestial harmonies, when considered apart each by itself.

Seventhly, in case anyone chances to think of those diurnal motions that are apparent, not to the assumed observer on the Sun, but to the observer on the Earth, with regard to which motions Book VI of *Epitome Astronomiae Copernicae* deals, let him know that these do not come under consideration at all in the present inquiry; clearly they should not, since the Earth is not the source of their motion, nor can they, since these motions, being referred to a false appearance, change not only into absolute rest or apparent motionlessness, but even into retrograde motion; whereby all the infinity of relations is attributed to all the planets at one and the same time and equally. That we may determine, therefore, what the inherent relations are that are established by the diurnal motions of the true individual eccentric orbits (although as yet even they are apparent, being supposed to be seen from the Sun, the source of motion), we must first separate from these inherent motions this appearance of extrinsic annual motion common to all five planets, whether that motion is due, as Copernicus holds, to the

motion of the Earth itself, or, as Tycho Brahe holds, to the
annual motion of the whole system, and these motions
peculiar to each planet must be presented to our view freed
from what is extraneous.

Eighthly, thus far we have dealt with the various times
of arcs of one and the same planet. Now we must deal also
with the motions of the planets taken two at a time and
compare these motions with each other. And here note the
definition of the terms that we shall find it necessary to use.
By the proximate apsides of two planets we shall mean the
perihelion of the higher and the aphelion of the lower, notwithstanding the fact that they turn not towards the same
quarter of the heavens, but towards different and possibly
opposite quarters. Extreme motions, understand to be the
slowest and the fastest of the entire planetary circuit; con-
vergent extreme or converse, those that are in the nearest
apsides of two orbits, that is, in the perihelion of the superior,
and the aphelion of the inferior; divergent or diverse, those
that are in opposite apsides, that is in the aphelion of the
superior, and the perihelion of the inferior. Again, therefore,
a part of my *Mysterium cosmographicum*, suspended twenty-
two years ago, because I did not then see my way clear,
must be completed and introduced here. For, after I had
by unceasing toil through a long period of time, using the
observations of Brahe, discovered the true distances of the
orbits, at last, the true relation of the periodic times to the
orbits and, if you ask for the exact time,

> ... though late, yet looked upon me idle
> And after long time came;

conceived on the 8th of March of this year, 1618, but un-
successfully brought to the test and for that reason rejected
as false, but, finally returning on the 15th of May, by a new
onset it overcame by storm the shadows of my mind, with
such fullness of agreement between my seventeen-years'
labour on the observations of Brahe and this present study
of mine that I at first believed that I was dreaming and was
assuming as an accepted principle what was still a subject of

inquiry. But the principle is unquestionably true and quite exact: the periodic times of any two planets are to each other exactly as the cubes of the square roots of their median distances; this fact should be observed, however, that the arithmetic mean between the two diameters of the elliptical orbit is a little less than the longer diameter. And so, if one takes from the period, say, of the Earth, which is one year, and from Saturn's period of thirty years, the third part of the ratio, that is the cubic roots, and doubles this ratio by squaring the roots, one has in the resulting numbers the exact ratio of the median distances from the Sun of the Earth and Saturn. For the cubic root of 1 is 1 and the square of that is 1; and the cubic root of 30 is greater than 3, and the square of that, therefore, is greater than 9. And Saturn, when at its mean distance from the Sun, is a little higher than nine times the mean distance of the Earth from the Sun.

Ninthly, if now you wish to measure as by the same ten-foot rule the exact journeys made by each planet daily through the sky, you will have to combine two ratios, one of the real (not apparent) daily arcs of the eccentric, the other of the mean distance of each planet from the Sun, because this is likewise the ratio of the amplitudes of the orbits; that is, the real daily arc of each planet must be multiplied into the semidiameter of its own orbit. This done, there will result numbers suitable for use in ascertaining whether those journeys have harmonic relations.

Tenthly, that you may know how great the apparent length of any such daily journey is when the eye is supposed to be on the Sun – although this may be obtained directly from astronomical observation, still it will also result if you add to the ratio of the journeys the inverse ratio of the mean, not real, distances of any point of the eccentrics, the journey of the superior eccentric being multiplied into the distance from the Sun of the inferior, and, on the other hand, the journey of the inferior being multiplied into the distance from the Sun of the superior.

Eleventhly, furthermore, given the apparent motions, the aphelion of one and the perihelion of the other, or conversely, or alternately, there are elicited ratios of the distances, of the aphelion of one to the perihelion of the other; in which case, however, the mean motions must be known beforehand, that is the inverse ratio of the periodic times, from which is deduced the proportion relating to the orbits found in paragraph VIII. Then, taking the mean proportional between either apparent motion and its own mean, the result is that, as this mean proportional is to the semidiameter of its orbit (which is already given), so is the mean motion to the distance or interval sought. Let the periodic times of two planets be 27 and 8; then their mean diurnal motions are to each other as 8 is to 27. Therefore, the semidiameters of the orbits will be as 9 is to 4. For the cubic root of 27 is 3, and that of 8 is 2, and the squares of these roots, 3 and 2, are 9 and 4. Now let the apparent motions be, the aphelion of one 2, and the perihelion of the other $33\frac{1}{3}$. The mean proportionals between the mean motions, 8 and 27, and these apparent motions will be 4 and 30. If, therefore, the mean 4 gives the mean distance of the planet 9, then the mean motion 8 gives the aphelion distance 18, corresponding to the apparent motion 2; and if the other mean 30 gives the mean distance of the other planet 4, then the mean motion of that planet 27 gives its perihelion distance $3\frac{3}{5}$. I say, therefore, that the aphelion distance of the former planet is to the perihelion of this as 18 is to $3\frac{3}{5}$. From which it is clear that, the harmonies between the extreme motions of two planets having been found, and the periodic times assigned to each, there must result the extreme and mean distances, and, therefore, also the eccentricities.

Twelfthly, it is given also, from different extreme motions of one and the same planet, to find the mean motion. For this is not exactly the arithmetical mean between the extreme motions, nor is it exactly the geometrical mean, but it is as much less than the geometrical mean as the geometrical mean is less than the (arithmetical) mean between the two. Let the two extreme motions be 8 and 10. The mean motion will be less than 9, less even than the root of 80 by a half of the difference between the two, 9 and the root of 80.

So, if the aphelion is 20, and the perihelion 24, the mean motion will be less than 22, less even than the root of 480 by a half of the difference between this root and 22.

———————

GALILEO GALILEI
1564–1642

THE CONSTRUCTION OF A TELESCOPE
AND ITS USE IN
ASTRONOMICAL OBSERVATION
and
THE LAWS OF ACCELERATION AND OF
FALLING BODIES ARE ESTABLISHED

ACCORDING to Alfred North Whitehead, 'the worship of God . . . is an adventure of the spirit, a flight after the un-attainable'. Most people today probably accept this state-ment as the basis for a working distinction between religion and science: the latter, by definition, can examine only the attainable. Yet this distinction, which to us seems obvious, was established neither quickly nor easily, and the experience of Galileo is an almost legendary example of the struggle to obtain recognition of science's more limited objectives.

Galileo's life covered precisely the period between the death of Michelangelo and the birth of Newton, a co-incidence that dramatizes the shift of scientific leadership from Italy to countries further north. Galileo's reference to 'trans-alpine diligence', in the second of the two readings that follow, suggests his awareness of this transition. This 'diligence' had, no doubt, been brought to his attention not only by the work of Kepler, with whom he was in correspondence in 1597, but also by the death of Giordano Bruno, who was burned at the stake in 1600 for the heresy of his scientific ideas.

Galileo was born at Pisa and educated in a monastery, as was customary for a nobleman's son. His original interest was medicine, but an accidental encounter with geometry changed the course of his career. His mathematical studies led him, at the age of twenty-five, to a lectureship at the .

University of Pisa. Three years later he was appointed Professor of Mathematics at the University of Padua, then one of the intellectual meccas of Europe. For eighteen years, Galileo developed his studies of bodies in motion – inspired, it is said, by his observation of the swing of a lamp suspended from the roof of the Cathedral of Pisa. The study of the pendulum followed, leading to Galileo's suggestion for a clock regulated by a pendulum – actually accomplished, however, not by Galileo but by Huygens in 1617.

Galileo remained an avowed Copernican. His development in 1609 of the telescope, from ideas about lenses reported from the Netherlands, opened up a new world of observation. Protuberances in the sun, the mountains of the moon, new stars, and the Milky Way were now revealed. Galileo's descriptions of these discoveries – and exposure of his Copernican views – brought about his first contact with the theologians, who apparently for the first time realized the effect on religious teaching of the view that the earth was not the centre of the universe. Galileo was reprimanded but allowed, in effect, to continue his studies provided that he treated the Copernican thesis of a daily revolution of the earth not as an absolute truth but as a hypothesis to facilitate mathematical calculations. This was in 1613. From then until 1632, when he published his *Dialogue on the Two Chief World Systems* (from which the second reading is taken), Galileo worked without much opposition from the Church; but the *Dialogue* (which, like all his works, was written in Italian and was thus available to any reader) brought him once more before the Inquisition. Galileo and the whole Copernican doctrine were condemned and he was compelled to sign a recognition of the Church's authority in these matters. Though Galileo kept himself out of controversy from this time on, others did not: the march of science continued at a rapidly accelerating speed.

The characters in the *Dialogue* are the Copernican, Salviati, whose propositions are stimulated by the questions of Sagredo, in the role of the intelligent layman. The objections of the anti-Copernicans are put forward by Simplicius, who is sometimes presented as a stupid person and sometimes as representative of those who were honestly convinced of the soundness of Ptolemy and the Aristotelian philosophy. The dialogue form was adopted to meet the conditions imposed on his continued work – that Galileo present the views of the Church.

Of the two readings on Astronomy which follow, the first, on the construction of the telescope, is taken from *The Sidereal Messenger* of 1610, translated by E. S. Carlos in 1880; the second, the comparison of the Ptolemaic with the Copernican system, is taken from *Dialogue on the Two Chief World Systems*, translated by Stillman Drake in 1953 (University of California Press). The original frontispiece of the latter is reproduced in Plate 4.

The second main extract is concerned with Galileo's great contribution to the founding of classical mechanics, and is taken from the *Dialogues Concerning Two New Sciences*, translated by Henry Crew and A. DeSalvio (1914).

¶ The Foundation of Telescopic Astronomy

Introduction. In the present small treatise I set forth some matters of great interest for all observers of natural phenomena to look at and consider. They are of great interest, I think, first, from their intrinsic excellence; secondly, from their absolute novelty; and lastly, also on account of the instrument by the aid of which they have been presented to my apprehension.

The number of Fixed Stars which observers have been able to see without artificial powers of sight up to this day can be counted. It is therefore decidedly a great feat to add to their number, and to set distinctly before the eyes other stars in myriads, which have never been seen before, and which surpass the old, previously known, stars in number more than ten times.

Again, it is a most beautiful and delightful sight to behold the body of the Moon, which is distant from us nearly sixty semidiameters of the Earth, as near as if it was at a distance of only two of the same measures; so that the diameter of this same Moon appears about thirty times larger, its surface about nine hundred times, and its solid mass nearly 27,000 times larger than when it is viewed only with the naked eye: and consequently any one may know with the certainty that is due to the use of our senses, that the Moon certainly does not possess a smooth and polished surface, but one rough and uneven, and, just like the face of the Earth itself, is everywhere full of vast protuberances, deep chasms, and sinuosities.

Then to have got rid of disputes about the Galaxy or Milky Way, and to have made its nature clear to the very senses, not to say to the understanding, seems by no means a matter which ought to be considered of slight importance. In addition to this, to point out, as with one's finger, the nature of those stars which every one of the astronomers up to this time has called nebulous, and to demonstrate that it is very different from what has hitherto been believed, will be pleasant, and very fine. But that which will excite the greatest astonishment by far, and which indeed especially moved me to call the attention of all astronomers and philosophers, is this, namely, that I have discovered four planets, neither known nor observed by any one of the astronomers before my time, which have their orbits round a certain bright star, one of those previously known like Venus and Mercury round the Sun, and are sometimes in front of it, sometimes behind it, though they never depart from it beyond certain limits. All which facts were discovered and observed a few days ago by the help of a telescope devised by me, through God's grace first enlightening my mind.

Perchance, other discoveries still more excellent will be made from time to time by me or by other observers, with assistance of a similar instrument, so I will first briefly record its shape and preparation, as well as the occasion of its being devised, and then I will give an account of the observations made by me.

The Telescope. About ten months ago a report reached my ears that a Dutchman had constructed a telescope, by the aid of which visible objects, although at a great distance from the eye of the observer, were seen distinctly as if near; and some proofs of its most wonderful performances were reported, which some gave credence to, but others contradicted. A few days after, I received confirmation of the report in a letter written from Paris by a noble Frenchman, Jaques Badovere, which finally determined me to give myself up first to inquire into the principle of the telescope, and then to consider the means by which I might compass the invention of a similar instrument, which after a little while I succeeded in doing, through deep study of the theory of Refraction; and I prepared a tube, at first of lead, in the ends of which I fitted two glass lenses, both plane on one side, but on the other side one spherically convex, and the other concave. Then bringing my eye to the concave lens I saw objects satisfactorily large and near, for they appeared one-third of the distance off and nine times larger than when they are seen with the natural eye alone. I shortly afterwards constructed another telescope with more nicety, which magnified objects more than sixty times. At length, by sparing neither labour nor expense, I succeeded in constructing for myself an instrument so superior that objects seen through it appear magnified nearly a thousand times and more than thirty times nearer than if viewed by the natural powers of sight alone.

First Telescopic Observations. It would be altogether a waste of time to enumerate the number and importance of the benefits which this instrument may be expected to confer, when used by land or sea. But without paying attention to its use for terrestrial objects, I betook myself to observations of the heavenly bodies; and first of all, I viewed the Moon as near as if it was scarcely two semidiameters of the Earth distant. After the Moon, I frequently observed other heavenly bodies, both fixed stars and planets, with incredible delight; and, when I saw their very great number, I began to consider about a method by which I might be able to measure their distances apart, and at length I found one. And here it is fitting that all who intend to turn their attention to observations of this kind should receive certain cautions. For, in the first place, it is absolutely necessary for them to prepare a most perfect telescope, one which will show very bright objects distinct and free from any mistiness, and will magnify them at least 400 times, for then it will show them as if only one-twentieth of their distance off. For, unless the instrument be of such power, it will be in vain to attempt to view all the things which have been seen by me in the heavens, or which will be enumerated hereafter.

Observations of Lunar Mountains and Valleys. Let me first speak of the surface of the Moon, which is turned towards us. For the sake of being understood more easily, I distinguish two parts in it, which I call respectively the brighter and the darker. The brighter part seems to surround and pervade the whole hemisphere; but the darker part, like a sort of cloud, discolours the Moon's surface and makes it appear covered with spots. Now these spots, as they are somewhat dark and of considerable size, are plain to everyone, and every age has seen them, wherefore I shall call them great or ancient spots to distinguish them from other spots, smaller in size, but so thickly scattered that they sprinkle the whole surface of the Moon, but especially the brighter portion of it. These spots have never been observed by anyone before me; and from my observations of them, often repeated, I have been led to that opinion which I have expressed, namely, that I feel sure that the surface of the Moon is not perfectly smooth, free from inequalities, and exactly spherical, as a large school of philosophers considers with regard to the Moon and the other heavenly bodies, but that, on the contrary, it is full of inequalities, uneven, full of hollows and protuberances, just like the surface of the Earth itself, which is varied everywhere by lofty mountains and deep valleys.

The appearances from which we may gather these conclusions are of the following nature: On the fourth or fifth day after new-moon, when the Moon presents itself to us with bright horns, the boundary which divides the part in shadow from the enlightened part does not extend continuously in an ellipse, as would happen in the case of a perfectly spherical body, but it is marked out by an irregular, uneven, and very wavy line ... for several bright excrescences, as they may be called, extend beyond the boundary of light and shadow into the dark part, and on the other hand pieces of shadow encroach upon the light – nay, even a great quantity of small blackish spots, altogether separated from the dark part, sprinkle everywhere almost the whole space which is at the time flooded with the Sun's light, with the exception of that part alone which is occupied by the great and ancient spots. I have noticed that the small spots just mentioned have this common characteristic always and in every case, that they have the dark part towards the Sun's position, and on the side away from the Sun they have brighter boundaries, as if they were crowned with shining summits. Now we have an appearance quite similar on the Earth about sunrise, when we behold the valleys, not yet flooded with light, but the mountains surrounding them on the side opposite to the Sun already ablaze with the splendour of his beams; and just as the shadows in the hollows of the Earth diminish in size as the Sun rises higher, so also these spots on the Moon lose their blackness as the illuminated part grows larger and larger. Again, not only are the boundaries of light and shadow in the Moon seen to be uneven and sinuous, but – and this produces still greater astonishment – there appear very many bright points within the darkened portion of the Moon, altogether divided and broken off from the illuminated tract, and separated from it by no inconsiderable interval, which, after a little while, gradually increase in size and brightness, and after an hour or two become joined on to the rest of the main portion, now become somewhat larger; but in the meantime others, one here and another there, shooting up as if growing, are lighted up within the shaded portion, increase in size, and at last are linked on to the same luminous surface, now still more extended. ... Now, is it not the case on the Earth before sunrise, that while the level plain is still in shadow, the peaks of the most lofty mountains are illuminated by the Sun's rays? After a little while does not the light spread further, while the middle and larger parts of those mountains are becoming illuminated; and at length, when the Sun has risen, do not the illuminated parts of the plains and hills join together? The grandeur, however, of such prominences and depressions in the Moon seems to surpass both in magnitude and extent the ruggedness of the Earth's surface, as I shall hereafter show. . . .

Appearance of Stars in the Telescope. Hitherto I have spoken of the observations which I have made concerning the Moon's body; now I will briefly announce the phenomena which have been, as yet, seen by me with reference to the Fixed Stars. And first of all the following fact is worthy of consideration: The stars, fixed as well as erratic, when seen with a telescope, by no means appear to be increased in magnitude in the same proportion as other objects, and the Moon herself, gain increase of size: but in the case of the stars such an increase appears much less, so that you may consider that a telescope, which (for the sake of illustration) is powerful enough to magnify other objects a hundred times, will scarcely render the stars magnified four or five times. But the reason of this is as follows: When stars are viewed with our natural eyesight they do not present themselves to us of their bare, real size, but beaming with a certain vividness, and fringed with sparkling rays, especially when the night is far advanced; and from this circumstance they appear much larger than they would if they were stripped of those adventitious fringes, for the angle which they subtend at the eye is determined not by the primary disc of the star, but by the brightness which so widely surrounds it. . . . A telescope . . . removes from the stars their adventitious and accidental splendours before it enlarges their true discs (if indeed they are of that shape), and so they seem less magnified than other objects, for a star of the fifth or sixth magnitude seen through a telescope is shown as of the first magnitude only.

The difference between the appearance of the planets and the fixed stars seems also deserving of notice. The planets present their discs perfectly round, just as if described with a pair of compasses, and appear as so many little moons, completely illuminated and of a globular shape; but the fixed stars do not look to the naked eye bounded by a circular circumference, but rather like blazes of light, shooting out beams on all sides and very sparkling, and with a telescope they appear of the same shape as when they are viewed by simply looking at them, but so much larger that a star of the fifth or sixth magnitude seems to equal Sirius, the largest of all the fixed stars.

The Infinite Multitude of Telescopic Stars. But beyond the stars of the sixth magnitude you will behold through the telescope a host of other stars, which escape the unassisted sight, so numerous as to be almost beyond belief, for you may see more than six other differences of magnitude, and the largest of these, which I may call stars of the seventh magnitude, or of the first magnitude of invisible stars, appear with the aid of the telescope larger and brighter than stars of the second magnitude seen with the unassisted sight. But in order that you may see one or two proofs of the inconceivable manner in which they are crowded together, I have determined to make out a case against two star-clusters that from them as a specimen you may decide about the rest.

As my first example, I had determined to depict the entire constellation of Orion, but I was overwhelmed by the vast quantity of stars and by want of time, and so I have deferred attempting this to another occasion, for there are adjacent to, or scattered among, the old stars more than five hundred new stars within the limits of one or two degrees. For this reason I have selected the three stars in Orion's Belt and the six in his Sword, which have been long well-known groups, and I have added eighty other stars recently discovered in their vicinity, and I have preserved as exactly as possible the intervals between them. The well-known or old stars, for the sake of distinction, I have depicted of larger size, and I have outlined them with a double line; the others, invisible to the naked eye, I have marked smaller and with one line only. I have also preserved the differences of magnitude as much as I could. As a second example, I have depicted the six stars of the constellation Taurus, called the Pleiades (I say six intentionally, since the seventh is scarcely ever visible), a group of stars which is enclosed in the heavens within very narrow precincts. Near these there lie more than forty others invisible to the naked eye, no one of which is more than half a degree off any of the aforesaid six; of these I have noticed only thirty-six in my diagram. I have preserved their intervals, magnitudes, and the distinction between the old and the new stars, just as in the case of the constellation Orion.

Telescopic Appearance of Milky Way. The next object which I have observed is the essence or substance of the Milky Way. By the aid of a telescope anyone may behold this in a manner which so distinctly appeals to the senses that all the disputes which have tormented philosophers through so many ages are exploded at once by the irrefragable evidence of our eyes, and we are freed from wordy disputes upon this subject, for the Galaxy is nothing else but a mass of innumerable stars planted together in clusters. Upon whatever part of it you direct the telescope straightway a vast crowd of stars presents itself to view; many of them are tolerably large and extremely bright, but the number of small ones is quite beyond determination. . . .

Discovery of Jupiter's Satellites. I have now finished my brief account of the observations which I have thus far made with regard to the Moon, the Fixed Stars, and the Galaxy. There remains the matter, which seems to me to deserve to be considered the most important in this work, namely, that I should disclose and publish to the world the occasion of discovering and observing four Planets, never seen from the very beginning of the world up to our own times, their positions, and the observations made during the last two months about their movements and their changes of magnitude; and I summon all astronomers to apply

offen den rouch vß zelassen/also dz dz blech
wol vstrichē sy mit leymē.vn vff dem blech
werd d offen gehöcht mit steynē eyns halbē
steyns dick mit vier hülsen/vn in der mitte
des offens ein loch gelassen / also das ouch

des rouchloch werd gemacht ein zapffen dz
füer domit zů regieren groß od clein nach di
nem gefallē/vñ d offen soll gehitziget wer
dē mit kolen od seg spen oder lose klötz vō
eym rot gerber vñ kein holtz. Des form also,

Jñ sollicher massen magstu ouch eyn
offen machē dz du mit holtz dar i bre
nest/also dz d offen läg ist/vñ von d
höche des rosts biß zů dem blech soll sin ey/
ner ecken hoch/vñ für die blech so werd ge

sens sy vff einer siten in d wyte ein halß ellē
vñ in d höhe.iii. viertel eyner ecken der offen
hab ouch zwei groß rouchlöct er.sölliche offē
magstu machē mit wie vil helmē du wilt
oder beteeren du bist. nach dinem gefallen.

A distillation furnace used by alchemists. From Hieronymus Brunschwig's
Das Buch der Rechten Kunst zu Distillieren, Strasburg, 1500.

net, in quo terram cum orbe lunari tanquam epicyclo contineri diximus. Quinto loco Venus nono mense reducitur. Sextum deniᶜᵖ locum Mercurius tenet, octuaginta dierum spacio circū currens. In medio uero omnium residet Sol. Quis enim in hoc

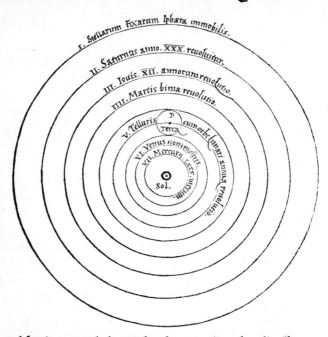

pulcherimo templo lampadem hanc in alio uel meliori loco po neret, quàm unde totum simul possit illuminare? Siquidem non inepte quidam lucernam mundi, aliῄ mentem, aliῄ rectorem uo= cant. Trimegistus uisibilem Deum, Sophoclis Electra intuentē omnia. Ita profecto tanquam in solio re gali Sol residens circum agentem gubernat Astrorum familiam. Tellus quoᶜᵖ minime fraudatur lunari ministerio, sed ut Aristoteles de animalibus ait, maximā Luna cū terra cognationē habet. Concipit interea à Sole terra, & impregnatur annuo partu. Inuenimus igitur sub hac

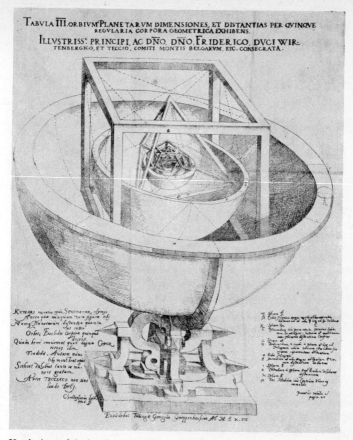

Kepler's model of a planetary system in which five regular solids – cube, tetrahedron, octahedron, dodecahedron, and icosahedron – are shown inscribed in and circumscribed by spheres. The spheres are shown in proportion to the distances of the planets from the sun. From Kepler's *Harmonices mundi libri V*, Linz, 1619.

Frontispiece of Galileo's *Dialogue on the Two Chief World Systems*, Florence, 1632. The three figures are Aristotle, Ptolemy, and Copernicus.

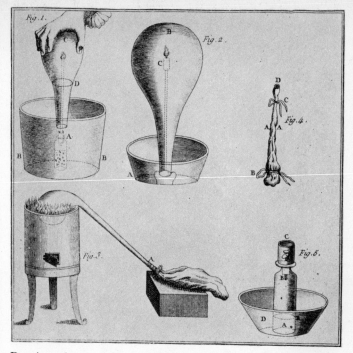

Drawings of some of the apparatus used by Scheele in his experiments on gases. From his *Chemische Abhandlung von der Luft und dem Feuer*, Uppsala and Leipzig, 1777.

A demonstration by Von Guericke of the pressure exerted by the atmosphere on a globe of fitted bronze hemispheres from which the air had been exhausted. Two teams of eight horses each could not pull the globe apart, although it fell apart when air was permitted to enter. From Otto von Guericke's *Experimenta nova (ut vocantur) magdeburgica de vacuo spatio*, Amsterdam, 1672.

6

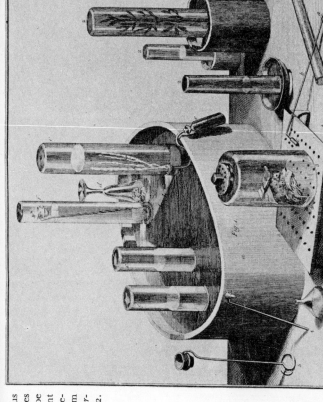

Some of Priestley's apparatus for experiments on the gases of the atmosphere. The tube on the right contains a mint plant, and the jar in the foreground contains mice. From Priestley's *Observations on Different Kinds of Air*, London, 1772.

7

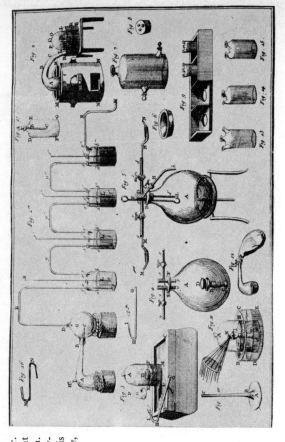

Apparatus used by Lavoisier. Figure 2 is the arrangement he used in preparing oxygen. His wife did most of the drawings for his writings. From his *Traité élémentaire de chimie*, Paris, 1789.

themselves to examine and determine their periodic times, which it has not been permitted me to achieve up to this day, owing to the restriction of my time. I give them warning, however, again, so that they may not approach such an inquiry to no purpose, that they will want a very accurate telescope, and such as I have described in the beginning of this account.

On the 7th day of January in the present year, 1610, in the first hour of the following night, when I was viewing the constellations of the heavens through a telescope, the planet Jupiter presented itself to my view, and as I had prepared for myself a very excellent instrument, I noticed a circumstance which I had never been able to notice before, owing to want of power in my other telescope, namely that three little stars, small but very bright, were near the planet; and although I believed them to belong to the number of the Fixed Stars, yet they made me somewhat wonder, because they seemed to be arranged exactly in a straight line, parallel to the ecliptic, and to be brighter than the rest of the stars, equal to them in magnitude. The position of them with reference to one another and to Jupiter was as follows:

Ori.   *   * O   *   Occ.

On the east side there were two stars, and a single one towards the west. The star which was furthest towards the east, and the western star, appeared rather larger than the third.

I scarcely troubled at all about the distance between them and Jupiter, for, as I have already said, at first I believed them to be Fixed Stars; but when on 8 January led by some fatality, I turned again to look at the same part of the heavens, I found a very different state of things, for there were three little stars all west of Jupiter, and nearer together than on the previous night, and they were separated from one another by equal intervals, as the accompanying figure shows. Ori.   O * * *   Occ.

At this point, although I had not turned my thoughts at all

upon the approximation of the stars to one another, yet my surprise began to be excited, how Jupiter could one day be found to the east of all the aforesaid fixed stars when the day before it had been west of two of them; and forthwith I became afraid lest the planet might have moved differently from the calculation of astronomers, and so had passed those stars by its own proper motion. I, therefore, waited for the next night with the most intense longing, but I was disappointed of my hope, for the sky was covered with clouds in every direction.

But on 10 January the stars appeared in the following position with regard to Jupiter, the third, as I thought, being

Ori.   *   * O   Occ.

hidden by the planet. They were situated just as before, exactly in the same straight line with Jupiter, and along the Zodiac. . . .

When I had seen these phenomena, as I knew that corresponding changes of position could not by any means belong to Jupiter, and as, moreover, I perceived that the stars which I saw had always been the same, for there were no others either in front or behind, within a great distance, along the Zodiac – at length, changing from doubt into surprise, I discovered that the interchange of position which I saw belonged not to Jupiter, but to the stars to which my attention had been drawn, and I thought therefore that they ought to be observed henceforward with more attention and precision.

Accordingly, on 11 January I saw an arrangement of the following kind:

Ori.   *   *   O   Occ.

namely, only two stars to the east of Jupiter, the nearer of which was distant from Jupiter three times as far as from the star further to the east; and the star furthest to the east was nearly twice as large as the other one; whereas on the previous night they had appeared nearly of equal magnitude. I, therefore, concluded, and decided unhesitatingly, that there are three stars in the heavens moving about Jupiter, as Venus and Mercury round the Sun; which at length was established as clear as daylight by numerous other subsequent observations. These observations also established that there are not only three, but four, erratic sidereal bodies performing their revolutions round Jupiter. . . .

These are my observations upon the four Medicean planets, recently discovered for the first time by me; and although it is not yet permitted me to deduce by calculation from these observations the orbits of these bodies, yet I may be allowed to make some statements, based upon them, well worthy of attention.

Orbits and Periods of Jupiter's Satellites. And, in the first place, since they are sometimes behind, sometimes before Jupiter, at like distances, and withdraw from this planet towards the east and towards the west only within very narrow limits of divergence, and since they accompany this planet alike when its motion is retrograde and direct, it can be a matter of doubt to no one that they perform their revolutions about this planet, while at the same time they all accomplish together orbits of twelve years' length about the centre of the world. Moreover, they revolve in unequal circles, which is evidently the conclusion to be drawn from the fact that I have never been permitted to see two satellites in conjunction when their distance from Jupiter was great, whereas near Jupiter two, three, and sometimes all four, have been found closely packed together. Moreover, it may be detected that the revolutions of the satellites which describe the smallest circles round Jupiter are the most rapid, for the satellites nearest to Jupiter are often to be seen in the east, when the day before they have appeared in the west, and contrariwise. Also, the satellite moving in the greatest orbit seems to me, after carefully weighing the occasions of its returning to positions previously noticed, to have a periodic time of half a month. Besides, we have a notable and splendid argument to remove the scruples of those who can tolerate the revolution of the planets round the Sun in the Copernican system, yet are so disturbed by the motion of one Moon about the Earth, while both accomplish an orbit of a year's length about the Sun, that they consider that this theory of the universe must be upset as impossible: for now we have not one planet only revolving about another, while both traverse a vast orbit about the Sun, but our sense of sight presents to us four satellites circling about Jupiter, like the Moon about the Earth, while the whole system travels over a mighty orbit about the Sun in the space of twelve years.

¶ To the Discerning Reader

Several years ago there was published in Rome a salutary edict which, in order to obviate the dangerous tendencies of our present age, imposed a seasonable silence upon the Pythagorean opinion that the earth moves. There were those who impudently asserted that this decree had its origin not in judicious inquiry, but in passion none too well informed. Complaints were to be heard that advisers who were totally unskilled at astronomical observations ought not to clip the wings of reflective intellects by means of rash prohibitions.

Upon hearing such carping insolence, my zeal could not be contained. Being thoroughly informed about that prudent determination, I decided to appear openly in the theatre of the world as a witness of the sober truth. I was at that time in Rome; I was not only received by the most eminent prelates of that Court, but had their applause; indeed, this decree was not published without some previous notice of it having been given to me. Therefore I propose in the present work to show to foreign nations that as much is understood of this matter in Italy, and particularly in Rome, as transalpine diligence can ever have imagined. Collecting all the reflections that properly concern the Copernican system, I shall make it known that everything was brought before the attention of the Roman censorship, and that there proceed from this clime not only dogmas for the welfare of the soul, but ingenious discoveries for the delight of the mind as well.

To this end I have taken the Copernican side in the discourse, proceeding as with a pure mathematical hypothesis and striving by every artifice to represent it as superior to supposing the earth motionless —

not, indeed, absolutely, but as against the arguments of some professed Peripatetics. These men indeed deserve not even that name, for they do not walk about; they are content to adore the shadows, philosophizing not with due circumspection but merely from having memorized a few ill-understood principles.

Three principal headings are treated. First, I shall try to show that all experiments practicable upon the earth are insufficient measures for proving its mobility, since they are indifferently adaptable to an earth in motion or at rest. I hope in so doing to reveal many observations unknown to the ancients. Secondly, the celestial pheno-mena will be examined, strengthening the Copernican hypothesis until it might seem that this must triumph absolutely. Here new reflections are adjoined which might be used in order to simplify astronomy, though not because of any necessity imposed by nature. In the third place, I shall propose an ingenious speculation. It happens that long ago I said that the unsolved problem of the ocean tides might receive some light from assuming the motion of the earth. This assertion of mine, passing by word of mouth, found loving fathers who adopted it as a child of their own ingenuity. Now, so that no stranger may ever appear who, arming himself with our weapons, shall charge us with want of attention to such an important matter, I have thought it good to reveal those probabilities which might render this plausible, given that the earth moves.

I hope that from these considerations the world will come to know that if other nations have navigated more, we have not theorized less. It is not from failing to take count of what others have thought that we have yielded to asserting that the earth is motionless, and holding the contrary to be a mere mathematical caprice, but (if for nothing else) for those reasons that are supplied by piety, religion, the knowledge of Divine Omnipotence, and a consciousness of the limitations of the human mind.

I have thought it most appropriate to explain these concepts in the form of dialogues, which not being restricted to the rigorous observ-ance of mathematical laws, make room also for digressions which are sometimes no less interesting than the principal argument.

Many years ago I was often to be found in the marvellous city of Venice, in discussions with Signore Giovanni Francesco Sagredo, a man of noble extraction and trenchant wit. From Florence came

Signore Filippo Salviati, the least of whose glories were the eminence of his blood and the magnificence of his fortune. His was a sublime intellect which fed no more hungrily upon any pleasure than it did upon fine meditations. I often talked with these two of such matters in the presence of a certain Peripatetic philosopher whose greatest obstacle in apprehending the truth seemed to be the reputation he had acquired by his interpretations of Aristotle.

Now, since bitter death has deprived Venice and Florence of those two great luminaries in the very meridian of their years, I have resolved to make their fame live on in these pages, so far as my poor abilities will permit, by introducing them as interlocutors in the present argument. (Nor shall the good Peripatetic lack a place; because of his excessive affection toward the Commentaries of Simplicius, I have thought fit to leave him under the name of the author he so much revered, without mentioning his own.) May it please those two great souls, ever venerable to my heart, to accept this public monument of my undying love. And may the memory of their eloquence assist me in delivering to posterity the promised reflections.

It happened that several discussions had taken place casually at various times among these gentlemen, and had rather whetted than satisfied their thirst for learning. Hence very wisely they resolved to meet together on certain days during which, setting aside all other business, they might apply themselves more methodically to the contemplation of the wonders of God in the heavens and upon the earth. They met in the palace of the illustrious Sagredo; and, after the customary but brief exchange of compliments, Salviati commenced as follows.

*

SALVIATI: Then let the beginning of our reflections be the consideration that whatever motion comes to be attributed to the earth must necessarily remain imperceptible to us and as if nonexistent, so long as we look only at terrestrial objects; for as inhabitants of the earth, we consequently participate in the same motion. But on the other hand it is indeed just as necessary that it display itself very generally in all other visible bodies and objects which, being separated from the earth, do not take part in this movement. So the true method of investigating whether any motion can be attributed to the earth, and if so what it may be, is to observe and consider whether bodies separated from the earth exhibit some appearance of motion which belongs equally to all. For a motion which is perceived only, for example, in the moon, and which does not affect Venus or Jupiter or the other stars, cannot in any way be the earth's or anything but the moon's.

Now there is one motion which is most general and supreme over all, and it is that by which the sun, moon, and all other planets and fixed stars – in a word, the whole universe, the earth alone excepted – appear to be moved as a unit from east to west in the space of twenty-four hours. This, in so far as first appearances are concerned, may just as logically belong to the earth alone as to the rest of the universe, since the same appearances would prevail as much in the one situation as in the other. Thus it is that Aristotle and Ptolemy, who thoroughly understood this consideration, in their attempt to prove the earth immovable do not argue against any other motion than this diurnal one, though Aristotle does drop a hint against another motion ascribed to it by an ancient writer, of which we shall speak in the proper place.

SAGREDO: I am quite convinced of the force of your argument, but it raises a question for me from which I do not know how to free myself, and it is this: Copernicus attributed to the earth another motion than the diurnal. By the rule just affirmed, this ought to remain imperceptible to all observations on the earth, but be visible in the rest of the universe. It seems to me that one may deduce as a necessary consequence either that he was grossly mistaken in assigning to the earth a motion corresponding to no appearance in the heavens generally, or that if the correspondent motion does exist, then Ptolemy was equally at fault in not explaining it away, as he explained away the other.

SALVIATI: This is very reasonably questioned, and when we come to treat of the other movement you will see how greatly Copernicus surpassed Ptolemy in acuteness and penetration of mind by seeing what the latter did not – I mean the wonderful correspondence with which such a movement is reflected in all the other heavenly bodies. But let us postpone this for the present and return to the first consideration, with respect to which I shall set forth, commencing with the most general things, those reasons which seem to favour the earth's motion, so that we may then hear their refutation from Simplicio.

First, let us consider only the immense bulk of the starry sphere in contrast with the smallness of the terrestrial globe, which is contained in the former so many millions of times. Now if we think of the velocity of motion required to make a complete rotation in a single day and night, I cannot persuade myself that anyone could be found who would think it the more reasonable and credible thing that it was the celestial sphere which did the turning, and the terrestrial globe which remained fixed.

SAGREDO: If, throughout the whole variety of effects that could exist in nature as dependent upon these motions, all the same consequences followed indifferently to a hairsbreadth from both positions, still my first general impression of them would be this: I should think that anyone who considered it more reasonable for the whole universe to move in order to let the earth remain fixed would be more irrational than one who should climb to the top of your cupola just to get a view of the city and its environs, and then demand that the whole countryside should revolve around him so that he would not have to take the trouble to turn his head. Doubtless there are many and great advantages to be drawn from the new theory and not from the previous one (which to my mind is comparable with or even surpasses the above in absurdity), making the former more credible than the latter. But perhaps Aristotle, Ptolemy, and Simplicio ought to marshal their advantages against us and set them forth, too, if such there are; otherwise it will be clear to me that there are none and cannot be any.

SALVIATI: Despite much thinking about it, I have not been able to find any difference, so it seems to me I have found that there can be no difference; hence I think it vain to seek one further. For consider: Motion, in so far as it is and acts as motion, to that extent exists relatively to things that lack it; and among things which all share equally in any motion, it does not act, and is as if it did not exist. Thus the goods with which a ship is laden leaving Venice, pass by Corfu, by Crete, by Cyprus and go to Aleppo. Venice, Corfu, Crete, etc. stand still and do not move with the ship; but as to the sacks, boxes, and bundles with which the boat is laden and with respect to the ship itself, the motion from Venice to Syria is as nothing, and in no way alters their relation among themselves. This is so because it is common to all of them and all share equally in it. If, from the cargo in the ship, a sack were shifted from a chest one single inch, this alone would be more of a movement for it than the two-thousand-mile journey made by all of them together.

SIMPLICIUS: This is good, sound doctrine, and entirely Peripatetic.

SALVIATI: I should have thought it somewhat older. And I question whether Aristotle entirely understood it when selecting it from some good school of thought, and whether he has not, by altering it in his writings, made it a source of confusion among those who wish to maintain everything he said. When he wrote that everything which is moved is moved upon something immovable, I think he only made equivocal the saying that whatever moves, moves with respect to something motionless. This proposition suffers no difficulties at all, whereas the other has many.

SAGREDO: Please do not break the thread, but continue with the argument already begun.

SALVIATI: It is obvious, then, that motion which is common to many moving things is idle and inconsequential to the relation of these movables among themselves, nothing being changed among them, and that it is operative only in the relation that they have with other bodies lacking that motion, among which their location is changed. Now, having divided the universe into two parts, one of which is necessarily movable and the other motionless, it is the same thing to make the earth alone move, and to move all the rest of the universe, so far as concerns any result which may depend upon such movement. For the action of such a movement is only in the relation between the celestial bodies and the earth, which relation alone is changed. Now if precisely the same effect follows whether the earth is made to move and the rest of the universe stay still, or the earth alone remains fixed while the whole universe shares one motion, who is going to believe that nature (which by general agreement does not act by means of many things when it can do so by means of few) has chosen to make an immense number of extremely large bodies move with inconceivable velocities, to achieve what could have been done by a moderate movement of one single body around its own centre?

SIMPLICIUS: I do not quite understand how this very great motion is as nothing for the sun, the moon, the other planets, and the innumerable host of the fixed stars. Why do you say it is nothing for the sun to pass from one meridian to the other, rise above this horizon and sink beneath that, causing now the day and now the night; and for the moon, the other planets, and the fixed stars to vary similarly?

SALVIATI: Every one of these variations which you recite to me is nothing except in relation to the earth. To see that this is true, remove the earth; nothing remains in the universe of rising and setting of the sun and moon, nor of horizons and meridians, nor day and night, and in a word from this movement there will never originate any changes in the moon or sun or any stars you please, fixed or moving. All these changes are in relation to the earth, all of them meaning nothing except that the sun shows itself now over China, then to Persia, afterwards to Egypt, to Greece, to France, to Spain, to America, etc. And the same holds for the moon and the rest of the heavenly bodies, this effect taking place in exactly the same way if, without embroiling the biggest part of the universe, the terrestrial globe is made to revolve upon itself.

And let us redouble the difficulty with another very great

one, which is this. If this great motion is attributed to the heavens, it has to be made in the opposite direction from the specific motion of all the planetary orbs, of which each one incontrovertibly has its own motion from west to east, this being very gentle and moderate, and must then be made to rush the other way; that is, from east to west, with this very rapid diurnal motion. Whereas by making the earth itself move, the contrariety of motions is removed, and the single motion from west to east accommodates all the observations and satisfies them all completely.

*

SAGREDO: O Nicholas Copernicus, what a pleasure it would have been for you to see this part of your system confirmed by so clear an experiment!

SALVIATI: Yes, but how much less would this sublime intellect be celebrated among the learned! For as I said before, we may see that with reason as his guide he resolutely continued to affirm what sensible experience seemed to contradict. I cannot get over my amazement that he was constantly willing to persist in saying that Venus might go around the sun and be more than six times as far from us at one time as at another, and still look always equal, when it should have appeared forty times larger.

SAGREDO: I believe then that in Jupiter, Saturn, and Mercury one ought also to see differences of size corresponding exactly to their varying distances.

SALVIATI: In the two outer planets I have observed this with precision in almost every one of the past twenty-two years. In Mercury no observations of importance can be made, since it does not allow itself to be seen except at its maximum angles with the sun, in which the inequalities of its distances from the earth are imperceptible. Hence such differences are unobservable, and so are its changes of shape, which must certainly take place as in Venus. But when we do see it, it would necessarily show itself to us in the shape of a semicircle, just as Venus does at its maximum angles, though its disc is so small and its brilliance so lively that the power of the telescope is not sufficient to strip off its hair so that it may appear completely shorn.

It remains for us to remove what would seem to be a great objection to the motion of the earth. This is that though all the planets turn about the sun, the earth alone is not solitary like the others, but goes together in the company of the moon and the whole elemental sphere around the sun in one year, while at the same time the moon moves around the earth every month. Here one must once more exclaim over and exalt the admirable perspicacity of Copernicus, and simultaneously regret his misfortune at not being alive in our day. For now Jupiter removes this apparent anomaly of the earth and moon moving conjointly. We see Jupiter, like another earth, going around the sun in twelve years accompanied not by one but by four moons, together with everything that may be contained within the orbits of its four satellites.

SAGREDO: And what is the reason for your calling the four Jovian planets 'moons'?

SALVIATI: That is what they would appear to be to anyone who saw them from Jupiter. For they are dark in themselves, and receive their light from the sun; this is obvious from their being eclipsed when they enter into the cone of Jupiter's shadow. And since only that hemisphere of theirs is illuminated which faces the sun, they always look entirely illuminated to us who are outside their orbits and closer to the sun; but to anyone on Jupiter they would look completely lighted only when they were at the highest points of their circles. In the lowest part – that is, when between Jupiter and the sun – they would appear horned from Jupiter. In a word, they would make for Jovians the same changes of shape which the moon makes for us Terrestrials.

Now you see how admirably these three notes harmonize with the Copernican system, when at first they seemed so discordant with it. From this, Simplicio will be much better able to see with what great probability one may conclude that not the earth, but the sun, is the centre of rotation of the planets. And since this amounts to placing the earth among the world bodies which indubitably move about the sun (above Mercury and Venus but beneath Saturn, Jupiter, and Mars), why will it not likewise be probable, or perhaps even necessary, to admit that it also goes around?

SIMPLICIUS: These events are so large and so conspicuous that it is impossible for Ptolemy and his followers not to have had knowledge of them. And having had, they must also have found a way to give reasons sufficient to account for such sensible appearances; congruous and probable reasons, since they have been accepted for so long by so many people.

SALVIATI: You argue well, but you must know that the principal activity of pure astronomers is to give reasons just for the appearances of celestial bodies, and to fit to these and to the motions of the stars such a structure and arrangement of circles that the resulting calculated motions correspond with those same appearances. They are not much worried about admitting anomalies which might in fact be troublesome in other respects. Copernicus himself writes, in his first studies, of having rectified astronomical science upon the old Ptolemaic assumptions, and corrected the motions of the planets in such a way that the computations corresponded much better with the appearances, and vice versa. But this was still taking them separately, planet by planet. He goes on to say that when he wanted to put together the whole fabric from all individual constructions, there resulted a monstrous chimera composed of mutually disproportionate members, incompatible as a whole. Thus however well the astronomer might be satisfied merely as a calculator, there was no satisfaction and peace for the astronomer as a scientist. And since he very well understood that although the celestial appearances might be saved by means of assumptions essentially false in nature, it would be very much better if he could derive them from true suppositions, he set himself to inquiring diligently whether any one among the famous men of antiquity had attributed to the universe a different structure from that of Ptolemy's which is commonly accepted. Finding that some of the Pythagoreans had in particular attributed the diurnal rotation to the earth, and others the annual revolution as well, he began to examine under these two new suppositions the appearances and peculiarities of the planetary motions, all of which he had readily at hand. And seeing that the whole then corresponded to its parts with wonderful simplicity, he embraced this new arrangement, and in it he found peace of mind.

SIMPLICIUS: But what anomalies are there in the Ptolemaic arrangement which are not matched by greater ones in the Copernican?

SALVIATI: The illnesses are in Ptolemy, and the cures for them in Copernicus. First of all, do not all philosophical schools hold it to be a great impropriety for a body having a natural circular movement to move irregularly with respect to its own centre and regularly around another point? Yet Ptolemy's structure is composed of such uneven movements, while in the Copernican system each movement is equable around its own centre. With Ptolemy it is necessary to assign to the celestial bodies contrary movements, and make everything move from east to west and at the same time from west to east, whereas with Copernicus all celestial revolutions are in one direction, from west to east. And what are we to say of the apparent movement of a planet, so uneven that it not only goes fast at one time and slow at another, but sometimes stops entirely and even goes backwards a long way after doing so? To save these appearances, Ptolemy introduces vast epicycles, adapting them one by one to each planet, with certain rules about incongruous motions – all of which can be done away with by one very simple motion of the earth. Do you not think it extremely absurd, Simplicio, that in Ptolemy's construction where all planets are assigned their own orbits, one above another, it should be necessary to say that Mars, placed above the sun's sphere, often falls so far that it breaks through the sun's orb, descends below this and gets closer to the earth than the body of the sun is, and then a little later soars immeasurably above it? Yet these and other anomalies are cured by a single and simple annual movement of the earth.

SAGREDO: I should like to arrive at a better understanding of how these stoppings, retrograde motions, and advances, which have always seemed to me highly improbable, come about in the Copernican system.

SALVIATI: Sagredo, you will see them come about in such a way that the theory of this alone ought to be enough to gain assent for the rest of the doctrine from anyone who is neither stubborn nor unteachable. I tell you, then, that no change occurs in the movement of Saturn in thirty years, in that of Jupiter in twelve, that of Mars in two, Venus in nine months, or in that of Mercury in about eighty days. The annual movement of the earth alone, between Mars and Venus, causes all the apparent irregularities of the five stars named. For an easy and full understanding of this, I wish to draw you a picture of it. Now suppose the sun to be located in the centre O, around which we shall designate the orbit described by the earth with its annual movement, BGM. The circle described by Jupiter (for example) in twelve years will be BGM here, and in the stellar sphere we shall take the circle of the zodiac to be PUA. In addition, in the earth's annual orbit we shall take a few equal arcs, BC, CD, DE, EF, FG, GH, HI, IK, KL, and LM, and in the circle of Jupiter we shall indicate these other arcs passed over in the same times in which the earth is passing through these. These are BC, CD, DE, EF, FG, GH, HI, IK, KL, and LM, which will be proportionately smaller than those noted on the earth's orbit, as the motion of Jupiter through the zodiac is slower than the annual celestial motion.

Now suppose that when the earth is at B, Jupiter is at B; then it will appear to us as being in the zodiac at P, along the straight line BBP. Next let the earth move from B to C and Jupiter from B to C in the same time; to us, Jupiter will appear to have arrived at Q in the zodiac, having advanced in the order of the signs from P to Q. The earth then passing to D and Jupiter to D, it will be seen in the zodiac at R; and from E, Jupiter being at E, it will appear in the zodiac at S, still advancing. But now when the earth begins to get directly between Jupiter and the sun (having arrived at F and Jupiter at *F*), to us Jupiter will appear to be ready to commence returning backwards through the zodiac, for during the time in which the earth will have passed through the arc EF, Jupiter will have been slowed down between the points *S* and *T*, will look to us almost stationary. Later the earth coming to G, Jupiter at *G* (in opposition to the sun) will be seen in the zodiac at *U*, turned far back through the whole arc *TU* in the zodiac; but in reality, following always its uniform course, it has advanced not only in its own circle but in the zodiac too, with respect to the centre of the zodiac and to the sun which is located there.

The earth and Jupiter then continuing their movements, when the earth is at H and Jupiter is at *H*, it will be seen as having returned far back through the zodiac by the whole arc *UX*; but the earth having arrived at I and Jupiter at *I*, it will apparently have moved in the zodiac by only the small space *XY*, and will there appear stationary. Then when the earth shall have progressed to K and Jupiter to *K*, Jupiter will have advanced through the arc *YN*, in the zodiac; and, continuing its course, from L the earth will see Jupiter at *L* in the point *Z*. Finally, Jupiter at *M* will be seen from the earth at M to have passed to *A*, still advancing. And its whole apparent retrograde motion in the zodiac will be as much as the arc *TX*, made by Jupiter while it is passing in its own circle through the arc *FH*, the earth going through FH in its orbit.

Now what is said here of Jupiter is to be understood of Saturn and Mars also. In Saturn these retrogressions are somewhat more frequent than in Jupiter, because its motion is slower than Jupiter's, so that the earth overtakes it in a shorter time. In Mars they are rarer, its motion being faster than that of Jupiter, so that the earth spends more time in catching up with it.

Next, as to Venus and Mercury, whose circles are included within that of the earth, stoppings and retrograde motions appear in them also, due not to any motion that really exists in them, but to the annual motion of the earth. This is acutely demonstrated by Copernicus, enlisting the

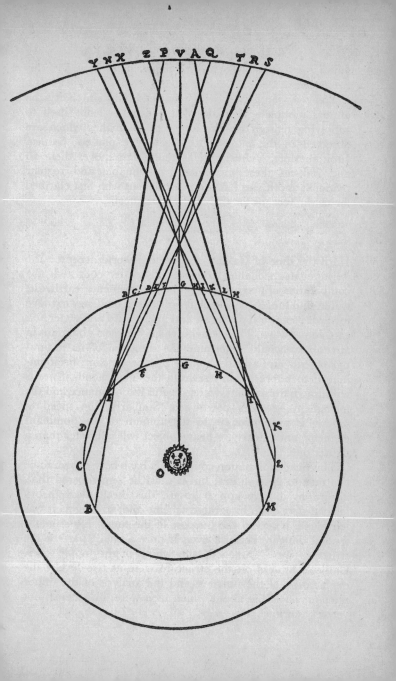

aid of Apollonius of Perga, in Chapter 35 of Book V in his *Revolutions*.

You see, gentlemen, with what ease and simplicity the annual motion – if made by the earth – lends itself to supplying reasons for the apparent anomalies which are observed in the movements of the five planets, Saturn, Jupiter, Mars, Venus, and Mercury. It removes them all and reduces these movements to equable and regular motions; and it was Nicholas Copernicus who first clarified for us the reasons for this marvellous effect.

Until the time of Galileo, the western world accepted the Aristotelian mechanical theory. All matter consisted of a combination of two or more of the four elements: earth, air, water, and fire. Every element possessed a tendency to move towards its natural place: air and fire upward and water and earth downward. The element which was most abundant in any object would determine the direction of its natural movement. Fire added to water produces steam; fire dominates; therefore steam rises. On the other hand, if fire is withdrawn from steam, water regains its dominance and the movement becomes downward. Similarly, the speed of motion is proportionate to the amount of the dominant element; and, clearly, a heavy object will fall faster than a lighter one.

This neat explanation could easily have been shown to be contrary to observation; but it must be remembered that, absurd as it may appear to us, this mechanical theory formed part of an integrated scheme and, so long as it was left alone, it served the purpose of the times. Experiments spelled danger, because even if only a small part of the structure were damaged, the whole might topple over. Galileo's attacks on the structure were at two levels: the explanation of the universe and the analysis of the minor phenomena of life about which men were, in general, not yet very curious.

In recalling Galileo's experiments demonstrating that bodies fall with velocities which increase regularly with the time of the fall, we must remember that Galileo lacked any means of recording the minute fractions of time involved. His experiments with vertically falling bodies (such as the legendary tests made from the Leaning Tower at Pisa) could not properly be verified. Resorting to inclined planes, Galileo found that he could obtain the same data by observing the time taken by a brass sphere to roll down a groove designed to minimize friction. To measure the short intervals of time fairly accurately, or rather to discover the relationship between the time intervals, Galileo weighed the quantities of water which escaped from a hole in a container during the various movements of the ball; a masterpiece of laboratory improvisation.

Galileo was also able to show that a body would, in the absence of friction, continue in motion after the force which provided it was withdrawn. This principle was afterwards developed by Newton in his first law of motion.

It will be noted in the selection that Simplicius, the anti-Copernican, appears to be out of his depth for he intervenes in the discussion hardly at all. Here was less meat for controversy than in the discussions about the mechanics of the universe.

§ NATURALLY ACCELERATED MOTION

SAGREDO: Although I can offer no rational objection to this or indeed to any other definition, devised by any author whomsoever, since all definitions are arbitrary, I may nevertheless without offence be allowed to doubt whether such a definition as the above, established in an abstract manner, corresponds to and describes that kind of accelerated motion which we meet in nature in the case of freely falling bodies. And since the Author apparently maintains that the motion described in his definition is that of freely falling bodies, I would like to clear my mind of certain difficulties in order that I may later apply myself more earnestly to the propositions and their demonstrations.

SALVIATI: It is well that you and Simplicio raise these difficulties. They are, I imagine, the same which occurred to me when I first saw this treatise, and which were removed either by discussion with the Author himself, or by turning the matter over in my own mind.

SAGREDO: When I think of a heavy body falling from rest, that is, starting with zero speed and gaining speed in proportion to the time from the beginning of the motion; such a motion as would, for instance, in eight beats of the pulse acquire eight degrees of speed; having at the end of the fourth beat acquired four degrees; at the end of the second, two; at the end of the first, one: and since time is divisible without limit, it follows from all these considerations that if the earlier speed of a body is less than its present speed in a constant ratio, then there is no degree of speed however small (or, one may say, no degree of slowness however great) with which we may not find this body travelling after starting from infinite slowness, i.e., from rest. So that if that speed which it had at the end of the fourth beat was such that, if kept uniform, the body would traverse two miles in an hour, and if keeping the speed which it had at the end of the second beat, it would traverse one mile an hour, we must infer that, as the instant of starting is more and more nearly approached, the body moves so slowly that, if it kept on moving at this rate, it would not traverse a mile in an hour, or in a day, or in a year or in a thousand years; indeed, it would not traverse a span in an even greater time; a phenomenon which baffles the imagination, while our senses show us that a heavy falling body suddenly acquires great speed.

SALVIATI: This is one of the difficulties which I also at the beginning, experienced, but which I shortly afterwards removed; and the removal was effected by the very experiment which creates the difficulty for you. You say the experiment appears to show that immediately after a heavy body starts from rest it acquires a very considerable speed: and I say that the same experiment makes clear the fact that the initial motions of a falling body, no matter how heavy, are very slow and gentle. Place a heavy body upon a yielding material, and leave it there without any pressure except that owing to its own weight; it is clear that if one lifts this body a cubit or two and allows it to fall upon the same material, it will, with this impulse, exert a new and greater pressure than that caused by its mere weight; and this effect is brought about by the [weight of the] falling body together with the velocity acquired during the fall, an effect which will be greater and greater according to the height of the fall, that is according as the velocity of the falling body becomes greater. From the quality and intensity of the blow we are thus enabled to accurately estimate the speed of a falling body. But tell me, gentlemen, is it not true that if a block be allowed to fall upon a stake from a height of four cubits and drives it into the earth, say, four finger-breadths, that coming from a height of two cubits it will drive the stake a much less distance, and from the height of one cubit a still less distance; and finally if the block be lifted only one finger-breadth how much more will it accomplish than if merely laid on top of the stake without percussion? Certainly very little. If it be lifted only the thickness of a leaf, the effect will be altogether imperceptible. And since the effect of the blow depends upon the velocity of this striking body, can anyone doubt the motion is very slow and the speed more than small whenever the effect [of the blow] is imperceptible? See now the power of truth; the same experiment which at first glance seemed to show one thing, when more carefully examined, assures us of the contrary.

But without depending upon the above experiment, which is doubtless very conclusive, it seems to me that it ought not to be difficult to establish such a fact by reasoning alone. Imagine a heavy stone held in the air at rest; the support is removed and the stone set free; then since it is heavier than the air it begins to fall, and not with uniform motion but slowly at the beginning and with a continuously accelerated motion. Now since velocity can be increased and diminished without limit, what reason is there to believe that such a moving body starting with infinite slowness, that is, from rest, immediately acquires a speed of ten degrees rather than one of four, or of two, or of one, or of a half, or of a hundredth; or, indeed, of any of the infinite number of small values [of speed]? Pray listen. I hardly think you will refuse to grant that the gain of speed of the stone falling from rest follows the same sequence as the diminution and loss of this same speed when, by some impelling force, the stone is thrown to its former elevation: but even if you do not grant this, I do not see how you can doubt that the ascending stone, diminishing in speed, must before coming to rest pass through every possible degree of slowness.

SIMPLICIUS: But if the number of degrees of greater and greater slowness is limitless, they will never be all exhausted, therefore such an ascending heavy body will never reach rest, but will continue to move without limit always at a slower rate; but this is not the observed fact.

SALVIATI: This would happen, Simplicio, if the moving body were to maintain its speed for any length of time at each degree of velocity; but it merely passes each point without delaying more than an instant: and since each time-interval however small may be divided into an infinite number of instants, these will always be sufficient [in number] to correspond to the infinite degrees of diminished velocity.

That such a heavy rising body does not remain for any length of time at any given degree of velocity is evident from the following: because if, some time-interval having been assigned, the body moves with the same speed in the last as in the first instant of that time-interval, it could from this second degree of elevation be in like manner raised through an equal height, just as it was transferred from the first elevation to the second, and by the same reasoning would pass from the second to the third and would finally continue in uniform motion forever.

SAGREDO: From these considerations it appears to me that we may obtain a proper solution of the problem dis-

cussed by philosophers, namely, what causes the acceleration in the natural motion of heavy bodies? Since, as it
seems to me, the force [*virtù*] impressed by the agent pro-
jecting the body upwards diminishes continuously, this
force, so long as it was greater than the contrary force of
gravitation, impelled the body upwards; when the two are
in equilibrium the body ceases to rise and passes through
the state of rest in which the impressed impetus [*impeto*] is
not destroyed, but only its excess over the weight of the body
has been consumed – the excess which caused the body to
rise. Then as the diminution of the outside impetus [*impeto*]
continues, and gravitation gains the upper hand, the fall
begins, but slowly at first on account of the opposing
impetus [*virtù impressa*], a large portion of which still remains
in the body; but as this continues to diminish it also continues to be more and more overcome by gravity, hence
the continuous acceleration of motion.

SIMPLICIUS: The idea is clever, yet more subtle than
sound; for even if the argument were conclusive, it would
explain only the case in which a natural motion is preceded
by a violent motion, in which there still remains active a
portion of the external force [*virtù esterna*]; but where there
is no such remaining portion and the body starts from an
antecedent state of rest, the cogency of the whole argument
fails.

SAGREDO: I believe that you are mistaken and that this
distinction between cases which you make is superfluous or
rather non-existent. But, tell me, cannot a projectile receive
from the projector either a large or a small force [*virtù*] such
as will throw it to a height of a hundred cubits, and even
twenty or four or one?

SIMPLICIUS: Undoubtedly, yes.

SAGREDO: So therefore this impressed force [*virtù
impressa*] may exceed the resistance of gravity so slightly as
to raise it only a finger-breadth; and finally the force
[*virtù*] of the projector may be just large enough to exactly
balance the resistance of gravity so that the body is not
lifted at all but merely sustained. When one holds a stone in

his hand does he do anything but give it a force impelling [*virtù impellente*] it upwards equal to the power [*facoltà*] of gravity drawing it downwards? And do you not continuously impress this force [*virtù*] upon the stone as long as you hold it in the hand? Does it perhaps diminish with the time during which one holds the stone?

And what does it matter whether this support which prevents the stone from falling is furnished by one's hand or by a table or by a rope from which it hangs? Certainly nothing at all. You must conclude, therefore, Simplicio, that it makes no difference whatever whether the fall of the stone is preceded by a period of rest which is long, short, or instantaneous provided only the fall does not take place so long as the stone is acted upon by a force [*virtù*] opposed to its weight and sufficient to hold it at rest.

SALVIATI: The present does not seem to be the proper time to investigate the cause of the acceleration of natural motion concerning which various opinions have been expressed by various philosophers, some explaining it by attraction to the centre, others to repulsion between the very small parts of the body, while still others attribute it to a certain stress in the surrounding medium which closes in behind the falling body and drives it from one of its positions to another. Now, all these fantasies, and others too, ought to be examined; but it is not really worth while. At present it is the purpose of our Author merely to investigate and to demonstrate some of the properties of accelerated motion (whatever the cause of this acceleration may be) – meaning thereby a motion, such that the momentum of its velocity [*i momenti della sua velocità*] goes on increasing after departure from rest, in simple proportionality to the time, which is the same as saying that in equal time-intervals the body receives equal increments of velocity; and if we find the properties [of accelerated motion] which will be demonstrated later are realized in freely falling and accelerated bodies, we may conclude that the assumed definition includes such a motion of falling bodies and that their speed [*accelerazione*] goes on increasing as the time and the duration of the motion.

SAGREDO: So far as I see at present, the definition might have been put a little more clearly perhaps without changing the fundamental idea, namely, uniformly accelerated motion is such that its speed increases in proportion to the space traversed; so that, for example, the speed acquired by a body in falling four cubits would be double that acquired in falling two cubits and this latter speed would be double that acquired in the first cubit. Because there is no doubt but that a heavy body falling from the height of six cubits has, and strikes with, a momentum [*impeto*] double what it had at the end of three cubits, triple that which it had at the end of one.

SALVIATI: It is very comforting to me to have had such a companion in error; and moreover let me tell you that your proposition seems so highly probable that our Author himself admitted, when I advanced this opinion to him, that he had for some time shared the same fallacy. But what most surprised me was to see two propositions so inherently probable that they commanded the assent of everyone to whom they were presented, proven in a few simple words to be not only false, but impossible.

SIMPLICIUS: I am one of those who accept the proposition, and believe that a falling body acquires force [*vires*] in its descent, its velocity increasing in proportion to the space, and that the momentum [*momento*] of the falling body is doubled when it falls from a doubled height; these propositions, it appears to me, ought to be conceded without hesitation or controversy.

SALVIATI: And yet they are as false and impossible as that motion should be completed instantaneously; and here is a very clear demonstration of it. If the velocities are in proportion to the spaces traversed, or to be traversed, then these spaces are traversed in equal intervals of time; if, therefore, the velocity with which the falling body traverses a space of eight feet were double that with which it covered the first four feet (just as the one distance is double the other) then the time-intervals required for these passages would be equal. But for one and the same body to fall eight feet and four feet in the same time is possible only in the case of instantaneous [discontinuous] motion; but observation shows us that the motion of a falling body occupies time, and less of it in covering a distance of four feet than of eight feet; therefore it is not true that its velocity increases in proportion to the space.

The falsity of the other proposition may be shown with equal clearness. For if we consider a single striking body the difference of momentum in its blows can depend only upon difference of velocity; for if the striking body falling from a double height were to deliver a blow of double momentum, it would be necessary for this body to strike with a doubled velocity; but with this doubled speed it would traverse a doubled space in the same time-interval; observation however shows that the time required for fall from the greater height is longer.

SAGREDO: You present these recondite matters with too much evidence and ease; this great facility makes them less appreciated than they would be had they been presented in a more abstruse manner. For, in my opinion, people esteem more lightly that knowledge which they acquire with so little labour than that acquired through long and obscure discussion.

SALVIATI: If those who demonstrate with brevity and clearness the fallacy of many popular beliefs were treated with contempt instead of gratitude the injury would be quite bearable; but on the other hand it is very unpleasant and annoying to see men, who claim to be peers of anyone in a certain field of study, take for granted certain conclusions which later are quickly and easily shown by another to be false. I do not describe such a feeling as one of envy, which usually degenerates into hatred and anger against those who discover such fallacies; I would call it a strong desire to maintain old errors, rather than accept newly discovered truths. This desire at times induces them to unite against these truths, although at heart believing in them, merely for the purpose of lowering the esteem in which certain others are held by the unthinking crowd.

Indeed, I have heard from our Academician many such fallacies held as true but easily refutable; some of these I have in mind.

SAGREDO: You must not withhold them from us, but, at the proper time, tell us about them even though an extra session be necessary. But now, continuing the thread of our talk, it would seem that up to the present we have established the definition of uniformly accelerated motion which is expressed as follows: *A motion is said to be equally or uniformly accelerated when, starting from rest, its momentum* (celeritatis momenta) *receives equal increments in equal times.*

SALVIATI: This definition established, the Author makes a single assumption, namely: *The speeds acquired by one and the same body moving down planes of different inclinations are equal when the heights of these planes are equal.*

By the height of an inclined plane we mean the perpendicular let fall from the upper end of the plane upon the horizontal line drawn through the lower end of the same plane. Thus, to illustrate, let the line *AB* be horizontal, and let the planes *CA* and *CD* be inclined to it; then the Author calls the perpendicular *CB* the height of the planes *CA* and *CD*; he supposes that the speeds acquired by one and the same body, descending along the planes *CA* and *CD* to the terminal points *A* and *D* are equal since the heights of these planes are the same, *CB*; and also it must be understood that this speed is that which would be acquired by the same body falling from *C* to *B*.

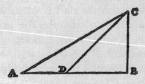

SAGREDO: Your assumption appears to me so reasonable that it ought to be conceded without question, provided of course there are no chance of outside resistances, and that the planes are hard and smooth, and that the figure of the moving body is perfectly round, so that neither plane nor moving body is rough. All resistance and opposition having been removed, my reason tells me at once that a heavy and perfectly round ball descending along the lines *CA*, *CD*, *CB* would reach the terminal points *A*, *D*, *B*, with equal momenta [*impeti eguali*].

SALVIATI: Your words are very plausible; but I hope by experiment to increase the probability to an extent which shall be little short of a rigid demonstration.

Imagine this page to represent a vertical wall, with a nail driven into it; and from the nail let there be suspended a lead bullet of one or two ounces by means of a fine vertical thread, *AB*, say from four to six feet long, on this wall draw a horizontal line *DC*, at right angles to the vertical thread *AB*, which hangs about two finger-breadths in front of the wall. Now bring the thread *AB* with the attached ball into the position *AC* and set it free; first it will be observed to descend along the arc *CBD*, to pass the point *B*, and to travel along the arc *BD*, till it almost reaches the horizontal *CD*, a slight shortage being caused by the resistance of the air and the string; from this we may rightly infer that the ball in its descent through the arc *CB* acquired a momentum [*impeto*] on reaching *B*, which was just sufficient to carry it through a similar arc *BD* to the same height. Having repeated this experiment many times, let us now drive a nail into the wall close to the perpendicular *AB*, say at *E* or *F*, so that it projects out some five or six finger-breadths in order that the thread, again carrying the bullet through the arc *CB*, may strike upon the nail *E* when the bullet reaches *B*, and thus compel it to traverse the arc *BG*, described about *E* as centre. From this we can see what can be done by the same momentum [*impeto*] which previously starting at the same point *B* carried the same body through the arc *BD* to the horizontal *CD*. Now, gentlemen, you will observe with pleasure that the ball swings to the point *G* in the horizontal, and you would see the same thing happen if the obstacle were placed at some lower point, say at *F*, about which the ball would describe the arc *BI*, the rise of the ball always terminating exactly on the line *CD*. But when the nail is placed so low that the remainder of the thread below it will not reach to the height *CD* (which would happen if the nail were placed nearer *B* than to the intersection of *AB* with the horizontal *CD*) then the thread leaps over the nail and twists itself about it.

This experiment leaves no room for doubt as to the truth of our supposition; for since the two arcs *CB* and *DB* are equal and similarly placed, the momentum [*momento*] acquired by the fall through the arc *CB* is the same as that gained by fall through the arc *DB*; but the momentum [*momento*] acquired at *B*, owing to fall through *CB*, is able to lift the same body [*mobile*] through the arc *BD*; therefore, the momentum acquired in the fall *BD* is equal to that which lifts the same body through the same arc from *B* to *D*; so, in general, every momentum acquired by fall through an arc is equal to that which can lift the same body through the same arc. But all these momenta [*momenti*] which cause a rise through the arcs *BD*, *BG*, and *BI* are equal, since they are produced by the same momentum, gained by fall through *CB*, as experiment shows. Therefore all the momenta gained by fall through the arcs *DB*, *GB*, *IB* are equal.

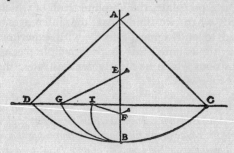

SAGREDO: The argument seems to me so conclusive and the experiment so well adapted to establish the hypothesis that we may, indeed, consider it as demonstrated.

SALVIATI: I do not wish, Sagredo, that we trouble

ourselves too much about this matter, since we are going to apply this principle mainly in motions which occur on plane surfaces, and not upon curved, along which acceleration varies in a manner greatly different from that which we have assumed for planes.

So that, although the above experiment shows us that the descent of the moving body through the arc *CB* confers upon it momentum [*momento*] just sufficient to carry it to the same height through any of the arcs *BD*, *BG*, *BI*, we are not able, by similar means, to show that the event would be identical in the case of a perfectly round ball descending along planes whose inclinations are respectively the same as the chords of these arcs. It seems likely, on the other hand, that, since these planes form angles at the point *B*, they will present an obstacle to the ball which has descended along the chord *CB*, and starts to rise along the chord *BD*, *BG*, *BI*.

In striking these planes some of its momentum [*impeto*] will be lost and it will not be able to rise to the height of the line *CD*; but this obstacle, which interferes with the experiment, once removed, it is clear that the momentum [*impeto*] (which gains in strength with descent) will be able to carry the body to the same height. Let us then, for the present, take this as a postulate, the absolute truth of which will be established when we find that the inferences from it correspond to and agree perfectly with experiment. The author having assumed this single principle passes next to the propositions which he clearly demonstrates; the first of these is as follows:

§ THEOREM I, PROPOSITION I. *The time in which any space is traversed by a body starting from rest and uniformly accelerated is equal to the time in which that same space would be traversed by the same body moving at a uniform speed whose value is the mean of the highest speed and the speed just before acceleration began.*

Let us represent by the line *AB* the time in which the space *CD* is traversed by a body which starts from rest at *C*

and is uniformly accelerated; let the final and highest value
of the speed gained during the interval *AB* be represented
by the line *EB* drawn at right angles to *AB*; draw the line
AE, then all lines drawn from equidistant points on *AB*
and parallel to *BE* will represent the increasing values of the
speed, beginning with the instant *A*. Let the point *F* bisect
the line *EB*; draw *FG* parallel to *BA*, and *GA* parallel to
FB, thus forming a parallelogram *AGFB* which will be equal
in area to the triangle *AEB*, since the side *GF* bisects the
side *AE* at the point *I*; for if the parallel lines in the triangle

AEB are extended to *GI*, then the sum of all the parallels
contained in the quadrilateral is equal to the sum of those
contained in the triangle *AEB*; for those in the triangle
IEF are equal to those contained in the triangle *GIA*, while
those included in the trapezium *AIFB* are common. Since
each and every instant of time in the time-interval *AB* has
its corresponding point on the line *AB*, from which points
parallels drawn in and limited by the triangle *AEB* represent
the increasing values of the growing velocity, and since
parallels contained within the rectangle represent the values

of a speed which is not increasing, but constant, it appears, in like manner, that the momenta [*momenta*] assumed by the moving body may also be represented, in the case of the accelerated motion, by the increasing parallels of the triangle *AEB*, and, in the case of the uniform motion, by the parallels of the rectangle *GB*. For, what the momenta may lack in the first part of the accelerated motion (the deficiency of the momenta being represented by the parallels of the triangle *AGI*) is made up by the momenta represented by the parallels of the triangle *IEF*.

Hence it is clear that equal spaces will be traversed in equal times by two bodies, one of which, starting from rest, moves with a uniform acceleration, while the momentum of the other, moving with uniform speed, is one-half its maximum momentum under accelerated motion.   Q. E. D.

§ THEOREM II, PROPOSITION 2. *The spaces described by a body falling from rest with a uniformly accelerated motion are to each other as the squares of the time-intervals employed in traversing these distances.*

Let the time beginning with any instant *A* be represented by the straight line *AB* in which are taken any two time-intervals *AD* and *AE*. Let *HI* represent the distance through which the body, starting from rest at *H*, falls with uniform acceleration. If *HL* represents the space traversed during the time-interval *AD*, and *HM* that covered during the interval *AE*, then the space *MH* stands to the space *LH* in a ratio which is the square of the ratio of the time *AE* to the time *AD*; or we may say simply that the distances *HM* and *HL* are related as the squares of *AE* and *AD*.

Draw the line *AC* making any angle whatever with the line *AB*; and from the points *D* and *E*, draw the parallel lines *DO* and *EP*; of these two lines, *DO* represents the greatest velocity attained during the interval *AD*, while *EP* represents the maximum velocity acquired during the interval *AE*. But it has just been proved that so far as distances traversed are concerned it is precisely the same whether a body falls from rest with a uniform acceleration or whether it falls during an equal time-interval with a constant speed which is one-half the maximum speed attained during the accelerated motion. It follows therefore that the distances *HM* and *HL* are the same as would be traversed, during the time-intervals *AE* and *AD*, by uniform velocities equal to one-half those represented by *DO* and *EP* respectively. If, therefore, one can show that the distances *HM* and *HL* are in the same ratio as the squares of the time-intervals *AE* and *AD*, our proposition will be proven.

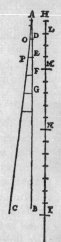

But in the fourth proposition of the first book ... it has been shown that the spaces traversed by two particles in uniform motion bear to one another a ratio which is equal to the product of the ratio of the velocities by the ratio of the times. But in this case the ratio of the velocities is the same as the ratio of the time-intervals (for the ratio of *AE* to *AD* is the same as that of ½*EP* to ½*DO* or of *EP* to *DO*). Hence the ratio of the spaces traversed is the same as the squared ratio of the time-intervals.   Q. E. D.

Evidently then the ratio of the distances is the square of the ratio of the final velocities, that is, of the lines *EP* and *DO*, since these are to each other as *AE* to *AD*.

ISAAC NEWTON
1642–1727

THE UNIVERSAL LAWS OF MOTION ARE
ESTABLISHED

ISAAC NEWTON was born in the hamlet of Woolsthorpe, in the county of Lincolnshire. That Newton was possessed of exceptional talents appears to have first been recognized by an uncle, the Reverend William Ayscough, on whose advice the young boy was sent to Grantham Grammar School, in preparation for Cambridge University, rather than assisting his mother with the management of the family farm.

Newton entered Cambridge University in 1661, but of his undergraduate years little record remains. The Great Plague of 1664–5 made it necessary for all Cambridge scholars to return to their homes, and it was in the isolation of his country home that Newton was to display clear indication of his genius. To this period belongs a series of achievements which were to revolutionize both physics and mathematics. The binomial theorem, the method of 'fluxions' (which we now know as the differential calculus), the composite nature of white light (which is the subject of a later extract), and the law of gravitation; in two brief years Newton had accomplished a body of work that, in terms of personal achievement, is without equal in the history of science.

He returned to Cambridge in 1667, and in 1669 became a Professor of Mathematics. His greatest work, the *Philosophiae naturalis principia mathematica*, from which this reading is taken in a translation by Andrew Motte (in 1729), was not, however, written until nearly twenty years later. Newton's wide range of interests, which included alchemy and theology, may well have contributed to his reluctance to publish the great discoveries he had made, and it was the insistent coaxing of Edmund Halley that finally persuaded Newton to take up the task of presenting his theories in a form appropriate to the magnitude of the achievement.

Two years of intense and continuous thought resulted in the completion of the *Principia*, and in 1687 the work was published at Halley's expense. The significance of this event was many-fold, and no brief commentary such as can be given here can hope to do full justice to the occasion. Yet in terms of the development of the history of physics, as shown in the earlier extracts of this section, one can see in outline the synthesis of scientific thought which Newton had brought about. The Copernican picture of the solar system, Kepler's laws of planetary motion, and Galileo's general laws of motion; all became part of a unified conception which was to provide both the foundation and the inspiration for more than two centuries of scientific investigation.

The publication of the *Principia* represents the climax of Newton's scientific career. Worn out by the labours of creation he became seriously ill, and with his recovery in 1693 he gradually became embroiled in a bitter controversy with Leibniz concerning the discovery of the calculus. Over-zealous patriots on both sides fed the flames of dissension and the futile struggle is one of the saddest episodes in the history of mathematics.

In 1696 Newton left Cambridge and became first Warden, and then Master, of the Mint. The story of these later years is a sad conclusion to the high achievement of his earlier scientific career. The genius of Newton was far from dead and in his response to the occasional challenge of the continental mathematicians he showed himself to be without peer. Yet during the last half of his long life it was the problems of monetary reform, not the problems of science, that were to receive the benefits of his great talents.

¶ *The Mathematical Principles of Natural Philosophy*

§ DEFINITIONS

Definition 1. *The quantity of matter is the measure of the same, arising from its density and bulk conjunctly.*

Thus air of a double density, in a double space, is quadruple in quantity; in a triple space, sextuple in quantity. The same thing is be understood of snow, and fine dust or powders, that are condensed by compression or liquefaction; and of all bodies that are by any causes whatever differently condensed. I have no regard in this place to a medium, if any such there is, that freely pervades the interstices between the parts of bodies. It is this quantity that I mean hereafter everywhere under the name of body or mass: And the same is known by the weight of each body; for it is proportional to the weight, as I have found by experiments on pendulums, very accurately made, which shall be shewn hereafter.

Definition 2. *The quantity of motion is the measure of the same, arising from the velocity and quantity of matter conjunctly.*

The motion of the whole is the sum of the motions of all the parts; and therefore in a body double in quantity, with equal velocity, the motion is double; with twice the velocity, it is quadruple.

Definition 3. *The* vis insita, *or innate force of matter, is a power of resisting, by which every body, as much as in it lies, endeavours to persevere in its present state, whether it be of rest, or of moving uniformly forward in a right line.*

This force is ever proportional to the body whose force it is; and differs nothing from the inactivity of the mass, but in our manner of conceiving it. A body, from the inactivity of matter, is not without difficulty put out of its state of rest or motion. Upon which account, this *vis insita*, may, by a most significant name, be called *vis inertiae*, or force of inactivity. But a body exerts this force only, when another force, impressed upon it, endeavours to change its condition; and the exercise of this force may be considered both as resistance and impulse; it is resistance, in so far as the body, for maintaining its present state, withstands the force impressed; it is impulse, in so far as the body, by not easily giving way to the impressed force of another, endeavours to change the state of that other. Resistance is usually ascribed to bodies at rest, and impulse to those in motion; but motion and rest, as commonly conceived, are only relatively distinguished; nor are those bodies always truly at rest, which commonly are taken to be so.

Definition 4. *An impressed force is an action exerted upon a body, in order to change its state, either of rest, or of moving uniformly forward in a right line.*

This force consists in the action only; and remains no longer in the body, when the action is over. For a body maintains every new state it acquires, by its *vis inertiae* only. Impressed forces are of different origins; as from percussion, from pressure, from centripetal force.

Definition 5. *A centripetal force is that by which bodies are drawn or impelled, or any way tend, towards a point as to a centre.*

Of this sort is gravity, by which bodies tend to the centre of the earth's magnetism, by which iron tends to the loadstone; and that force, what ever it is, by which the planets are perpetually drawn aside from the rectilinear motions, which otherwise they would pursue, and made to revolve in curvilinear orbits. A stone, whirled about in a sling, endeavours to recede from the hand that turns it; and by that endeavour, distends the sling, and that with so much the greater force, as it is revolved with the greater velocity, and as soon as ever it is let go, flies away. That force which opposes itself to this endeavour, and by which the sling perpetually draws back the stone towards the hand and retains it in its orbit, because it is directed to the hand, as the centre of the orbit, I call the centripetal force. And the same thing is to be understood of all bodies, revolved in any orbits. They all endeavour to recede from the centres of their orbits; and were it not for the opposition of a contrary force which restrains them to, and detains them in their orbits, which I therefore call centripetal, would fly off in right lines, with a uniform motion. A projectile, if it was not for the force of gravity, would not deviate towards the earth, but would go off from it in a right line, and that with a uniform motion, if the resistance of the air was taken away. It is by its gravity that it is drawn aside perpetually from its rectilinear course, and made to deviate towards the earth, more or less, according to the force of its gravity, and the velocity of its motion. The less its gravity is, for the quantity of its matter, or the greater the velocity with which it is projected, the less will it deviate from a rectilinear course, and the farther it will go. If a leaden ball, projected from the top of a mountain by the force of gunpowder with a given velocity, and in a direction parallel to the horizon, is carried in a curved line to the distance of two miles before it falls to the ground; the same, if the resistance of the air were taken away, with a double or decuple velocity, would fly twice or ten times as far. And by increasing the velocity, we may at pleasure increase the distance to which it might be projected, and diminish the curvature of the line, which it might describe, till at last it should fall at the distance of 10, 30, or 90 degrees, or even might go quite round the whole earth before it falls; or lastly, so that it might never fall to the earth, but go forward into the celestial spaces, and proceed in its motion *in infinitum*. And after the same manner that a projectile, by the force of gravity, may be made to revolve in an orbit, and go round the whole earth, the moon also, either by the force of gravity, if it is endued with gravity, or by any other force that impels it towards the earth, may be perpetually drawn aside towards the earth, out of the rectilinear way, which by its innate force it would pursue; and would be made to revolve in the orbit which it now describes; nor could the moon without some such force, be retained in its orbit. If this force was too small, it would not sufficiently turn the moon out of a rectilinear course: if it was too great, it would turn it too much, and draw down the moon from its orbit towards the earth. It is necessary, that the force be of a just quantity, and it belongs to the mathematicians to find the force, that may serve exactly to retain a body in a given orbit, with a given velocity; and *vice versa*, to determine the curvilinear way, into which a body projected from a given place, with a given velocity, may be made to deviate from its natural rectilinear way, by means of a given force.

The quantity of any centripetal force may be considered as of three kinds; absolute, accelerative, and motive.

Definition 6. *The absolute quantity of a centripetal force is the measure of the same proportional to the efficacy of the cause that propagates it from the centre, through the spaces round about.*

Thus the magnetic force is greater in one load-stone and less in another according to their sizes and strength of intensity.

Definition 7. *The accelerative quantity of a centripetal force is the measure of the same, proportional to the velocity which it generates in a given time.*

Thus the force of the same loadstone is greater at a less distance, and less at a greater: also the force of gravity is greater in valleys, less on tops of exceeding high mountains; and yet less (as shall hereafter be shown), at greater distances from the body of the earth; but at equal distances, it is the same everywhere; because (taking away, or allowing for, the resistance of the air), it equally accelerates all falling bodies, whether heavy or light, great or small.

Definition 8. *The motive quantity of a centripetal force, is the measure of the same, proportional to the motion which it generates in a given time.*

Thus the weight is greater in a greater body, less in a less body; and, in the same body, it is greater near to the earth, and less at remoter distances. This sort of quantity is the centripetency, or propension of the whole body towards the centre, or, as I may say, its weight; and it is always known by the quantity of an equal and contrary force just sufficient to hinder the descent of the body.

These quantities of forces, we may, for brevity's sake, call by the names of motive, accelerative, and absolute forces; and, for distinction's sake, consider them, with respect to the bodies that tend to the centre; to the places of those bodies; and to the centre of force towards which they tend; that is to say, I refer the motive force to the body as an endeavour and propensity of the whole towards a centre, arising from the propensities of the several parts taken together; the accelerative force to the place of the body, as a certain power or energy diffused from the centre to all places around to move the bodies that are in them; and the absolute force to the centre, as endued with some cause, without which those motive forces would not be propagated through the spaces round about; whether that cause be some central body (such as is the loadstone, in the centre of the magnetic force, or the earth in the centre of the gravitating force), or anything else that does not yet appear. For I here design only to give a mathematical notion of those forces, without considering their physical causes and seats.

Wherefore the accelerative force will stand in the same relation to the motive, as celerity does to motion. For the quantity of motion arises from the celerity drawn into the quantity of matter; and the motive force arises from the accelerative force drawn into the same quantity of matter. For the sum of the actions of the accelerative force, upon the several particles of the body, is the motive force of the whole. Hence it is, that near the surface of the earth, where the accelerative gravity, or force productive of gravity, in all bodies is the same, the motive gravity or the weight is as the body: but if we should ascend to higher regions, where the accelerative gravity is less, the weight would be equally diminished, and would always be as the product of the body, by the accelerative gravity. So in those regions, where the accelerative gravity is diminished into one half, the weight of a body two or three times less, will be four or six times less.

I likewise call attractions and impulses, in the same sense, accelerative, and motive; and use the words attraction, impulse, or propensity of any sort towards a centre, promiscuously, and indifferently, one for another; considering those forces not physically, but mathematically: wherefore, the reader is not to imagine, that by those words, I anywhere take upon me to define the kind, or the manner of any action, the causes or the physical reason thereof, or that I attribute forces, in a true and physical sense, to certain centres (which are only mathematical points); when at any time I happen to speak of centres as attracting, or as endued with attractive powers.

Scholium. Hitherto I have laid down the definitions of such words as are less known, and explained the sense in which I would have them to be understood in the following discourse. I do not define time, space, place, and motion, as being well known to all. Only I must observe, that the vulgar conceive those quantities under no other notions but from the relation they bear to sensible objects. And thence arise certain prejudices, for the removing of which, it will be convenient to distinguish them into absolute and relative, true and apparent, mathematical and common.

I. Absolute, true, and mathematical time, of itself, and from its own nature flows equably without regard to anything external, and by another name is called duration: relative, apparent, and common time, is some sensible and external (whether accurate or unequable) measure of duration by the means of motion, which is commonly used instead of true time; such as an hour, a day, a month, a year.

II. Absolute space, in its own nature, without regard to anything external, remains always similar and immovable. Relative space is some movable dimension or measure of the absolute spaces; which our senses determine by its position to bodies; and which is vulgarly taken for immovable space; such is the dimension of a subterraneous, an aereal, or celestial space, determined by its position in respect of the earth. Absolute and relative space, are the same in figure and magnitude; but they do not remain always numerically the same. For if the earth, for instance, moves, a space of our air, which relatively and in respect of the earth remains always the same, will at one time be one part of the absolute space into which the air passes; at another time it will be another part of the same, and so, absolutely understood, it will be perpetually mutable.

III. Place is a part of space which a body takes up, and is according to the space, either absolute or relative. I say, a part of space; not the situation, nor the external surface of the body. For the places of equal solids are always equal; but their superficies, by reason of their dissimilar figures, are often unequal. Positions properly have no quantity, nor are they so much the places themselves, as the properties of places. The motion of the whole is the same thing with the sum of the motions of the parts; that is, the translation of the whole, out of its place, is the same thing with the sum of the translations of the parts out of their places; and therefore the place of the whole is the same thing with the sum of the places of the parts, and for that reason, it is internal, and in the whole body.

IV. Absolute motion is the translation of a body from one absolute place into another; and relative motion, the translation from one relative place into another. Thus in a ship under sail, the relative place of a body is that part of the ship which the body possesses; or that part of its cavity which the body fills, and which therefore moves together with the ship: and relative rest is the continuance of the body in the same part of the ship, or of its cavity. But real, absolute rest, is the continuance of the body in the same part of that immovable space, in which the ship itself, its cavity, and all that it contains, is moved. Wherefore, if the earth is really at rest, the body, which relatively rests in the ship, will really and absolutely move with the same velocity which the ship has on the earth. But if the earth also moves, the true and absolute motion of the body will arise, partly from the true motion of the earth, in immovable space; partly from the relative motion of the ship on the earth; and if the body moves also relatively in the ship; its true motion will arise, partly from the true motion of the earth, in immovable space, and partly from the relative motions as well of the ship on the earth, as of the body in the ship; and from these relative motions will arise the relative motion of the body on the earth. As if that part of the earth, where the ship is, was truly moved towards the east, with a velocity of 10010 parts; while the ship itself, with a fresh gale, and full sails, is carried towards the west, with a velocity expressed by 10 of those parts; but a sailor walks in the ship towards the east, with 1 part of the said velocity; then the sailor will be moved truly in immovable space towards the east, with a velocity of 10001 parts, and relatively on the earth towards the west, with a velocity of 9 of those parts.

Absolute time, in astronomy, is distinguished from relative, by the equation or correction of the vulgar time. For the natural days are truly unequal, though they are commonly considered as equal, and used for a measure of time; astronomers correct this inequality for their more accurate deducing of the celestial motions. It may be, that there is no such thing as an equable motion, whereby time may be accurately measured. All motions may be accelerated and retarded, but the true, or equable, progress of absolute time is liable to no change. The duration or perseverance of the existence of things remains the same, whether the motions are swift or slow, or none at all: and therefore it ought to be distinguished from what are only sensible measures thereof; and out of which we collect it, by means of the astronomical equation. The necessity of which equation, for determining the times of a phenomenon, is evinced as well from the experiments of the pendulum clock, as by eclipses of the satellites of *Jupiter*.

As the order of the parts of time is immutable, so also is the order of the parts of space. Suppose those parts to be moved out of their places, and they will be moved (if the expression may be allowed) out of themselves. For times and spaces are, as it were, the places as well of themselves as of all other things. All things are placed in time as to order of succession; and in space as to order of situation. It is from their essence or nature that they are places; and that the primary places of things should be movable, is absurd. These are therefore the absolute places; and translations out of those places, are the only absolute motions.

But because the parts of space cannot be seen, or distinguished from one another by our senses, therefore in their stead we use sensible measures of them. For from the positions and distances of things from any body considered as immovable, we define all places; and then with respect to such places, we estimate all motions, considering bodies as transferred from some of those places into others. And so, instead of absolute places and motions, we use relative ones; and that without any inconvenience in common affairs; but in philosophical disquisitions, we ought to abstract from our senses, and consider things themselves, distinct from what are only sensible measures of them. For it may be that there is no body really at rest, to which the places and motions of others may be referred.

But we may distinguish rest and motion, absolute and relative, one from the other by their properties, causes, and effects. It is a property of rest, that bodies really at rest do rest in respect to one another. And therefore as it is possible, that in the remote regions of the fixed stars, or perhaps far beyond them, there may be some body absolutely at rest; but impossible to know, from the position of bodies to one another in our regions whether any of these do keep the same position to that remote body; it follows that absolute rest cannot be determined from the position of bodies in our regions.

It is a property of motion, that the parts, which retain given positions to their wholes, do partake of the motions of those wholes. For all the parts of revolving bodies endeavour to recede from the axis of motion; and the impetus of bodies moving forward, arises from the joint impetus of all the parts. Therefore, if surrounding bodies are moved, those that are relatively at rest within them, will partake of their motion. Upon which account, the true and absolute motion of a body cannot be determined by the translation of it from those which only seem to rest; for the external bodies ought not only to appear at rest, but to be really at rest. For otherwise, all included bodies, beside their translation from near the surrounding ones, partake likewise of their true motions; and though that translation were not made they would not be really at rest, but only seem to be so. For the surrounding bodies stand in the like relation to the surrounded as the exterior part of a whole does to the interior, or as the shell does to the kernel; but, if the shell moves, the kernel will also move, as being part of the whole, without any removal from near the shell.

A property, near akin to the preceding, is this, that if a place is moved, whatever is placed therein moves along with it; and therefore a body, which is moved 'from a place in motion, partakes also of the motion of its place. Upon which account, all motions, from places in motion, are no other than parts of entire and absolute motions; and every entire motion is composed of the motion of the body out of its first place, and the motion of this place out of its place; and so on, until we come to some immovable place, as in the before-mentioned example of the sailor. Wherefore, entire and absolute motions can be no otherwise determined than by immovable places; and for that reason I did before refer those absolute motions to immovable places, but relative ones to movable places. Now no other places are immovable but those that, from infinity to infinity, do all retain the same given position one to another; and upon this account must ever remain unmoved; and do thereby constitute immovable space.

The causes by which true and relative motions are distinguished, one from the other, are the forces impressed upon bodies to generate motion. True motion is neither generated nor altered, but by some force impressed upon the body moved; but relative motion may be generated or altered without any force impressed upon the body. For it is sufficient only to impress some force on other bodies with which the former is compared, that by their giving way, that relation may be changed, in which the relative rest or motion of this other body did consist. Again, true motion suffers always some change from any force impressed upon the moving body; but relative motion does not necessarily undergo any change by such forces. For if the same forces are likewise impressed on those other bodies, with which the comparison is made, that the relative position may be preserved, then that condition will be preserved in which the relative motion consists. And therefore any relative motion may be changed when the true motion remains unaltered, and the relative may be preserved when the true suffers some change. Upon which accounts, true motion does by no means consist in such relations.

The effects which distinguish absolute from relative motion are, the forces of receding from the axis of circular motion. For there are no such forces in a circular motion purely relative, but in a true and absolute circular motion, they are greater or less, according to the quantity of the motion. If a vessel, hung by a long cord, is so often turned about that the cord is strongly twisted, then filled with water, and held at rest together with the water; after, by the sudden action of another force, it is whirled about the contrary way, and while the cord is untwisting itself, the vessel continues for some time in this motion; the surface of the water will at first be plain, as before the vessel began to move; but the vessel by gradually communicating its motion to the water, will make it begin sensibly to revolve, and recede by little and little from the middle, and ascend to the sides of the vessel, forming itself into a concave figure (as I have experienced), and the swifter the motion becomes, the higher will the water rise, till at last, performing its revolutions in the same times with the vessel, it becomes relatively at rest in it. This ascent of the water shows its endeavour to recede from the axis of its motion; and the true and absolute circular motion of the water, which is here directly contrary to the relative, discovers itself, and may be measured by this endeavour. At first, when the relative motion of the water in the vessel was greatest, it produced no endeavour to recede from the axis; the water showed no tendency to the circumference, nor any ascent towards the sides of the vessel, but remained of a plain surface, and therefore its true circular motion had not yet begun. But afterwards, when the relative motion of the water had decreased, the ascent thereof towards the sides of the vessel proved its endeavour to recede from the axis; and this endeavour showed the real circular motion of the water perpetually increasing, till it had acquired its greatest quantity, when the water rested relatively in the vessel. And therefore this endeavour does not depend upon any translation of the water in respect of the ambient bodies, nor can true circular motion be defined by such translation. There is only one real circular motion of any one revolving body, corresponding to only one power of endeavouring to recede from its axis of motion, as its proper and adequate effect; but relative motions, in one and the same body, are innumerable, according to the various relations it bears to external bodies, and like other relations, are altogether destitute of any real effect, any otherwise than they may perhaps partake of that one only true motion. And therefore in their system who suppose that our heavens, revolving below the sphere of the fixed stars, carry the planets along with them; the several parts of those heavens, and the planets, which are indeed relatively at rest in their heavens, do yet really move. For they change their position one to another (which never happens to bodies truly at rest), and being carried together with their heavens, partake of their motions, and as parts of revolving wholes, endeavour to recede from the axis of their motions.

Wherefore relative quantities are not the quantities themselves, whose names they bear, but those sensible measures of them (either accurate or inaccurate), which are commonly used instead of the measured quantities themselves. And if the meaning of words is to be determined by their use, then by the names time, space, place, and motion, their measures are properly to be understood; and the expression will be unusual, and purely mathematical, if the measured quantities themselves are meant. Upon which account, they do strain the sacred writings, who there interpret those words for the measured quantities. Nor do those less defile the purity of mathematical and philosophical truths, who confound real quantities themselves with their relations and vulgar measures.

It is indeed a matter of great difficulty to discover, and effectually to distinguish, the true motions of particular bodies from the apparent; because the parts of that immovable space, in which those motions are performed, do by no means come under the observation of our senses. Yet the thing is not altogether desperate; for we have some arguments to guide us, partly from the apparent motions, which are the differences of the true motions; partly from the forces, which are the causes and effects of the true motions. For instance, if two globes, kept at a given distance one from the other by means of a cord that connects them, were revolved about their common centre of gravity, we might, from the tension of the cord, discover the endeavour of the globes to recede from the axis of their motion, and from thence we might compute the quantity of their circular motions. And then if any equal forces should be impressed at once on the alternate faces of the globes to augment or diminish their circular motions, from the increase or decrease of the tension of the cord, we might infer the increment or decrement of their motions; and thence would be found on what faces those forces ought to be impressed, that the motions of the globes might be most augmented; that is, we might discover their hindermost faces, or those which, in the circular motion, do follow. But the faces which follow being known, and consequently the opposite ones that precede, we should likewise know the determination of their motions. And thus we might find both the quantity and the determination of this circular motion, even in an immense vacuum, where there was nothing external or sensible with which the globes could be compared. But now, if in that space some remote bodies were placed that kept always a given position one to another, as the fixed stars do in our regions, we could not indeed determine from the relative translation of the globes among those bodies, whether the motion did belong to the globes or to the bodies. But if we observed the cord, and found that its tension was that very tension which the motions of the globes required, we might conclude the motion to be in the globes, and the bodies to be at rest; and then, lastly, from the translation of the globes among the bodies, we should find the determination of their motions. But how we are to collect the true motions from their causes, effects, and apparent differences; and, vice versa, how from the motions, either true or apparent, we may come to the knowledge of their causes and effects, shall be explained more at large in the following tract. For to this end it was that I composed it.

§ Axioms, or Laws of Motion

Law 1. *Everybody perseveres in its state of rest, or of uniform motion in a right line, unless it is compelled to change that state by forces impressed thereon.*

Projectiles persevere in their motions, so far as they are not retarded by the resistance of the air, or impelled downwards by the force of gravity. A top, whose parts by their cohesion are perpetually drawn aside from rectilinear motions, does not cease its rotation, otherwise than as it is retarded by the air. The greater bodies of the planets and comets, meeting with less resistance in more free spaces, preserve their motions both progressive and circular for a much longer time.

Law 2. *The alteration of motion is ever proportional to the motive force impressed; and is made in the direction of the right line in which that force is impressed.*

If any force generates a motion, a double force will generate double the motion, a triple force will generate triple the motion, whether that force be impressed altogether and at once, or gradually and successively. And this motion (being always directed the same way with the generating force), if the body moved before, is added to or subducted from the former motion, according as they directly conspire with or are directly contrary to each other; or obliquely joined, when they are oblique, so as to produce a new motion compounded from the determination of both.

Law 3. *To every action there is always opposed an equal reaction: or the mutual actions of two bodies upon each other are always equal, and directed to contrary parts.*

Whatever draws or presses another is as much drawn or pressed by that other. If you press a stone with your finger, the finger is also pressed by the stone. If a horse draws a stone tied to a rope, the horse (if I may so say) will be equally drawn back towards the stone: for the distended rope, by the same endeavour to relax or unbend itself, will draw the horse as much towards the stone, as it does the stone towards the horse, and will obstruct the progress of the one as much as it advances that of the other. If a body impinge upon another, and by its force change the motion of the other, that body also (because of the equality of the mutual pressure) will undergo an equal change, in its own motion, towards the contrary part. The changes made by these actions are equal, not in the velocities but in the motions of bodies; that is to say, if the bodies are not hindered by any other impediments. For, because the motions are equally changed, the changes of the velocities made towards contrary parts are reciprocally proportional to the bodies. This law takes place also in attractions, as will be proved in the next scholium.

Corollary 1. *A body by two forces conjoined will describe the diagonal of a parallelogram, in the same time that it would describe the sides, by those forces apart.*

If a body in a given time, by the force M impressed apart in the place A, should with a uniform motion be carried from A to B; and by the force N impressed apart in the same place, should be carried from A to C; complete the parallelogram $ABCD$, and, by both forces acting together, it will in the same time be carried in the diagonal from A to D. For since the force N acts in the direction of the line AC, parallel to BD, this force (by the second law) will not at all alter the velocity generated by the other force M, by which the body is carried towards the line BD. The body therefore will arrive at the line BD in the same time, whether the force N be impressed or not; and therefore at the end of that time it will be found somewhere in the line BD. By the same argument, at the end of the same time it will be found somewhere in the line CD. Therefore it will be found in the point D, where both lines meet. But it will move in a right line from A to D, by Law 1.

Corollary 2. *And hence is explained the composition of any one direct force AD, out of any two oblique forces AC and CD; and, on* *the contrary, the resolution of any one direct force AD into two oblique forces AC and CD: which composition and resolution are abundantly confirmed from mechanics.*

As if the unequal radii *OM* and *ON* drawn from the centre *O* of any wheel, should sustain the weights *A* and *P* by the cords *MA* and *NP*; and the forces of those weights to move the wheel were required. Through the centre *O* draw the right line *KOL*, meeting the cords perpendicularly in *K* and *L*; and from the centre *O*, with *OL* the greater of the distances *OK* and *OL*, describe a circle, meeting the cord *MA* in *D*: and drawing *OD*, make *AC* parallel and *DC* perpendicular thereto. Now, it being indifferent whether the points *K,L,D,* of the cords be fixed to the plane of the wheel or not, the weights will have the same effect whether they are suspended from the points *K* or *L*, or from *D* and *L*. Let the whole force of the weight *A* be represented by the line *AD*, and let it be resolved into the forces *AC* and *CD*; of which the force *AC*, drawing the radius *OD* directly from the centre, will have no effect to move the wheel: but the other force *DC*, drawing the radius *DO* perpendicularly, will have the same effect as if it drew perpendicularly the radius *OL* equal to *OD*; that is, it will have the same effect as the weight *P*, if that weight is to the weight *A* as the force *DC* is to the force *DA*; that is (because of the similar triangles *ADC*, *DOK*), as *OK* to *OD* or *OL*. Therefore the weights *A* and *P*, which are reciprocally as the radii *OK* and *OL* that lie in the same right line, will be equipollent, and so remain in equilibrio; which is the well known property of the balance, the lever, and the wheel. If either weight is greater than in this ratio, its force to move the wheel will be so much greater.

If the weight *p*, equal to the weight *P*, is partly suspended by the cord *Np*, partly sustained by the oblique plane *pG*; draw *pH*, *NH*, the former perpendicular to the horizon, the latter to the plane *pG*; and if the force of the weight *p* tending downwards is represented by the line *pH*, it may be resolved into the forces *pN*, *HN*. If there was any plane *pQ*, perpendicular to the cord *pN*, cutting the other plane *pG* in a line parallel to the horizon, and the weight *p* was supported only by those planes pQ, pG, it would press those planes perpendicularly with the forces pN, HN; to wit, the plane pQ with the force pN, and the plane pG with the force HN. And therefore if the plane pQ was taken away, so that the weight might stretch the cord, because the cord now sustaining the weight, supplies the place of the plane that was removed, it will be strained by the same force pN which pressed upon the plane before. Therefore, the tension of this oblique cord pN will be to that of the other perpendicular cord PN as pN to pH. And therefore if the weight p is to the weight A in a ratio compounded of the reciprocal ratio of the least distances of the cords PN, AM, from the centre of the wheel, and of the direct ratio of pH to pN, the weights will have the same effect towards moving the wheel, and will therefore sustain each other; as anyone may find by experiment.

But the weight p pressing upon those two oblique planes, may be considered as a wedge between the two internal surfaces of a body split by it; and hence the forces of the wedge and the mallet may be determined; for because the force with which the weight p presses the plane pQ is to the force with which the same, whether by its own gravity, or by the blow of a mallet, is impelled in the direction of the line pH towards both the planes, as pN to pH; and to the force with which it presses the other plane pG, as pN to NH. And thus the force of the screw may be deduced from a like resolution of forces; it being no other than a wedge impelled with the force of a lever. Therefore the use of this Corollary spreads far and wide, and by that diffusive extent the truth thereof is farther confirmed. For on what has been said depends the whole doctrine of mechanics variously demonstrated by different authors. For from hence are easily deduced the forces of machines, which are compounded of wheels, pullies, levers, cords, and weights, ascending directly or obliquely, and other mechanical powers; as also the force of the tendons to move the bones of animals.

Corollary 3. *The quantity of motion, which is collected by taking the sum of the motions directed towards the same parts, and the difference of those that are directed to contrary parts, suffers no change from the action of bodies among themselves.*

For action and its opposite reaction are equal, by Law III, and therefore, by Law II, they produce in the motions equal changes towards opposite parts. Therefore if the motions are directed towards the same parts, whatever is added to the motion of the preceding body will be subducted from the motion of that which follows; so that the sum will be the same as before. If the bodies meet, with contrary motions, there will be an equal deduction from the motions of both; and therefore the difference of the motions directed towards opposite parts will remain the same.

Thus if a spherical body *A* with two parts of velocity is triple of a spherical body *B* which follows in the same right line with ten parts of velocity, the motion of *A* will be to that of *B* as 6 to 10. Suppose, then, their motions to be of 6 parts and of 10 parts, and the sum will be 16 parts. Therefore, upon the meeting of the bodies, if *A* acquire 3, 4, or 5 parts of motion, *B* will lose as many; and therefore after reflection *A* will proceed with 9, 10, or 11 parts, and *B* with 7, 6, or 5 parts; the sum remaining always of 16 parts as before. If the body *A* acquire 9, 10, 11, or 12 parts of motion, and therefore after meeting proceed with 15, 16, 17, or 18 parts, the body *B*, losing so many parts as *A* has got, will either proceed with 1 part, having lost 9, or stop and remain at rest, as having lost its whole progressive motion of 10 parts; or it will go back with 1 part, having not only lost its whole motion, but (if I may so say) one part more; or it will go back with 2 parts, because a progressive motion of 12 parts is taken off. And so the sums of the conspiring motions 15+1, or 16+0, and the differences of the contrary motions 17−1 and 18−2, will always be equal to 16 parts, as they were before the meeting and reflection of the bodies. But, the motions being known with which the bodies proceed after reflection, the velocity of either will be also known, by taking the velocity after to the velocity before reflection, as the motion after is to the motion before. As in the last case, where the motion of the body *A* was of 6 parts before reflection and of 18 parts after, and the velocity was of 2 parts before reflection, the velocity thereof after reflection will be found to be of 6 parts; by saying, as the 6 parts of motion before to 18 parts after, so are 2 parts of velocity before reflection to 6 parts after.

But if the bodies are either not spherical, or, moving in different right lines, impinge obliquely one upon the other, and their motions after reflection are required, in those cases we are first to determine the position of the plane that touches the concurring bodies in the point of concourse; then the motion of each body (by Corol. 2) is to be resolved into two, one perpendicular to that plane, and the other parallel to it. This done, because the bodies act upon each other in the direction of a line perpendicular to this plane, the parallel motions are to be retained the same after reflection as before; and to the perpendicular motions we are to assign equal changes towards the contrary parts; in such manner that the sum of the conspiring and the difference of the contrary motions may remain the same as before. From such kind of reflections also sometimes arise the circular motions of bodies about their own centres. But these are cases which I do not consider in what follows, and it would be too tedious to demonstrate every particular that relates to this subject.

Corollary 4. *The common centre of gravity of two or more bodies does not alter its state of motion or rest by the actions of the bodies among themselves; and therefore the common centre of gravity of all bodies acting upon each other (excluding outward actions and impediments) is either at rest, or moves uniformly in a right line.*

For if two points proceed with a uniform motion in right lines, and their distance be divided in a given ratio, the dividing point will be either at rest, or proceed uniformly in a right line. This is demonstrated hereafter in Lem. XXIII and its Corol., when the points are moved in the same plane; and by a like way of arguing, it may be demonstrated when the points are not moved in the same plane. Therefore if any number of bodies move uniformly in right lines, the common centre of gravity of any two of them is either at rest, or proceeds uniformly in a right line; because the line which connects the centres of those two bodies so moving is divided at that common centre in a given ratio. In like manner the common centre of those two and that of a third body will be either at rest or moving uniformly in a right line; because at that centre the distance between the common centre of the two bodies, and the centre of this last, is divided in a given ratio. In like manner the common centre of these three, and of a fourth body, is either at rest, or moves uniformly in a right line; because the distance between the common centre of the three bodies, and the centre of the fourth is there also divided in a given ratio, and so on *in infinitum*. Therefore, in a system of bodies where there is neither any mutual action among themselves, nor any foreign force impressed upon them from without, and which consequently move uniformly in right lines, the common centre of gravity of them all is either at rest or moves uniformly forward in a right line.

Moreover, in a system of two bodies mutually acting upon each other, since the distances between their centres and the common centre of gravity of both are reciprocally as the bodies, the relative motions of those bodies, whether of approaching to or of receding from that centre, will be equal among themselves. Therefore since the changes which happen to motions are equal and directed to contrary parts, the common centre of those bodies, by their mutual action between themselves, is neither promoted nor retarded, nor suffers any change as to its state of motion or rest. But in a system of several bodies, because the common centre of gravity of any two acting mutually upon each other suffers no change in its state by that action; and much less the common centre of gravity of the others with which that action does not intervene; but the distance between those two centres is divided by the common centre of gravity of all the bodies into parts reciprocally proportional to the total sums of those bodies whose centres they are; and therefore while those two centres retain their state of motion or rest, the common centre of all does also retain its state: it is manifest that the common centre of all never suffers any change in the state of its motion or rest from the actions of any two bodies between themselves. But in such a system all the actions of the bodies among themselves either happen between two bodies, or are composed of actions interchanged between some two bodies; and therefore they do never produce any alteration in the common centre of all as to its state of motion or rest. Wherefore since that centre, when the bodies do not act mutually one upon another, either is at rest or moves uniformly forward in some right line, it will, notwithstanding the mutual actions of the bodies among themselves, always persevere in its state, either of rest, or of proceeding uniformly in a right line, unless it is forced out of this state by the action of some power impressed from without upon the whole system. And therefore the same law takes place in a system consisting of many bodies as in one single body, with regard to their persevering in their state of motion or of rest. For the progressive motion, whether of one single body, or of a whole system of bodies, is always to be estimated from the motion of the centre of gravity.

Corollary 5. *The motions of bodies included in a given space are the same among themselves, whether that space is at rest, or moves uniformly forward in a right line without any circular motion.*

For the differences of the motions tending towards the same parts, and the sums of those that tend towards contrary parts, are, at first (by supposition), in both cases the same; and it is from those sums and differences that the collisions and impulses do arise with which the bodies mutually impinge one upon another. Wherefore (by Law 2), the effects of those collisions will be equal in both cases; and therefore the mutual motions of the bodies among themselves in the one case will remain equal to the mutual motions of the bodies among themselves in the other. A clear proof of which we have from the experiment of a ship; where all motions happen after the same manner, whether the ship is at rest, or is carried uniformly forwards in a right line.

Corollary 6. *If bodies, anyhow moved among themselves, are urged in the direction of parallel lines by equal accelerative forces, they will all continue to move among themselves, after the same manner as if they had been urged by no such forces.*

For these forces acting equally (with respect to the quantities of the bodies to be moved), and in the direction of parallel lines, will (by Law 2) move all the bodies equally (as to velocity), and therefore will never produce any change in the positions or motions of the bodies among themselves.

Scholium. Hitherto I have laid down such principles as have been received by mathematicians, and are confirmed by abundance of experiments. By the first two Laws and the first two Corollaries, Galileo discovered that the descent of bodies observed the duplicate ratio of the time, and that the motion of projectiles was in the curve of a parabola; experience agreeing with both, unless so far as these motions are a little retarded by the resistance of the air. When a body is falling, the uniform force of its gravity acting equally, impresses, in equal particles of time, equal forces upon that body, and therefore generates equal velocities; and in the whole time impresses a whole force, and generates a whole velocity proportional to the time. And the spaces described in proportional times are as the velocities and the times conjunctly; that is, in a duplicate ratio of the times. And when a body is thrown upwards, its uniform gravity impresses forces and takes off velocities proportional to the times; and the times of ascending to the greatest heights are as the velocities to be taken off, and those heights are as the velocities and the times conjunctly, or in the duplicate ratio of the velocities. And if a body be projected in any direction, the motion arising from its projection is compounded with the motion arising from its gravity. As if the body *A* by its motion of projection alone could describe in a given time the right line *AB*, and with its motion of falling alone could describe in the same time the altitude *AC*; complete the parallelogram *ABDC*, and the body by that compounded motion will at the end of the time be found in the place *D*; and the curve line *AED*, which that body describes, will be a parabola, to which the right line *AB* will be a tangent in *A*; and whose ordinate *BD* will be as the square of the line *AB*. On the same Laws and Corollaries depend those things which have been demonstrated concerning the times of the vibration of pendulums, and are confirmed by the daily experiments of pendulum clocks. By the same, together with the third Law, Sir Christopher Wren, Dr Wallis, and Mr Huygens, the greatest geometers of our times, did severally determine the rules of the congress and reflection of hard bodies, and much about the same time communicated their discoveries to the Royal Society, exactly agreeing among themselves as to those rules. Dr Wallis, indeed, was something more early in the publication; then followed Sir Christopher Wren, and, lastly, Mr Huygens. But Sir Christopher Wren confirmed the truth of the thing before the Royal Society by the experiment of pendulums, which Mr Mariotte soon after thought fit to explain in a treatise entirely upon that subject. But to bring this experiment to an accurate agreement with the theory, we are to have a due regard as well to the resistance of the air as to the elastic force of the concurring bodies. Let the spherical bodies A, B be suspended by the parallel and equal strings AC, BD, from the centres C, D. About these centres, with those intervals, describe the semicircles EAF, GBH, bisected by the radii CA, DB. Bring the body A to any point R of the arc EAF, and (withdrawing the body B) let it go from thence, and after one oscillation suppose it to return to the point V: then RV will be the retardation arising from the resistance of the air. Of this RV let ST be a fourth part, situated in the middle, to wit, so as RS and TV may be equal, and RS may be to ST as 3 to 2 then will ST represent very nearly the retardation during the descent from S to A. Restore the body B to its place: and, supposing the body A to be let fall from the point S, the velocity thereof in the place of reflection A, without sensible error, will be the same as if it had descended *in vacuo* from the point T. Upon which account this velocity may be represented by the chord of the arc TA. For it is a proposition well known to geometers, that the velocity of a pendulous body in the lowest point is as the chord of the arc which it has described in its descent. After reflection, suppose the body A comes to the place s, and the body B to the place k. Withdraw the body B, and find the place v, from which if the body A, being let go, should after one oscillation return to the place r, st may be a fourth part of rv, so placed in the middle thereof as to leave rs equal to tv, and let the chord of the arc tA represent the velocity which the body A had in the place A immediately after reflection. For t will be the true and correct place to which the body A should have ascended, if the resistance of the air had been taken off. In the same way we are to correct the place k to which the body B ascends, by finding the place l to which it should have ascended *in vacuo*. And thus everything may be subjected to experiment, in the same manner as if we were really placed *in vacuo*. These things being done, we are to take the product (if I may so say) of the body A, by the chord of the arc TA (which represents its velocity), that we may have its motion in the place A immediately before reflection; and then by the chord of the arc tA, that we may have its motion in the place A immediately after reflection. And so we are to take the product of the body B by the chord of the arc Bl, that we may have the motion of the same immediately after reflection. And in like manner, when two bodies are let go together from different places, we are to find the motion of each, as well before as after reflection; and then we may compare the motions between themselves, and collect the effects of the reflection. Thus trying the thing with pendulums of ten feet, in unequal as well as equal bodies, and making the bodies to concur after a descent through large spaces, as of 8, 12, or 16 feet, I found always, without an error of 3 inches, that when the bodies concurred together directly, equal changes towards the contrary parts were produced in their motions, and, of consequence, that the action and reaction were always equal. As if the body A impinged upon the body B at rest with 9 parts of motion, and losing 7, proceeded after reflection with 2, the body B was carried backwards with those 7 parts. If the bodies concurred with contrary motions, A with twelve parts of motion, and B with six, then if A receded with 2, B receded with 8; to wit, with a deduction of 14 parts of motion on each side. For from the motion of A subducting twelve parts, nothing will remain; but subducting 2 parts more, a motion will be generated of 2 parts towards the contrary way; and so, from the motion of the body B of 6 parts, subducting 14 parts, a motion is generated of 8 parts towards the contrary way. But if the bodies were made both to move towards the same way, A, the swifter, with 14 parts of motion, B, the slower, with 5, and after reflection A went on with 5, B likewise went on with 14 parts; 9 parts being transferred from A to B. And so in other cases. By the congress and collision of bodies, the quantity of motion, collected from the sum of the motions directed towards the same way, or from the difference of those that were directed towards contrary ways, was never changed. For the error of an inch or two in measures may be easily ascribed to the difficulty of executing everything with accuracy. It was not easy to let go the two pendulums so exactly together that the bodies should impinge one upon the other in the lowermost place AB; nor to mark the places s, and k, to which the bodies ascended after congress. Nay, and some errors, too, might have happened from the unequal density of the parts of the pendulous bodies themselves, and from the irregularity of the texture proceeding from other causes.

But to prevent an objection that may perhaps be alleged against the rule, for the proof of which this experiment was made, as if this rule did suppose that the bodies were either absolutely hard, or at least perfectly elastic (whereas no such bodies are to be found in nature), I must add, that the experiments we have been describing, by no means depending upon that quality of hardness, do succeed as well in soft as in hard bodies. For if the rule is to be tried in bodies not perfectly hard, we are only to diminish the reflection in such a certain proportion as the quantity of the elastic force requires. By the theory of Wren and Huygens, bodies absolutely hard return one from another with the same velocity with which they meet. But this may be affirmed with more certainty of bodies perfectly elastic. In bodies imperfectly elastic the velocity of the return is to be diminished together with the elastic force; because that force (except when the parts of bodies are bruised by their congress, or suffer some such extension as happens under the strokes of a hammer) is (as far as I can perceive) certain and determined, and makes the bodies to return one from the other with a relative velocity, which is in a given ratio to that relative velocity with which they met. This I tried in balls of wool, made up tightly, and strongly compressed. For, first, by letting go the pendulous bodies, and measuring their reflection, I determined the quantity of their elastic force; and then, according to this force, estimated the reflections that ought to happen in other cases of congress. And with this computation other experiments made afterwards did accordingly agree; the balls always receding one from the other with a relative velocity, which was to the relative velocity with which they met as about 5 to 9. Balls of steel returned with almost the same velocity; those of cork with a velocity something less; but in balls of glass the proportion was as about 15 to 16. And thus the third Law, so far as it regards percussions and reflections, is proved by a theory exactly agreeing with experience.

In attractions, I briefly demonstrate the thing after this manner. Suppose an obstacle is interposed to hinder the congress of any two bodies *A*, *B*, mutually attracting one the other: then if either body, as *A*, is more attracted towards the other body *B*, than that other body *B* is towards the first body *A*, the obstacle will be more strongly urged by the pressure of the body *A* than by the pressure of the body *B*, and therefore will not remain in equilibrio: but the stronger pressure will prevail, and will make the system of the two bodies, together with the obstacle, to move directly towards the parts on which *B* lies; and in free spaces, to go forward *in infinitum* with a motion perpetually accelerated; which is absurd and contrary to the first Law. For, by the first Law, the system ought to persevere in its state of rest, or of moving uniformly forward in a right line; and therefore the bodies must equally press the obstacle, and be equally attracted one by the other. I made the experiment on the loadstone and iron. If these, placed apart in proper vessels, are made to float by one another in standing water, neither of them will propel the other; but, by being equally attracted, they will sustain each other's pressure, and rest at last in an equilibrium.

So the gravitation betwixt the earth and its parts is mutual. Let the earth *FI* be cut by any plane *EG* into two parts *EGF* and *EGI*, and their weights one towards the other will be mutually equal. For if by another plane *HK*, parallel to the former *EG*, the greater part *EGI* is cut into two parts *EGKH* and *HKI*, whereof *HKI* is equal to the part *EFG*, first cut off, it is evident that the middle part *EGKH*, will have no propension by its proper weight towards either side, but will hang as it were, and rest in an equilibrium betwixt both. But the one extreme part *HKI* will with its whole weight bear upon and press the middle part towards the other extreme part *EGF*; and therefore the force with which *EGI*, the sum of the parts *HKI* and *EGKH*, tends towards the third part *EGF*, is equal to the weight of the part *HKI*, that is, to the weight of the third part *EGF*. And therefore the weights of the two parts *EGI* and *EGF*, one towards the other, are equal, as I was to prove. And indeed if those weights were not equal, the whole earth floating in the nonresisting ether would give way to the greater weight, and, retiring from it, would be carried off *in infinitum*.

And as those bodies are equipollent in the congress and reflection, whose velocities are reciprocally as their innate forces, so in the use of mechanic instruments those agents are equipollent, and mutually sustain each the contrary pressure of the other, whose velocities, estimated according to the determination of the forces, are reciprocally as the forces.

So those weights are of equal force to move the arms of a balance; which during the play of the balance are reciprocally as their velocities upwards and downwards; that is, if the ascent or descent is direct, those weights are of equal force, which are reciprocally as the distances of the points at which they are suspended from the axis of the balance; but if they are turned aside by the interposition of oblique planes, or other obstacles, and made to ascend or descend obliquely, those bodies will be equipollent, which are reciprocally as the heights of their ascent and descent taken according to the perpendicular; and that on account of the determination of gravity downwards.

And in like manner in the pully, or in a combination of pullies, the force of a hand drawing the rope directly, which is to the weight, whether ascending directly or obliquely, as the velocity of the perpendicular ascent of the weight to the velocity of the hand that draws the rope, will sustain the weight.

In clocks and such like instruments, made up from a combination of wheels, the contrary forces that promote and impede the motion of the wheels, if they are reciprocally as the velocities of the parts of the wheel on which they are impressed, will mutually sustain the one the other.

The force of the screw to press a body is to the force of the hand that turns the handles by which it is moved as the circular velocity of the handle in that part where it is impelled by the hand is to the progressive velocity of the screw towards the pressed body.

The forces by which the wedge presses or drives the two parts of the wood it cleaves are to the force of the mallet upon the wedge as the progress of the wedge in the direction of the force impressed upon it by the mallet is to the velocity with which the parts of the wood yield to the wedge, in the direction of lines perpendicular to the sides of the wedge. And the like account is to be given of all machines.

The power and use of machines consist only in this, that by diminishing the velocity we may augment the force, and the contrary: from whence in all sorts of proper machines, we have the solution of this problem; *To move a given weight with a given power*, or with a given force to overcome any other given resistance. For if machines are so contrived that the velocities of the agent and resistant are reciprocally as their forces, the agent will just sustain the resistant, but with a greater disparity of velocity will overcome it. So that if the disparity of velocities is so great as to overcome all that resistance which commonly arises either from the attrition of contiguous bodies as they slide by one another, or from the cohesion of continuous bodies that are to be separated, or from the weights of bodies to be raised, the excess of the force remaining, after all those resistances are overcome, will produce an acceleration of motion proportional thereto, as well in the parts of the machine as in the resisting body. But to treat of mechanics is not my present business. I was only willing to show by those examples the great extent and certainty of the third Law of motion. For if we estimate the action of the agent from its force and velocity conjunctly, and likewise the reaction of the impediment conjunctly from the velocities of its several parts, and from the forces of resistance arising from the attrition, cohesion, weight, and acceleration of those parts, the action and reaction in the use of all sorts of machines will be found always equal to one another. And so far as the action is propagated by the intervening instruments, and at last impressed upon the resisting body, the ultimate determination of the action will be always contrary to the determination of the reaction.

EDMUND HALLEY
1656–1742

THE RETURN OF A COMET IS PREDICTED

NEWTON's *Principia* was published in 1687, as the result of a revival of his interest in work done in his youth. The man directly responsible for this was Edmund Halley, a member of a group within the Royal Society, who desired Newton's views on the elliptical orbits of the planets. Halley had begun his study of the planets while he was a student at Queen's College, Oxford, and his first paper on the planetary orbits was published in 1676. After his graduation, he spent some time on the lonely island of St Helena, where, 170 years later, Napoleon Bonaparte died in exile. Here Halley studied the stars of the southern hemisphere, adding 341 to the catalogues.

Halley's whole life, first as professor of geometry at Oxford and later as Astronomer Royal at the Greenwich Observatory, was dedicated to the study of the heavens. Like Sarton, his interest in his field induced him even to learn Arabic, to give him access to early texts not otherwise available. He was always on hand to support Newton in his work, whether by financing the publication of the *Principia* or by helping to iron out the disputes which arose with Hooke.

Halley's principal project was an eighteen-year study (started when he was already sixty-four years old) of the moon, but his major, and perhaps best known, scientific contribution was his discovery of the comet of 1682, subsequently named after him. He connected the comet with earlier appearances of comets, in 1531 and 1607, which had followed the same course; and he ventured a prediction that this comet 'would reappear after approximately $75\frac{1}{2}$ years'. This certainty about an otherwise mysterious phenomenon helped to dissipate the superstitious fear of comets, long regarded as forerunners of disaster; more important, it offered strong confirmation for the belief that the universe was a comprehensible mechanism.

Halley was a practical astronomer and established many procedures which assisted later generations to work out the implications of Newton's synthesis.

The selection that follows has been taken from Gregory's *The Elements of Astronomy*, Vol. 2, 1715. It appears in *A Source Book in Astronomy*.

¶ *A Discussion of Elliptical Orbits of Comets*

Hitherto I have consider'd the Orbits of Comets as exactly Parabolic; upon which supposition it wou'd follow, that Comets being impell'd towards the Sun by a Centripetal Force, would descend as from spaces infinitely distant, and by their so falling acquire such a Velocity, as that they may again fly off into the remotest parts of the Universe, moving upwards with a perpetual tendency, so as never to return again to the Sun. But since they appear frequently enough, and since some of them can be found to move with a Hyperbolic Motion, or a Motion swifter than what a Comet might acquire by its Gravity to the Sun, 'tis highly probable they rather move in very Excentric Elliptic Orbits, and make their returns after long periods of Time: For so their number will be determinate, and, perhaps, not so very great. Besides, the space between the Sun and the Fix'd Stars is so immense, that there is room enough for a Comet to revolve, tho' the Period of its revolution be vastly long. Now, the *Latus Rectum* of an Ellipsis, is to the *Latus Rectum* of a Parabola, which has the same Distance in its Perihelium; as the Distance in the Aphelium in the Ellipsis, is to the whole Axis of the Ellipsis. And the Velocities are in a Sub-duplicate ratio of the same: Wherefore in very Excentric Orbits the ratio comes very near to a ratio of Equality; and the very small difference which happens on account of the greater Velocity in the Parabola, is easily compensated in determining the situation of the Orbit. The principal use therefore, of this Table of the Elements of their Motions, and that which indeed induced me to construct it, is, that whenever a new Comet shall appear, we may be able to know, by comparing together the Elements, whether it be any of those which has appear'd before, and consequently to determine its Period, and the Axis of its Orbit, and to foretell its Return. And, indeed there are many things which make me believe that the Comet which Apian observ'd in the Year 1531, was the same with that which Kepler and Longomontanus more accurately describ'd in the Year 1607; and which I myself have seen return, and observ'd in the Year 1682. All the Elements agree, and nothing seems to contradict this my opinion, besides the Inequality of the Periodic revolutions. Which Inequality is not so great neither, as that it may not be owing to Physical Causes. For the Motion of Saturn is so disturbed by the rest of the Planets, especially Jupiter, that the Periodic time of that Planet is uncertain for some whole days together. How much more therefore will a Comet be subject to such like errors, which rises almost four times higher than Saturn, and whose Velocity, tho' increased but a very little, would be sufficient to change its Orbit, from an Elliptical to a Parabolical one. And I am the more confirmed in my opinion of its being the same; for that in the Year 1456, in the Summer time, a Comet was seen passing Retrograde between the Earth and the Sun, much after the same manner: Which tho' nobody made observations upon it, yet from its Period and the manner of its Transit, I cannot think different from those I have just now mention'd. And since looking over the *Histories of Comets* I find, at an equal interval of Time, a Comet to have been seen about Easter in the Year 1305, which is another double Period of 151 Years before the former. Hence I think I may venture to foretell, that it will return again in the Year 1758. And, if it should then so return, we shall have no reason to doubt but the rest may return also: Therefore, Astronomers have a large field wherein to exercise themselves for many ages, before they will be able to know the number of these many and great Bodies revolving about the common Centre of the Sun, and to reduce their Motions to certain Rules.

———

PIERRE SIMON LAPLACE
1749–1827

THE NEBULAR HYPOTHESIS IS SUGGESTED
AS AN EXPLANATION OF THE ORIGIN
OF THE SOLAR SYSTEM

PIERRE SIMON LAPLACE, the man who examined Napoleon Bonaparte in mathematics, is sometimes called the French Newton. The son of a Norman farmer, Laplace was sent to school by wealthy neighbours and, in due course, became a professor of mathematics at the École Militaire in Paris. By the age of twenty-four he had published the first stage of his thesis to prove the essential stability of the solar system. In this he was to oppose Newton's view that the planets were affected in their movement not only by the sun but also by other planets, so that eventually an irregularity would develop which only Divine intervention could adjust!

By 1825 Laplace had published his six-volume *Mécanique céleste* (*Celestial Mechanics*), in which he provided 'a complete solution of the great mechanical problem presented by the solar system'. He also advanced his 'nebular hypothesis' (described in the following selection), in which he traced the origin of the planets to masses of hot, rotating gases thrown off by the sun because of its increasing acceleration. This would account for the similarity of the direction of the rotation of the planets and their satellites. It is not known if Laplace was aware that the philosopher Immanuel Kant (1724–1804) had, in 1755, when he was still a practising scientist, put forth the same idea. Laplace's theory held ground for some time until it was ascertained that, among other technical objections, the sun, instead of increasing its rate of rotation, is, in fact, hardly rotating at all.

With Laplace, the development of cosmology entered the nineteenth century. After three hundred years, a cosmic order had been discovered; the sun, stars, and earth had been observed in their true relations to one another; and a mathematical set of tools had been provided to serve those who wished to refine the theories of the great cosmic discoverers.

The following selection has been taken from *The System of the World*, translated by H. H. Harte in *A Source Book of Astronomy*.

¶ *The Nebular Hypothesis*

However arbitrary the elements of the system of the planets may be, there exists between them some very remarkable relations, which may throw light on their origin. Considering it with attention, we are astonished to see all the planets move round the Sun from west to east, and nearly in the same plane, all the satellites moving round their respective planets in the same direction, and nearly in the same plane with the planets. Lastly, the Sun, the planets, and those satellites in which a motion of rotation have been observed, turn on their own axes, in the same direction, and nearly in the same plane as their motion of projection.

The satellites exhibit in this respect a remarkable peculiarity. Their motion of rotation is exactly equal to their motion of revolution; so that they always present the same hemisphere to their primary. At least, this has been observed for the Moon, for the four satellites of Jupiter, and for the last satellite of Saturn, the only satellites whose rotation has been hitherto recognized.

Phenomena so extraordinary, are not the effect of irregular causes. By subjecting their probability to computation, it is found that there is more than two thousand to one against the hypothesis that they are the effect of chance, which is a probability much greater than that on which most of the events of history, respecting which there does not exist a doubt, depends. We ought, therefore, to be assured with the same confidence, that a primitive cause has directed the planetary motions.

Another phenomenon of the solar system, equally remarkable, is the small eccentricity of the orbits of the planets and their satellites, while those of comets are very much extended. The orbits of this system present no intermediate shades between a great and small eccentricity. We are here again compelled to acknowledge the effect of a regular cause; chance alone could not have given a form nearly circular to the orbits of all the planets. It is, therefore, necessary that the cause which determined the motions of these bodies, rendered them also nearly circular. This cause then must also have influenced the great eccentricity of the orbits of comets, and their motion in every direction; for, considering the orbits of retrograde comets, as being inclined more than one hundred degrees to the ecliptic, we find that the mean inclination of the orbits of all the observed comets, approaches near to one hundred degrees, which would be the case if the bodies had been projected at random.

What is this primitive cause? In the concluding note of this work I will suggest a hypothesis which appears to me to result with a great degree of probability, from the preceding phenomena, which, however, I present with that diffidence, which ought always to attach to whatever is not the result of observation and computation.

Whatever be the true cause, it is certain that the elements of the planetary system are so arranged as to enjoy the greatest possible stability, unless it is deranged by the intervention of foreign causes. From the sole circumstance that the motions of the planets and satellites are performed in orbits nearly circular, in the same direction, and in planes which are inconsiderably inclined to each other, the system will always oscillate about a mean state, from which it will deviate but by very small quantities. The mean motions of rotation and of revolution of these different bodies are uniform, and their mean distances from the foci of the principal forces which actuate them are constant; all the secular inequalities are periodic. ...

§Note vii, and Last

From the preceding chapter it appears, that we have the five following phenomena to assist us in investigating the cause of the primitive motions of the planetary system. The motions of the planets in the same direction, and very nearly in the same plane; the motions of the satellites in the same direction as those of the planets; the motions of rotation of these different bodies and also of the Sun, in the same direction as their motions of projection, and in planes very little inclined to each other; the small eccentricity of the orbits of the planets and satellites; finally, the great eccentricity of the orbits of the comets, their inclinations being at the same time entirely indeterminate.

Buffon is the only individual that I know of, who, since the discovery of the true system of the world, endeavoured to investigate the origin of the planets and satellites. He supposed that a comet, by impinging on the Sun, carried away a torrent of matter, which was reunited far off, into globes of different magnitudes, and at different distances from this star. These globes, when they cool and become hardened, are the planets and their satellites. This hypothesis satisfied the first of the five preceding phenomena for it is evident that all bodies thus formed should move very nearly in the plane which passes through the centre of the Sun, and through the direction of the torrent of matter which has produced them: but the four remaining phenomena appear to me inexplicable on this supposition. Indeed the absolute motion of the molecules of a planet ought to be in the same direction as the motion of its centre of gravity; but it by no means follows from this, that the motion of rotation of a planet should be also in the same direction. Thus the Earth may revolve from east to west, and yet the absolute motion of each of its molecules may be directed from west to east. This observation applies also to the revolution of the satellites, of which the direction, in the same hypothesis, is not necessarily the same as that of the motion of projection of the planets.

The small eccentricity of the planetary orbits is a phenomenon, not only difficult to explain on this hypothesis, but altogether inconsistent with it. We know from the theory of central forces, that if a body which moves in a re-entrant orbit about the Sun, passes very near the body of the Sun, it will return constantly to it, at the end of each revolution. Hence it follows that if the planets were originally detached from the Sun, they would touch it, at each return to this star; and their orbits, instead of being nearly circular, would be very eccentric. Indeed it must be admitted that a torrent of matter detached from the Sun, cannot be compared to a globe which just skims by its surface: from the impulsions which the parts of this torrent receive from each other, combined with their mutual attraction, they may, by changing the direction of their motions, increase the distances of their perihelions from the Sun. But their orbits should be extremely eccentric, or at least all the orbits would not be circular, except by the most extraordinary chance. Finally, no reason can be assigned on the hypothesis of Buffon, why the orbits of more than one hundred comets, which have been already observed, should be all very eccentric. This hypothesis, therefore, is far from satisfying the preceding phenomena. Let us consider whether we can assign the true cause.

Whatever may be its nature, since it has produced or influenced the direction of the planetary motions, it must have embraced them all within the sphere of its action; and considering the immense distance which intervenes between them, nothing could have effected this but a fluid of almost indefinite extent. In order to have impressed on them all a motion circular and in the same direction about the Sun, this fluid must environ this star, like an atmosphere. From a consideration of the planetary motions, we are, therefore, brought to the conclusion, that in consequence of an excessive heat, the solar atmosphere originally extended beyond the orbits of all the planets, and that it has successively contracted itself within its present limits.

In the primitive state in which we have supposed the Sun to be, it resembles those substances which are termed nebulae, which, when seen through telescopes, appear to be composed of a nucleus, more or less brilliant, surrounded by a nebulosity, which, by condensing on its surface, transforms it into a star. If all the stars are conceived to be similarly formed, we can suppose their anterior state of nebulosity to be preceded by other states, in which the nebulous matter was more or less diffuse, the nucleus being at the same time more or less brilliant. By going back in this manner, we shall arrive at a state of nebulosity so diffuse, that its existence can with difficulty be conceived.

For a considerable time back, the particular arrangement of some stars visible to the naked eye, has engaged the attention of philosophers. Mitchel remarked long since how extremely improbable it was that the stars composing the constellation called the Pleiades, for example, should be confined within the narrow space which contains them, by the sole chance of hazard; from which he inferred that this group of stars, and the similar groups which the heavens present to us, are the effects of a primitive cause, or of a primitive law of nature. These groups are a general result of the condensation of nebulae of several nuclei; for it is evident that the nebulous matter being perpetually attracted by these different nuclei, ought at length to form a group of stars, like to that of the Pleiades. The condensation of nebulae consisting of two nuclei, will in like manner form stars very near to each other, revolving the one about the other like to the double stars, whose respective motions have been already recognized.

But in what manner has the solar atmosphere determined the motions of rotation and revolution of the planets and satellites? If these bodies had penetrated deeply into this atmosphere, its resistance would cause them to fall on the Sun. We may, therefore, suppose that the planets were formed at its successive limits, by the condensation of zones of vapours, which it must, while it was cooling, have abandoned in the plane of its equator.

Let us resume the results which we have given in the tenth chapter of the preceding book. The Sun's atmosphere cannot extend indefinitely; its limit is the point where the centrifugal force arising from the motion of rotation balances the gravity; but according as the cooling contracts the atmosphere, and condenses the molecules which are near to it, on the surface of the star, the motion of rotation increases; for in virtue of the principle of areas, the sum of the areas described by the radius vector of each particle of the Sun and of its atmosphere, and projected on the plane of its equator, is always the same. Consequently, the rotation ought to be quicker, when these particles approach to the centre of the Sun. The centrifugal force arising from this motion becoming thus greater, the point where the gravity is equal to it, is nearer to the centre of the Sun. Supposing, therefore, what is natural to admit, that the atmosphere extended at any epoch as far as this limit, it ought, according as it cooled, to abandon the molecules, which are situated at this limit, and at the successive limits produced by the increased rotation of the Sun. These particles, after being abandoned, have continued to circulate about this star, because their centrifugal force was balanced by their gravity. But as this equality does not obtain for those molecules of the atmosphere which are situated on the parallels to the Sun's equator, these have come nearer by their gravity to the atmosphere according as it condensed, and they have not ceased to belong to it, inasmuch as by this motion, they have approached to the plane of this equator.

Let us now consider the zones of vapours, which have been successively abandoned. These zones ought, according to all probability, to form by their condensation, and by the mutual attraction of their particles, several concentrical rings of vapours circulating about the Sun. The mutual friction of the molecules of each ring ought to accelerate some and retard others, until they all had acquired the same angular motion. Consequently, the real velocities of the molecules which are farther from the Sun, ought to be greatest. The following cause ought, likewise, to contribute to this difference of velocities: The most distant particles of the Sun, which, by the effects of cooling and of condensation, have collected so as to constitute the superior part of the ring, have always described areas proportional to the times, because the central force by which they are actuated has been constantly directed to this star; but this constancy of areas requires an increase of velocity, according as they approach more to each other. It appears that the same cause ought to diminish the velocity of the particles, which, situated near the ring, constitute its inferior part.

If all the particles of a ring of vapours continued to condense without separating, they would at length constitute a solid or a liquid ring. But the regularity which this formation requires in all the parts of the ring, and in their cooling, ought to make this phenomenon very rare. Thus the solar system presents but one example of it; that of the rings of Saturn. Almost always each ring of vapours ought to be divided into several masses, which, being moved with velocities which differ little from each other, should continue to revolve at the same distance about the Sun. These masses should assume a spheroidical form, with a rotatory motion in the direction of that of their revolution, because their inferior particles have a less real velocity than the superior; they have, therefore, constituted so many planets in a state of vapour. But if one of them was sufficiently powerful, to unite successively by its attraction, all the others about its centre, the ring of vapours would be changed into one sole spheroidical mass, circulating about the Sun, with a motion of rotation in the same direction with that of revolution. This last case has been the most common; however, the solar system presents to us the first case, in the four small planets which revolve between Mars and Jupiter, at least unless we suppose with Olbers, that they originally formed one planet only, which was divided by an explosion into several parts, and actuated by different velocities. Now if we trace the changes which a further cooling ought to produce in the planets formed of vapours, and of which we have suggested the formation, we shall see to arise in the centre of each of them, a nucleus increasing continually, by the condensation of the atmosphere which environs it. In this state, the planet resembles the Sun in the nebulous state, in which we have first supposed it to be; the cooling should, therefore, produce at the different limits of its atmosphere, phenomena similar to those which have been described, namely, rings and satellites circulating about its centre in the direction of its motion of rotation, and revolving in the same direction on their axes. The regular distribution of the mass of rings of Saturn about its centre and in the plane of its equator, results naturally from this hypothesis, and, without it, is inexplicable. Those rings appear to me to be existing proofs of the primitive extension of the atmosphere of Saturn, and of its successive condensations. Thus the singular phenomena of the small eccentricities of the orbits of the planets and satellites, of the small inclination of these orbits to the solar equator, and of the identity in the direction of the motions of rotation and revolution of all those bodies with that of the rotation of the Sun, follow from the hypothesis which has been suggested, and render it extremely probable. If the solar system was formed with perfect regularity, the orbits of the bodies which compose it would be circles, of which the planes, as well as those of the various equators and rings, would coincide with the plane of the solar equator. But we may suppose that the innumerable varieties which must necessarily exist in the temperature and density of different parts of these great masses, ought to produce the eccentricities of their orbits, and the deviations of their motions, from the plane of this equator.

In the preceding hypothesis, the comets do not belong to the solar system. If they be considered, as we have done, as small nebulae, wandering from one solar system to another, and formed by the condensation of the nebulous matter, which is diffused so profusely throughout the universe, we may conceive that when they arrive in that part of space where the attraction of the Sun predominates, it should force them to describe elliptic or hyperbolic orbits. But as their velocities are equally possible in every direction, they must move indifferently in all directions, and at every possible inclination to the ecliptic; which is conformable to observation. Thus the condensation of the nebulous matter, which explains the motions of rotation and revolution of the planets and satellites in the same direction, and in orbits very little inclined to each other, likewise explains why the motions of the comets deviate from this general law.

The great eccentricity of the orbits of the comets, is also a result of our hypothesis. If those orbits are elliptic, they are very elongated, since their greater axes are at least equal to the radius of the sphere of activity of the Sun. But these orbits may be hyperbolic; and if the axes of these hyperbolae are not very great with respect to the mean distance of the Sun from the Earth, the motion of the comets which describe them will appear to be sensibly hyperbolic. However, with respect to the hundred comets, of which the elements are known, not one appears to move in a hyperbola; hence the chances which assign a sensible hyperbola, are extremely rare relatively to the contrary chances. The comets are so small, that they only become sensible when their perihelion distance is inconsiderable. Hitherto this distance has not surpassed twice the diameter of the Earth's orbit, and most frequently, it has been less than the radius of this orbit. We may conceive, that in order to approach so near to the Sun, their velocity at the moment of their ingress within its sphere of activity, must have an intensity and direction confined within very narrow limits. If we determine by the analysis of probabilities, the ratio of the chances which, in these limits, assign a sensible hyperbola to the chances which assign an orbit, which may without sensible error be confounded with a parabola, it will be found that there is at least six thousand to unity that a nebula which penetrates within the sphere of the Sun's activity so as to be observed, will either describe a very elongated ellipse, or a hyperbola, which, in consequence of the magnitude of its axis will be as to sense confounded with a parabola in the part of its orbit which is observed. It is not, therefore, surprising that hitherto no hyperbolic motions have been recognized.

The attraction of the planets, and perhaps also the resistance of the ethereal media, ought to change several cometary orbits into ellipses, of which the greater axes are much less than the radius of the sphere of the solar activity. It is probable that such a change was produced in the orbit of the comet of 1759, the greater axis of which was not more than thirty-five times the distance of the Sun from the Earth. A still greater change was produced in the orbits of the comets of 1770 and of 1805.

If any comets have penetrated the atmospheres of the Sun and planets at the moment of their formation, they must have described spirals, and consequently fallen on these bodies, and in consequence of their fall, caused the planes of the orbits and of the equators of the planets to deviate from the plane of the solar equator.

If in the zones abandoned by the atmosphere of the Sun, there are any molecules too volatile to be united to each other, or to the planets, they ought, in their circulation about this star, to exhibit all the appearances of the zodiacal light, without opposing any sensible resistance to the different bodies of the planetary system, both on account of their great rarity, and also because their motion is very nearly the same as that of the planets which they meet.

An attentive examination of all the circumstances of this system renders our hypothesis still more probable. The primitive fluidity of the planets is clearly indicated by the compression of their figure, conformably to the laws of the mutual attraction of their molecules; it is, moreover, demonstrated by the regular diminution of gravity, as we proceed from the equator to the poles. This state of primitive fluidity to which we are conducted by astronomical phenomena, is also apparent from those which natural history points out. But in order fully to estimate them, we should take into account the immense variety of combinations formed by all the terrestrial substances which were mixed together in a state of vapour, when the depression of their temperature enabled their elements to unite; it is necessary, likewise, to consider the wonderful changes which this depression ought to cause in the interior and at the surface of the earth, in all its productions, in the constitution and pressure of the atmosphere, in the ocean, and in all substances which it held in a state of solution. Finally, we should take into account the sudden changes, such as great volcanic eruptions, which must at different epochs have deranged the regularity of these changes. Geology, thus studied under the point of view which connects it with astronomy, may, with respect to several objects, acquire both precision and certainty.

One of the most remarkable phenomena of the solar system is the rigorous equality which is observed to subsist between the angular motions of rotation and revolution of each satellite. It is infinity to unity that this is not the effect of hazard. The theory of universal gravitation makes infinity to disappear from this improbability, by showing that it is sufficient for the existence of this phenomenon, that at the commencement these motions did not differ much. Then, the attraction of the planet would establish between them a perfect equality; but at the same time it has given rise to a periodic oscillation in the axis of the satellite directed to the planet, of which oscillation the extent depends on the primitive difference between these motions. As the observations of Mayer on the libration of the Moon, and those which Bouvard and Nicollet made for the same purpose, at my request, did not enable us to recognize this oscillation; the difference on which it depends must be extremely small, which indicates with every appearance of probability the existence of a particular cause, which has confined this difference within very narrow limits, in which the attraction of the planet might establish between the mean motions of rotation and revolution a rigid equality, which at length terminated by annihilating the oscillation which arose from this equality. Both these effects result from our hypothesis; for we may conceive that the Moon, in a state of vapour, assumed in consequence of the powerful attraction of the earth the form of an elongated spheroid, of which the greater axis would be

constantly directed towards this planet, from the facility
with which the vapours yield to the slightest force impressed
upon them. The terrestrial attraction continuing to act in
the same manner, while the Moon is in a state of fluidity,
ought at length, by making the two motions of this satellite
to approach each other, to cause their difference to fall
within the limits, at which their rigorous equality commences to establish itself. Then this attraction should
annihilate, by little and little, the oscillation which this
equality produced on the greater axis of the spheroid
directed towards the earth. It is in this manner that the
fluids which cover this planet, have destroyed by their
friction and resistance the primitive oscillations of its axis
of rotation, which is only now subject to the nutation
resulting from the actions of the Sun and Moon. It is easy
to be assured that the equality of the motions of rotation
and revolution of the satellites ought to oppose the formation of rings and secondary satellites, by the atmospheres of
these bodies. Consequently observation has not hitherto
indicated the existence of any such. The motions of the
three first satellites of Jupiter present a phenomenon still
more extraordinary than the preceding; which consists in
this, that the mean longitude of the first, minus three times
that of the second, plus twice that of the third, is constantly
equal to two right angles. There is the ratio of infinity to
one, that this equality is not the effect of chance. But we
have seen, that in order to produce it, it is sufficient, if at the
commencement, the mean motions of these three bodies
approached very near to the relation which renders the
mean motion of the first, minus three times that of the
second, plus twice that of the third, equal to nothing. Then
their mutual attraction rendered this ratio rigorously exact,
and it has moreover made the mean longitude of the first
minus three times that of the second, plus twice that of the
third, equal to a semicircumference. At the same time, it
gave rise to a periodic inequality, which depends on the
small quantity, by which the mean motions originally
deviated from the relation which we have just announced.

Notwithstanding all the care Delambre took in his observations, he could not recognize this inequality, which; while it evinces its extreme smallness, also indicates, with a high degree of probability, the existence of a cause which makes it to disappear. In our hypothesis, the satellites of Jupiter, immediately after their formation, did not move in a perfect *vacuo*; the less condensible molecules of the primitive atmospheres of the Sun and planet would then constitute a rare medium, the resistance of which being different for each of the [bodies], might make the mean motions to approach by degrees to the ratio in question; and when these movements had thus attained the conditions requisite, in order that the mutual attraction of the three satellites might render this relation accurately true, it perpetually diminished the inequality which this relation originated, and eventually rendered it insensible. We cannot better illustrate these effects than by comparing them to the motion of a pendulum, which, actuated by a great velocity, moves in a medium, the resistance of which is inconsiderable. It will first describe a great number of circumferences; but at length its motion of circulation perpetually decreasing, it will be converted into an oscillatory motion, which itself diminishing more and more, by the resistance of the medium, will eventually be totally destroyed, and then the pendulum, having attained a state of repose, will remain at rest for ever.

IV

THE SCIENCE OF GASES

THE seventeenth and eighteenth centuries in Europe were times of such change in comparison with the preceding centuries that individual events have been designated as revolutions – politically the French and American Revolutions, technologically and sociologically the Industrial Revolution, and in one aspect of intellectual activity, the Scientific Revolution.

The new spirit of inquiry and discussion could be exercised more widely, and in one way this was evidenced by the foundation of the national academies. In Britain, the Royal Society was founded in 1660, and received the first of its Royal Charters in 1662. In France the Académie des Sciences was founded in 1666, in Russia the St Petersburg Academy in 1724.

The Royal Society, having developed from a group which met weekly for 'Philosophical Inquiries', was widely based in its interests, though as to individual members the founders were very careful in selecting those 'judged willing and fit to joyne them in their design'. Besides those whom we should recognize as scientists, using the term in the present narrow sense, were Sir Christopher Wren the architect, John Evelyn the diarist, and Kenelm Digby, 'skilled in six tongues and learned in all the arts'; Pepys was the President a few years before Newton.

One kind of philosophical inquiry resulted in the changed outlook in cosmology recorded in the previous section. Although it appears in some ways remote from daily life, interest in astronomy was supported by a need for better aids to navigation, just as it was undoubtedly helped by the development of telescopes.

In less remote sciences, the combination of a 'philosophi-cal' interest in physical matters with a background of prac-tical utility is again apparent. The early invention of sailing ships showed that men were aware of the forces which the atmosphere could exert. The discoveries recorded in the next three extracts, however, showed how little they knew of its other properties – the density of air, the variation of its pressure with height above the earth's surface, still less its composition – although men had always lived 'submerged at the bottom of an ocean of the element air'.

The development of mines, however, brought with it an increased interest in water-pumps. Galileo observed the limit in height of a column of water which a pump would produce. Torricelli was able to relate this to atmos-pheric pressure in experiments which led to the barometer (after further work by Pascal) and to a great interest in vacuum. Von Guericke, in Magdeburg, developed an air pump with which a (partial) vacuum could be produced, and staged a splendid demonstration of the pressure of the atmosphere. He fitted together two large bronze hemi-spheres to form a globe and evacuated the space within. A team of eight horses was attached to each hemisphere; their combined efforts did not succeed in separating them, but on re-entry of the air, they fell apart.*

Hooke improved on von Guericke's design in making an air-pump with which Boyle experimented. Boyle developed the idea of gas pressure more quantitatively, concerning himself with measuring pressures of gas intermediate be-tween full atmospheric pressure and that of the vacuum then obtainable. In the course of this work he related the pressure exerted by the gas to the volume in which it was contained, a deduction now generally know as Boyle's Law, but occasionally named after Mariotte who rediscovered it independently.

Even the general concept of a 'gas' was late in develop-ing. Van Helmont (1577–1644) recognized the existence of different gases at a time when they were generally regarded

* See Plate 6.

as different kinds of 'air'. Any gas, when liberated into the atmosphere, mixes with it and diffuses away. If it is to be preserved for experiments, it must be kept in a closed vessel. It was van Helmont's misfortune not to realize that this was possible, and his conception was thus not readily taken up until the later developments, just described, had taken place.

When experiments on gases were later carried out, they had a considerable effect on the next stages of the development of chemistry. This was essentially the replacement of the idea of 'principles' by that of material unchangeable elements. The change in outlook is found clearly in Boyle's *The Sceptical Chymist*. He not only distinguished between mixtures and compounds but then defined an element by declaring that we 'must not look upon any body as a true principle or element but as yet compounded, which is not perfectly homogeneous, but is further resolvable into any number of distinct substances how small soever'. He did not develop this idea experimentally, but it formed a framework within which others could do so.

This took a considerable time, for the idea that earth, air, fire, and water were the essential constituents of matter continued to influence chemical thought for nearly a century after Boyle's death. Although it was coming to be recognized that there were different 'earths', the same attitude was not yet evident to 'air'. Black wrote of the carbon dioxide ('fixed air') which he obtained from magnesium carbonate as though he originally considered it as a form of atmospheric air, differing only in that it had been 'fixed' in the solid. His investigation of its properties brought him to recognize that there were greater differences, the significance of which was seen by others later. A very important part of his work was to show, by quantitative experiments, that calcined magnesia and chalk (i.e the oxides) and the corresponding hydroxides would react with almost the same quantities of acid as the original substances (i.e. the carbonates). The development of this quantitative approach to chemical reactions (stoicheiometry) played an enormous part in the development of chemical theory.

Priestley experimented extensively with gases, developing the technique of collecting them in gas jars over water (in a pneumatic trough); the method (which would have been valuable to van Helmont) had been used in the previous century by Mayow, but its value became much more obvious as a result of Priestley's work. Extending the principle, he collected some gases over mercury; this enabled him to isolate gases, such as hydrogen chloride and ammonia which are highly soluble in water and had consequently only been known previously in solution (spirits of salt, muriatic acid or marine acid, and caustic spirit of salt ammoniac).

His most important work, in terms of the development of chemical theory, was the preparation of oxygen from mercuric oxide, the realization of its identity with a part only of atmospheric air, and thus, from the discovery that atmospheric air is 'alterable', the conclusion 'that it is not an elementary substance, but a composition' (in present terminology, a mixture). Among the experiments from which he drew these conclusions were those in which oxygen reacted with 'nitrous air' (nitric oxide), the 'redness of the mixture' so produced being due to nitrogen dioxide. Priestley's experiments on combustion and respiration follow interestingly upon those of Boyle. Boyle examined the effect of absence of air on these processes; Priestley examined the effect of the absence of the relevant component (oxygen).

Priestley wrote not of oxygen, but of dephlogisticated air. He interpreted all his results in terms of the phlogiston theory, which he continued to uphold after he knew of Lavoisier's view. The importance of his contribution was in enthusiastic and deliberate experimenting and in the ability to relate his results logically to the theory which he had learnt at the start of his career. Although he was used to unorthodox political and religious ideas, his chemical thinking was not revolutionary enough for him to produce or even accept a fundamental change in chemical theory. By contrast, change came from Lavoisier who suffered at the hands of men politically more revolutionary than himself.

Priestley's failure to advance beyond the phlogiston theory emphasizes how much longer was required to establish the Scientific Revolution in chemistry than in physics. In part this may be attributed to the need, in chemistry, for the collection of more data than were available a century earlier when Newton produced such important developments in physics. Newton could use quantitative observations. In chemistry the need was not so much, in the first instance, for detailed numerical data, but for a wide range of precise and related observations. Among gases, the diffuse notion of 'air' as a principle had to be clarified by recognizing the individual properties of the separate 'nitrous air', 'dephlogisticated air', 'inflammable air', 'fixed air', and so on.

Scheele and Cavendish contributed substantially to this process. Scheele was a prolific experimenter who, living in Sweden, was isolated from the main centres of scientific work. His immediate impact on the chemical world would have been vastly greater had he been able to travel as easily as we can today to discuss results with colleagues in other countries. As it was, he and Priestley independently isolated both chlorine and oxygen. (This is not, however, to suggest that the efforts of either were wasted; their routes to oxygen were different and both routes are important chemically.)

Scheele's experiments showed the existence of oxygen and nitrogen in the air; Cavendish even recorded the existence of what we now know to be argon, though without appreciating its significance at the time. This would have been difficult to interpret in terms of the phlogiston theory, to which Cavendish adhered. When he prepared 'inflammable air' (hydrogen) by the action of sulphuric acid on zinc, he thought he had isolated phlogiston itself.

The crucial change came with Lavoisier. He had early distrusted the phlogiston theory, but was able to formulate a new theory only after careful experiments (in which he used the most accurate balances he could find) had shown that the products of combustion had exactly the same combined weight as the starting materials. He depended, inevitably, on previous work, especially that of Black, Scheele, Priestley, and Cavendish. His theory of combustion was that the burning substance combined with oxygen, and that its weight increased by the weight of oxygen used in the reaction.

The concept of 'principle' was thus almost completely destroyed. (A trace of it lingered in Lavoisier's view that oxygen was the acid-producing substance.) Undoubtedly his resolution of 'the burning question', as some books call it, cleared the way for a rapid growth of chemistry which he further helped by proposing a simplified nomenclature for chemical substances. The rise of modern chemistry is outlined in Volume 2.

EVANGELISTA TORRICELLI
1608–47

THE BAROMETER

WHEN Galileo found that his water pump would not raise water above the height of thirty-two feet, he explained the fact merely by saying that the column of water broke under its own weight. His pupils, Torricelli and Viviani, looked further for 'a plainly apparent cause for the resistance which is felt when one needs to produce a vacuum'. Their experiments led to a new understanding of atmospheric pressure.

The experiments, which they conducted in 1643, were made with forty-six-inch glass tubes which reflect the advance of the craft of glass-making in Italy at that time. It is unlikely that such tubes could have been produced anywhere else in Europe. Torricelli found that if one of these tubes was filled with mercury and then inverted into a dish of mercury, the level of mercury in the tube fell to leave a column of about thirty inches only. The remaining space in the tube contained a vacuum or possibly mercury 'highly rarified' (which we could now identify with mercury vapour).

Torricelli realized that the column of mercury was supported, not by the vacuum, as had been supposed previously, but by a corresponding column of air outside the tube. Because he saw this balancing of the two columns as a simple mechanical equilibrium, he was able to explain why the heights of the columns of water and mercury which could be supported by the atmosphere were inversely proportional to the densities of the two liquids.

The use of this assembly as a barometer for measuring atmospheric pressure was due to Pascal. Torricelli, who also devised improvements to the microscope and telescope, was more interested in the vacuum at the head of the tube (the 'Torricellian vacuum'), using it for experiments in the transmission of light, sound, and magnetic forces.

This selection has been taken from *The Physical Treatises of Pascal*, translated by I.H.B. and A.G.H. Spiers (Columbia, 1937).

¶ *On the Pressure of the Atmosphere*

Letter from Torricelli to Michelangelo Ricci

Florence, 11 June 1644

My most illustrious Sir and most cherished Master:

Several weeks ago I sent some demonstrations of mine on the area of the cycloid to Signor Antonio Nardi, entreating him to send them directly to you or to Signor Magiotti after he had seen them. I have already intimated to you that a certain physical experiment was being performed on the vacuum; not simply to produce a vacuum, but to make an instrument which would show the changes in the air, which is at times heavier and thicker and at times lighter and more rarefied. Many have said that a vacuum cannot be produced, others that it can be produced, but with repugnance on the part of Nature and with difficulty; so far, I know of no one who has said that it can be produced without effort and without resistance on the part of Nature. I reasoned in this way: if I were to find a plainly apparent cause for the resistance which is felt when one needs to produce a vacuum, it seems to me that it would be vain to try to attribute that action, which patently derives from some other cause, to the vacuum; indeed, I find that by making certain very easy calculations, the cause I have proposed (which is the weight of the air) should in itself have a greater effect than it does in the attempt to produce a vacuum. I say this because some Philosopher, seeing that he could not avoid the admission that the weight of the air causes the resistance which is felt in producing a vacuum, did not say that he admitted the effect of the weight of the air, but persisted in asserting that Nature also contributes at least to the abhorrence of a vacuum.

We live submerged at the bottom of an ocean of the element air, which by unquestioned experiments is known to have weight, and so much, indeed, that near the surface of the earth where it is most dense, it weighs [volume for volume] about the four-hundredth part of the weight of water.* Those who have written about twilight, moreover, have observed that the vaporous and visible air rises above us about fifty or fifty-four miles; I do not, however, believe its height is as great as this, since if it were, I could show that the vacuum would have to offer much greater resistance than it does – even though there is in their favour the argument that the weight referred to by Galileo applies to the air in very low places where men and animals live, whereas that on the tops of high mountains begins to be distinctly rare and of much less weight than the four-hundredth part of the weight of water.

We have made glass vessels like the following marked *A* and *B* with necks two cubits.† We filled these with quicksilver, and then, the mouths being stopped with a finger and being inverted in a basin where there was quicksilver *C*, they seemed to become empty and nothing happened in the vessel that was emptied; the neck *AD*, therefore, remained always filled to the height of a cubit and a quarter and an inch besides.‡ To show that the vessel was perfectly empty, the underlying basin was filled with water up to *D*, and as the vessel was slowly raised, when its mouth reached the water, one could see the quicksilver fall from the neck, whereupon with a violent impetus the vessel was filled with water completely to the mark *E*. This experiment was performed when the vessel *AE* was empty and the quicksilver,

*Modern computations show that the density of water is about 800 times that of air, at sea level; the exact figure depends on the temperature of the air.

†*Braccia*; each closely 23 inches. The 'vessels' *A* and *B*, according to Torricelli, are the parts *above* the 'necks' *BC*, *AD*, in the figure on the following page.

‡29¾ inches.

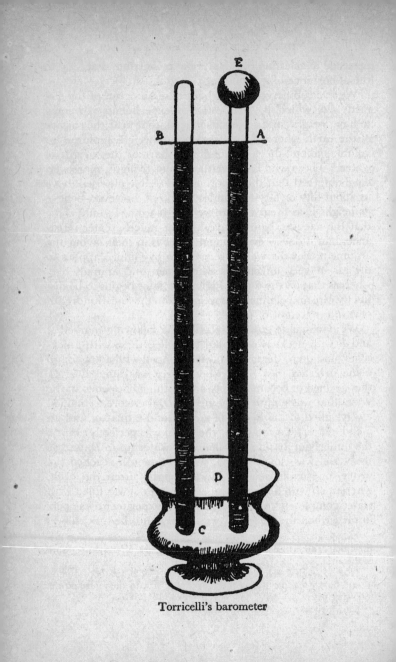

Torricelli's barometer

although very heavy, was held up in the neck *AD*.

The force which holds up that quicksilver against its nature to fall down again, has been believed hitherto to be inside of the vessel *AE*, and to be due either to vacuum or to that material [mercury] highly rarefied; but I maintain that it is external and that the force comes from without. On the surface of the liquid which is in the basin, there gravitates a mass of air fifty miles high; is it therefore to be wondered at if in the glass *CE*, where the mercury is not attracted nor indeed repelled, since there is nothing there, it enters and rises to such an extent as to come to equilibrium with the weight of this outside air which presses upon it? Water also, in a similar but much longer vessel, will rise up to almost eighteen cubits, that is, as much further than the quicksilver rises as quicksilver is heavier than water, in order to come to equilibrium with the same force, which presses alike the one and the other.

The above conclusion was confirmed by an experiment made at the same time with a vessel *A* and a tube *B*, in which the quicksilver always came to rest at the same level, *AB*. This is an almost certain indication that the force was not within; because if that were so, the vessel *AE* would have had greater force, since within it there was more rare-fied material to attract the quicksilver, and a material much more powerful than that in the very small space *B*, on account of its greater rarefaction.

I have since tried to consider from this point of view all the kinds of repulsions which are felt in the various effects attributed to vacuum, and thus far I have not encountered anything which does not go [to confirm my opinion]. I know that you will think up many objections, but I also hope that, as you think about them, you will overcome them. I must add that my principal intention – which was to determine with the instrument *EC* when the air was thicker and heavier and when it was more rarefied and light – has not been fulfilled; for the level *AB* changes from another cause (which I never would have believed), namely, on account of heat and cold; and changes very appreciably, exactly as if the vase *AE* were full of air.*

*Thus acting like Galileo's thermometer.

BLAISE PASCAL

1623–62

THE FACTS OF AIR PRESSURE ARE
DEMONSTRATED BY EXPERIMENT

BLAISE PASCAL is best remembered, perhaps, for his *Pensées*, which were the philosophical fruit of a short but intense life. A precocious child, Pascal was trained by the Jesuits, but afterwards he came under the influence of the Jansenists, a sect which denied the possibility of free will. All of his scientific work was done before the age of thirty-one, and the degree of his brilliance is indicated by its variety. His development of the theory of probability, a type of applied mathematics which was to prove of great importance in such fields as biological statistics, was in its time, what we should now call 'a major break-through'. At the age of nineteen, Pascal had devised and constructed an automatic machine which helped to avoid errors in reading the recently introduced logarithmic scales.

Pascal's studies in the equilibrium of fluids, which extended the work of Galileo, produced the discovery that pressures exerted by such fluids as the atmosphere were exerted equally in all directions. The laws of fluid pressures which Pascal developed became one of the foundation stones of the science of hydrodynamics. He carried Torricelli's work on the barometer on to its next logical stage. Reasoning, as we see from the following selection from *The Physical Treatises,* that if air has weight, the pressure exerted by it will vary according to the amount of it, he sent his brother to the high mountains of the Puy-de-Dôme in Central France with a Torricelli barometer. The results showed that the column of mercury supported by atmospheric pressure varied with the height of the land above sea level.

¶ *Treatise on the Weight of the Mass of the Air*

§ CHAPTER I *The Mass of the Air has Weight, And with this Weight presses upon all the Bodies it surrounds*

It is no longer open to discussion that the air has weight. It is common knowledge that a balloon is heavier when inflated than when empty, which is proof enough. For if the air were light, the more the balloon was inflated, the lighter the whole would be, since there would be more air in it. But since, on the contrary, when more air is put in, the whole becomes heavier, it follows that each part has a weight of its own, and consequently that the air has weight.

Whoever wishes for more elaborate proofs can find them in the writings of those who have devoted special treatises to the subject.

If it be objected that air is light when pure, but that the air that surrounds us is not pure, being mixed with vapour and impurities which alone give it weight, my answer is brief: I am not acquainted with 'pure air', and believe that it might be very difficult to find it. But throughout this treatise I am referring solely to the air such as we breathe, regardless of its component elements. Whether it be compound or simple, that is the body which I call the air, and which I declare to have weight. This cannot be denied, and I require nothing more for my further proof.

This principle being laid down, I will now proceed to draw from it certain consequences.

1. Since every part of the air has weight, it follows that the whole mass of the air, that is to say, the whole sphere of the air, has weight, and as the sphere of the air is not infinite in extent, but limited, neither is the weight of the whole mass of the air infinite.

2. The mass of the water of the sea presses with its weight that part of the earth which is beneath it; if it surrounded the whole earth instead of only a part, its weight would press upon the whole surface of the earth. In the same way,

since the mass of the air covers the whole face of the earth, its weight presses upon the earth at every point.

3. Just as the bottom of a bucket containing water is pressed more heavily by the weight of the water when it is full than when it is half empty, and the more heavily the deeper the water is, similarly the high places of the earth, such as the summits of mountains, are less heavily pressed than the lowlands are by the weight of the mass of the air. This is because there is more air above the lowlands than above the mountain tops; for all the air along a mountain side presses upon the lowlands but not upon the summit, being above the one but below the other.

4. Bodies immersed in water are pressed on all sides by the weight of the water above them, as we have shown in the *Treatise on the Equilibrium of Liquids*. In the same way bodies in the air are pressed on all sides by the weight of the air above them.

5. Animals in water do not feel its weight; neither do we feel the weight of the air, and for the same reason. Just as it would be a mistake to infer that, because we do not feel the weight of the water when immersed in it, water has no weight; so it would be a mistake to infer that air has no weight because we do not feel its pressure. We have shown the reason of this in the *Treatise on The Equilibrium of Liquids*.

6. If there were collected a great bulk of wool, say twenty or thirty fathoms high, this mass would be compressed by its own weight; the bottom layers would be far more compressed than the middle or top layers, because they are pressed by a greater quantity of wool. Similarly the mass of the air, which is a compressible and heavy body like wool, is compressed by its own weight, and the air at the bottom, in the lowlands, is far more compressed than the higher layers on the mountain tops, because it bears a greater load of air.

7. In the case of that bulk of wool, if a handful of it were taken from the bottom layer, compressed as it is and lifted, in the same state of compression, to the middle of the mass,

it would expand of its own accord; for it would then be nearer the top and subjected there to the pressure of a smaller quantity of wool. Similarly if a body of air, as found here below in its natural state of compression, were by some device transferred to a mountain top, it would necessarily expand and come to the condition of the air around it on the mountain; for then it would bear a lesser weight of air than it did below. Hence if a balloon, only half inflated – not fully so, as they generally are – were carried up a mountain, it would necessarily be more inflated at the mountain top, and would expand in the degree to which it was less burdened. The difference will be visible, provided the quantity of air along the mountain slope, from the pressure of which it is now relieved, has a weight great enough to cause a sensible effect.

There is so necessary a bond between these consequences and their principle that if the principle is true the consequences will be true also. Since, therefore, it is acknowledged that the air, reaching from the earth to the periphery of its sphere, has weight, all the conclusions we have inferred from this fact are equally correct.

But, however certain these conclusions may be deemed, it appears to me that all who accept them would nevertheless be eager to see this last consequence confirmed by experiment, because it involves all the others and indeed directly verifies the principle itself. There is no doubt that if a balloon such as we have described were seen to expand as it was lifted up, the conclusion could not be avoided that the expansion was due to a pressure, which was greater below than above. Nothing else could cause that expansion, the more so as the mountains are colder than the lowlands. The compression of the air in the balloon could have no other cause than the weight of the mass of the air, since this air was taken in its actual condition at low altitudes and was uncompressed, the balloon being even limp and only half inflated. This would be proof positive that air has weight; that the mass of the air is heavy; that its weight presses all the bodies it contains; that its pressure is greater on the lowlands than on the highlands; that it compresses itself by its own weight, and is more highly compressed below than above. And, since in physical science experience is far more convincing than argument, I do not doubt that everyone will wish to see this reasoning confirmed by experiment. Moreover, should the experiment be performed, I should enjoy this advantage: that if no expansion of the balloon were observed even on the highest mountains, my conclusions, nevertheless, would not be invalidated; for I might then claim that the mountains were still not high enough to cause a perceptible difference. Whereas if a considerable and very marked change occurred, say of one-eighth or one-ninth in volume, the proof, to me, would be absolutely convincing, and there could remain no doubt as to the truth of all that I had asserted.

But I delay too long. It is time to say, in a word, that the trial has been made and with the following successful result.

|| An Experiment Made at Two High Places, the One about 500 Fathoms Higher than the Other

If one takes a balloon half-filled with air, shrunken and flabby, and carries it by a thread to the top of a mountain 500 fathoms high, it will expand of its own accord as it rises, until at the top it will be fully inflated as if more air had been blown into it. As it is brought down it will gradually shrink by the same degrees, until at the foot of the mountain it has resumed its former condition.

This experiment proves all that I have said of the mass of the air, with wholly convincing force; but it must be fully confirmed, since the whole of my discourse rests on this foundation. Meanwhile it remains to be pointed out only that the mass of the air weighs more or less at different times, according as it is more charged with vapour or more contracted by cold.

Let it then be set down, (1) that the mass of air has weight; (2) that its weight is limited; (3) that it is heavier at some times than at others; (4) that its weight is greater in some places than in others, as in [highlands and] lowlands; (5) that by its weight it presses all the bodies it surrounds, the more strongly when its weight is greater.

§ CHAPTER II *The Weight of the Mass of the Air produces all the Effects hitherto ascribed to the Abhorrence of a Vacuum*

This chapter is divided into two parts: the first describes the principal effects which have been commonly ascribed to the abhorrence of a vacuum; the second shows that they are due to the weight of the air.

|| PART I An account of the effects ascribed to the abhorrence of a vacuum

There are several effects which nature is said to produce by an abhorrence of a vacuum, of which the most striking are the following:

I. When all the apertures of a bellows are closed, it is hard to open. Any attempt to do this meets with a resistance as if its two sides were stuck together. And similarly the piston of a sealed syringe resists the effort to withdraw it, as though it adhered to the base of its case.

This resistance is commonly explained as an instance of nature's abhorrence of the vacuum which would be produced if the bellows could be opened: and this theory is supported by the fact that the resistance ceases as soon as an aperture is made by which air can enter to fill the bellows when it is opened.

II. Two polished surfaces laid one upon the other are difficult to separate and seem glued together. Thus a hat laid on a table is hard to jerk up. A piece of leather pressed against a paving stone and jerked up, will wrench out and lift the stone.

It is claimed that this adhesion is due to nature's abhorrence of the vacuum that would exist while the air was passing from the periphery to the centre.

III. When a syringe is dipped in water and the piston is drawn back, the water follows it, and rises as if it adhered to the plunger. In the same way, in a suction pump, which is really but a long syringe, the water rises and follows its piston when this is drawn back, as if it adhered to it.

It is claimed that this rising of the water is due to nature's abhorrence of the vacuum which would be left when the piston is withdrawn, if water did not take its place, since air cannot enter. This explanation is supported by the fact that if slits are cut through which air can penetrate, the water no longer rises.

Similarly, if the nozzle of a bellows is thrust into water and the bellows is opened suddenly, water enters to fill it because no air can get in, especially if the vents in the sides are sealed.

Again, if a man sucks up water, the same cause produces the result; for the lungs act like a bellows of which the nozzle is the mouth.

Again, in breathing, the air is drawn in as a bellows draws in air, to fill its emptiness.

Again, if lighted tow is put in a saucer full of water and covered with an inverted glass, then, as the fire dies out the water rises in the glass, because the air within it, rarefied by the fire, is condensed as it cools and draws the water up with it to fill the place which its condensation has left empty; just as the piston of a syringe draws the water up behind it.*

Again, in cupping, the flesh is drawn up into a swelling; because the air inside the cup, rarefied by the flame of the candle, is condensed as it cools when the flame dies, and draws up the flesh to fill the vacated space, as the water was drawn up in the foregoing instance.

IV. If a bottle, filled with water, is set upside down in a water-filled vessel, the water hangs in the bottle and does not fall out.

It is claimed that this retention of the water is due to nature's abhorrence of the vacuum which would be produced were the water

---

*In this case, as is implied, the tow is only partially submerged, and is not at once extinguished. At first, some of the warmed air would probably bubble out through the water and thus suggest this interpretation. The chemistry of combustion was not, at this time, understood.

to drop away while no air could enter to fill the vacancy left behind. This explanation is supported by the fact that if a vent is made through which the air can flow in, the water drops immediately.

The same test may be made with a tube, say ten feet in length, sealed at the top and open at the bottom. If the tube is filled with water and the open end [temporarily closed] is dipped into a vessel full of water, the water will be wholly retained in the tube, whereas it would run out at once if the top were opened.

The same thing may be done with a similar tube, sealed at the top but bent backward at the lower [open] end, without dipping it in a water-filled vessel as in the preceding case. For if the tube is filled with water, the water will be retained, whereas if the top were opened a jet of water would instantly and violently escape from the bent extremity.*

Lastly, the same thing may be done with a simple straight tube, provided it be very narrow at its lower end. If it is sealed at the top the water will be retained, whereas the water would rush out below if the upper end were opened. This is why a wine-filled cask does not release a single drop, though the spigot be open, until a vent is opened at the top.

V. If a tube bent in the shape of an inverted horseshoe (which is commonly called a siphon) is filled with water, and its legs are placed so as to dip in separate water-filled vessels, then, however small the difference of level between the two vessels may be, all the water from the higher vessel will rise up the leg immersed in it to the top of the siphon and will pass down by the other leg into the lower vessel in which that leg is immersed; so that, if a sufficiency of water be supplied to the higher vessel, the flow will be continuous.

It is claimed that this retention of the water is due to nature's abhorrence of the vacuum that would be left in the siphon if the water from these two legs were to fall from each into its own. So it does, if any vent is made at the top of the siphon, whereby the air can enter.

There are several other similar effects which I do not

*The instrument now called the siphon barometer.

describe because they are all like those I have mentioned. In all of them the one outstanding cause is that all bodies in contact resist any effort to part them when the air cannot insinuate itself between them whether that effort be due to their own weight, as in the cases where the water rises and is retained in spite of its weight, or to the force exerted to part them as in the earlier examples.

Such are the effects commonly ascribed to nature's abhorrence of a vacuum. We will now show that they are due to the weight of the air.

|| PART II The weight of the mass of the air produces all the effects that are commonly ascribed to the abhorrence of a vacuum

If it has been well understood, from the *Treatise on the Equilibrium of Liquids*, how their weight presses all the bodies immersed in them, there will be no difficulty in understanding how the weight of the mass of the air bearing on all bodies produces on them the effects that might be ascribed to abhorrence of a vacuum: for they are quite alike, as we shall prove in each case.

I. The weight of the mass of the air causes the difficulty in opening a sealed bellows.

To make it clear how the weight of the mass of air causes the resistance encountered in opening a bellows from which the air is excluded, I will point to a similar resistance due to the weight of water. It needs only to be remembered, as I said in the *Equilibrium of Liquids*, that if a bellows with a tube twenty or more feet long is set in a tank full of water with the tip of the nozzle extending above the surface, it is hard to open; and that the greater the depth of water above it the harder it is to open. This is obviously due to the weight of the water above: for if there is no water there, it is easy to open. The more water you pour in, the greater is the resistance, which is always equal to the weight of the water sustained. The reason is that as the nozzle projects above the water, and therefore excludes it, the bellows cannot be opened without raising and holding up the whole mass of water. The water that is pushed aside in the act of opening cannot enter the bellows, is forced to find room elsewhere, and thus raises the water level – a process attended with some difficulty – whereas if the bellows were so perforated that water could get in, it could be freely opened and closed because the water could enter through the perforations as fast as room was made for it, and would not, therefore, be lifted. I do not think that anyone can be tempted to ascribe this resistance to the abhorrence of a vacuum. It is absolutely certain that it is due solely to the weight of water.

Now what we say about water must be taken to apply to any other liquid: for if the bellows is set in a vessel full of wine, the same resistance to its opening will be experienced; likewise with milk, oil, quicksilver, and indeed with any liquid whatsoever. Thus it is a general rule and a necessary effect of the weight of liquids, that if a bellows is so immersed in any one of them that the liquid is excluded from its interior, the weight of the liquid above makes it impossible to open the bellows without overcoming a resistance due to the fact that it has to be lifted. Applying this general rule to air in particular, it follows as a certain consequence that when a bellows is so sealed as to exclude all air, the weight of the air above prevents its opening without overcoming some resistance: since it cannot be opened without lifting the whole mass of air. But as soon as a perforation is made in the bellows, it can be freely opened and closed, because now the act of opening no longer lifts the mass of the air. All this is completely analogous to the action of the bellows immersed in water.

Whence it is evident that the difficulty in opening a sealed bellows is but a particular case of the general rule that it is hard to open a bellows in any fluid whatsoever which is prevented from entering it.

What we have said about this effect we will say of all the rest, but more briefly.

II. The weight of the mass of the air is the cause of the difficulty that one feels in separating two polished bodies in close contact.

To explain how the weight of the mass of the air causes the resistance felt when the attempt is made to separate two polished surfaces in close contact, I will give an example of a wholly similar resistance due to the weight of water, which will put it beyond doubt that the air causes this effect. Here again what was stated in the *Equilibrium of Liquids* must be recalled.

Let a copper cylinder carefully ground on a lathe be placed in the mouth of a funnel made with equal care, until they fit so perfectly that the cylinder enters smoothly into the funnel without any leakage of water between them; and let this device be plunged into a tank full of water so that the stem of the funnel – which may be made twenty feet long if necessary – just emerges. If, now, while the funnel is held in one hand, the cylinder, at a depth of fifteen feet in the water, is released and left to move as it will, not only will it remain in position, although it seems to be quite unsupported; but furthermore, there will be difficulty in withdrawing it from the funnel, although it is in no way attached to it. On the other hand it would drop violently of its own weight if it were only four feet below the surface of the water in the tank, and more violently still if it were entirely out of the water. The reason for this I have already made clear. It is that water is in contact with the cylinder below but not above (since the funnel prevents its contact with the upper surface); it presses the face it touches toward the face it does not touch, and thus drives the cylinder up against the funnel.

The same reasoning applies to any other liquid. Consequently, when two polished surfaces are laid together, if the upper is held in the hand while the lower is left free, the latter must remain suspended, because it is in contact with the air below, but not with the air above, since there is no opening between the two plates, and the air, consequently, cannot reach the surfaces in contact. Whence it follows, as a necessary effect of the weight of all fluids, that the weight of the air must drive the lower body up and press it against the upper so strongly that a great resistance will be felt to the effort of separating them: an effect completely analogous to the effect of the weight of water.

Thus it is evident that the difficulty of separating two smooth bodies is but a particular case of the general rule that applies to the pressure of all fluids whatever when they are in contact with one of the surfaces of a body, but not with the surface opposite.

III. The weight of the mass of the air is the cause of the rise of water in syringes and pumps.

To explain how the weight of the mass of the air makes water rise in pumps as the plunger is drawn back, I will explain an entirely similar effect of the weight of water, which will acount for it perfectly.

If a syringe is provided with a long piston, say ten feet in length and hollow throughout, with a valve at its base opening downwards and not upwards, it cannot suck water nor any other liquid above the level of the liquid, because air can freely enter through the hollow of the piston. When the mouth of this syringe is plunged into a vessel full of quicksilver, and the whole apparatus is placed in a tank full of water so that the top of the piston shall just emerge, then if the piston is drawn up, the quicksilver will also rise behind it, as though adhering; though it would not rise at all if there were no water in the tank, because the air would then have free access to the body of the syringe through the hollow neck of the piston.

There is here no abhorrence of a vacuum, for even if the quicksilver did not rise to fill the space vacated by the piston, there would be no vacuum; since the air could enter freely. The sole cause is the mass of water which presses on the quicksilver in the vessel from every side except at the mouth of the syringe (which it is prevented from reaching by the body of the syringe and by the piston). This quicksilver, then, pressed on all sides but one, is forced by the weight of the water towards that one side as soon as the rising piston leaves it entrance room, and balances, within the syringe, the weight of the water outside. But if slits are made to admit water into the syringe, the quicksilver will cease to rise, because the water enters by them and is now in the same contact with the mouth of the syringe as with the other parts. Since its pressure then affects all parts equally, no liquid rises. All this has been clearly demonstrated in the *Equilibrium of Liquids*.

This illustration makes it clear how the weight of the water causes the quicksilver to rise. The same effect might be produced by the weight of sand. If all the water is removed from this vessel, and sand is poured in, in its place, the weight of the sand will cause the quicksilver to rise in the syringe because, just as the water did before, the sand now presses it on every side save that which is at the mouth of the syringe; and pressing it, compels it to rise. And if you bear on the sand with your hands, you will drive the quicksilver further up the syringe until it reaches such a height that it can balance the extra pressure.

The explanation of these effects makes it very easy to see why the weight of the air causes water to rise in common syringes to the height that the piston is drawn back. The air, in contact with the water of the vessel on every side except at the mouth of the syringe (from which it is excluded by the syringe itself and by its piston), pressing by its weight upon that water on every side except that single one, cannot fail to drive it up as far as the withdrawing piston makes room for it to enter, and to counterbalance, within the syringe, the weight of the air outside. It does so for the same reason that the quicksilver rose under the pressure of the water, and under that of the sand in the case that we have just given, and by the same necessity.

Thus it is obvious that the rising of water in syringes is but a particular case of the general rule that any liquid pressed in every one of its parts save one by the weight of another fluid is thereby driven towards that part against which no pressure is exerted.

*

V. The weight of the mass of the air causes water to rise in siphons.

To make it apparent how the weight of the air causes water to rise in a siphon, we will show that the weight of water makes quicksilver rise in a siphon which is fully open at the top and to which, therefore, air has free access. From this it will be clearly seen how the weight of the air produces this effect. And we will do so thus:

Let a siphon with one leg some twelve inches long and the other thirteen be opened at the top and let a tube twenty feet in length be soldered hermetically to this opening. Then let it be filled with quicksilver and placed with its legs dipping into separate vessels also filled with quicksilver; and let the whole apparatus be set up in a water-filled tank to a depth of some fifteen or sixteen feet, the upper end of the open tube remaining out of water. Now if one of the vessels be never so little, say one inch, higher than the other, all the quicksilver in the higher vessel will rise to the top of the siphon and make its way by the other leg to the lower vessel in a continuous stream; and if more quicksilver is fed to the higher vessel the flow will be continuous. But if the siphon is punctured so that water may enter it, instantly the quicksilver will drop out of each leg into its vessel, and water will take its place.

This rising of the quicksilver is not due to the abhorrence of a vacuum, for the air has perfectly free access to the siphon. Again, if the water were removed from the tank, the quicksilver from each leg would drop into its separate vessel, and air would take its place through the now freely open tube. Thus manifestly it is the weight of the water that causes this rising, because it presses upon the quicksilver in the vessels and not upon that in the siphon. This weight forces the quicksilver to rise and to flow as it does. But no sooner is water admitted by a perforation than, pressing now inside as well as outside the siphon, it ceases to force the quicksilver upwards.

For the same reason that water must necessarily cause the quicksilver to rise in a siphon when it presses upon the vessels without any access to the inside of the siphon, similarly the weight of the air must cause the water to rise in common siphons: it exerts its weight upon the water held by the vessels into which their legs dip, without any access to the inside of the siphon; but if a perforation is made so as to provide that access, the water ceases to rise, and on the contrary drops into each vessel and is replaced by air which now exerts its weight both inside and outside the siphon.

It is apparent that this last effect is but a particular case of the general rule, and that if it is clearly understood why the weight of the water makes the quicksilver rise in the example we have given, it will be apparent likewise why the weight of the air raises the water in common siphons. Hence we must make very clear the reason why the weight of the water produces this effect, and explain why it is the higher vessel that empties itself into the lower and not the lower into the other.

To do so, it must be observed that the water weighs upon the quicksilver in each vessel, but not on the quicksilver inside the legs that dip into it. Thus the quicksilver in the vessels is pressed, by the weight of the water, up each leg of the siphon to its top, and would rise farther if this were possible, for the water in the tank is sixteen feet deep while the siphon is but one foot in height; and one foot of quicksilver is equal to only fourteen of water. So, obviously, the weight of the water drives the quicksilver to the top of each leg, with some power left over. Thus the quicksilver in each leg being driven up by the weight of the water, the pressures in the two legs oppose each other at the top, and the stronger must prevail. It will be easy to calculate which this will be. Since the water has a greater height by one inch above the lower vessel, it drives up the quicksilver in the longer leg with more power than in the other leg, by the margin of the power derived from one inch of height. From this it would seem at first glance that the result would be to drive the quicksilver from the longer leg into the shorter. But it must be taken into consideration that the weight of quicksilver in each leg opposes the effort of water to press it up. These two resistances are not equal. Since the quicksilver in the longer leg is the deeper, by one inch, it offers a resistance which is greater by the force derived from one inch of height. Hence the quicksilver in the longer leg is driven up by a force of water the greater by the height of one inch. But it is borne down by its own weight, that is by the excess weight of one inch of quicksilver. Now one inch of quicksilver weighs more than one inch of water; therefore the quicksilver in the shorter leg is driven up with the greater force and consequently must continue to rise so long as there is quicksilver in the vessel into which it dips.

From this it is apparent that the reason why the higher vessel empties itself into the lower is that quicksilver is heavier than water. The contrary would be the effect if the siphon, and also the vessels in which the siphon is plunged, were filled with oil, which is lighter than water, while the whole apparatus was immersed in the same tank of water. For then the oil from the lower vessel would rise and flow through the top of the siphon into the higher for the reasons aforesaid. The water would press the oil continuously from the lower vessel more strongly by the weight of one inch of height, and the oil of the longer leg would oppose this with the weight of one inch of greater height. As one inch of oil is lighter than one inch of water, the oil of the longer leg would be driven up more forcibly than that in the other and consequently would make its way from the lower vessel to the higher. And lastly, if the siphon were filled with a liquid of the same weight as the water in the tank, then there would be no exchange. Equilibrium would prevail. Calculating all the forces, you will find that they cancel one another.

Such are the effects that had to be clearly understood in order to grasp the reason for the rise of these liquids in siphons. After this it is perfectly easy to see why the weight of the air lifts the water in simple siphons from the higher to the lower vessel. We need not dilate upon the subject, as the case is only another one of the general rule that we have stated above.

*

IX. The weight of the mass of the air causes the in-drawing of air which occurs in breathing.

For the same reason, in breathing, the air enters the lungs. When the lungs open while the nose and all passages are also free and open, the air in these passages, driven by the weight of its whole mass, enters and drops down by the natural and necessary action of its weight. These facts are so intelligible, easy, and simple, that it is strange that recourse should have been had to the abhorrence of a vacuum, occult qualities, and other such far-fetched and chimerical causes for the purpose of accounting for them. It is just as natural for air to enter and drop down into the lungs when they open, as for wine to drop into a bottle when it is poured in.

Thus it is that the weight of the air produces all the effects hitherto ascribed to the abhorrence of a vacuum. I have now explained the more important of them. If any remain unexplained, they are so easy to account for by the same processes as the rest, that to look for them and explain them in detail would seem to me idle and tedious. Indeed they have all been seen, we may say, in their common origin, in the preceding treatise, since all these effects are but particular cases of the general rule concerning the Equilibrium of Fluids.

ROBERT BOYLE

1627–91

THE RELATIONSHIP BETWEEN THE
PRESSURE AND THE VOLUME OF A GAS IS
DEVELOPED EXPERIMENTALLY
(BOYLE'S LAW)

ROBERT BOYLE was a younger son of the second Earl of Cork. At the age of eleven, he was taken from school and sent abroad with a tutor, and when fourteen was studying the work of Galileo in Italy. Later, in England, his movements were influenced by those of the group of scientists and philosophers known sometimes as the 'Invisible College', sometimes as the 'Philosophical College', who met regularly to perform experiments and discuss theories, first at a tavern in Cheapside, later in Gresham College. Many of these men were called to Oxford to fill posts made vacant when the University was reformed under Parliamentarians during the Civil War. Wilkins became Warden of Wadham College, Wallis became Professor of Geometry and Petty Professor of Anatomy. Boyle moved to Oxford at that time, though not to a University post, and while there his work on the air-pump was carried out. Some years after the Restoration he moved to London, having in the meantime become a founder member of the Royal Society.

Boyle's activities covered a wide range of science. Within the field of physics he was actively interested not only in gases, but also in thermometry and in electricity and magnetism. His definition of a chemical element represents a further break from scholasticism beyond those due to such men as Galileo. His work on pigments derived from plants makes interesting reading to a chemist today. He experimented in physiology and wrote copiously on theology.

In partnership with Hooke, Boyle improved the first air-pump made by von Guericke. This enabled him to examine the effect of a vacuum on combustion and respiration. As the following passage shows, he developed the U-shaped form of Torricelli's barometer which is familar today. Using this apparatus he obtained the results which he generalized into what we now know as Boyle's Law.

The following selection is from the second edition (1662) of *A Defense of the Doctrine Touching the Spring and Weight of the Air*, as reprinted in W. F. Magie's *A Sourcebook in Physics* (Harvard, 1935).

¶ *Relations of Pressure and Volume of Air*

§ *Two New Experiments Touching the Measure of the Force of the Spring of Air Compressed and Dilated.*

We took then a long glass-tube, which, by a dexterous hand and the help of a lamp, was in such a manner crooked at the bottom, that the part turned up was almost parallel to the rest of the tube, and the orifice of this shorter leg of the siphon (if I may so call the whole instrument) being hermetically sealed, the length of it was divided into inches (each of which was subdivided into eight parts) by a streight list of paper, which containing those divisions, was carefully pasted all along it. Then putting in as much quicksilver as served to fill the arch or bended part of the siphon, that the mercury standing in a level might reach in the one leg to the bottom of the divided paper, and just to the same height or horizontal line in the other; we took care, by frequently inclining the tube, so that the air might freely pass from one leg into the other by the sides of the mercury (we took, I say, care) that the air at last included in the shorter cylinder should be of the same laxity with the rest of the air about it. This done, we began to pour quicksilver into the longer leg of the siphon, which by its weight pressing up that in the shorter leg, did by degrees streighten the included air: and continuing this pouring in of quicksilver till the air in the shorter leg was by condensation reduced to take up by half the space it possessed (I say, possessed, not filled) before; we cast our eyes upon the longer leg of the glass, on which was likewise pasted a list of paper carefully divided into inches and parts, and we observed, not without delight and satisfaction, that the quicksilver in that longer part of the tube was 29 inches higher than the other. Now that this observation does both very well agree with and confirm our hypothesis, will be easily discerned by him that takes notice what we teach; and Monsieur Paschal and our English friend's experiments prove, that the greater the weight is that leans upon the air, the more forcible is its endeavour of dilatation, and consequently its power of resistance (as other springs are stronger when bent by greater weights). For this being considered, it will appear to agree rarely-well with the hypothesis, that as according to it the air in that degree of density and correspondent measure of resistance, to which the weight of the incumbent atmosphere had brought it, was able to counter-balance and resist the pressure of a mercurial cylinder of about 29 inches, as we are taught by the Torricellian experiment; so here the same air being brought to a degree of density about twice as great as that it had before, obtains a spring twice as strong as formerly. As may appear by its being able to sustain or resist a cylinder of 29 inches in the longer tube, together with the weight of the atmospherical cylinder, that leaned upon those 29 inches of mercury; and, as we just now inferred from the Torricellian experiment, was equivalent to them.

We were hindered from prosecuting the trial at that time by the casual breaking of the tube. But because an accurate experiment of this nature would be of great importance to the doctrine of the spring of the air, and has not yet been made (that I know) by any man; and because also it is more uneasy to be made than one would think, in regard of the difficulty as well of procuring crooked tubes fit for the purpose, as of making a just estimate of the true place-of the protuberant mercury's surface; I suppose it will not be unwelcome to the reader to be informed, that after some other trials, one of which we made in a tube whose longer

A TABLE OF THE CONDENSATION OF THE AIR*

A	A	B	C	D	E
48	12	00	29 2/16	29 2/16	
46	11½	01 7/16	30 9/16	30 6/16	
44	11	02 13/16	31 15/16	31 12/16	
42	10½	04 6/16	33 8/16	33 1/7	
40	10	06 3/16	35 5/16	35	
38	9½	07 14/16	37	36 15/19	
36	9	10 2/16	39 5/16	38 7/8	
34	8½	12 8/16	41 10/16	41 2/17	
32	8	15 1/16	44 3/16	43 11/16	
30	7½	17 15/16	47 1/16	46 3/5	
28	7	21 3/16	50 5/16	50	
26	6½	25 3/16	54 5/16	53 10/13	
24	6	29 11/16	58 13/16	58 2/8	
23	5¾	32 3/16	61 5/16	60 18/23	
22	5½	34 15/16	64 1/16	63 6/11	
21	5¼	37 15/16	67 1/16	66 4/7	
20	5	41 9/16	70 11/16	70	
19	4¾	45	74 2/16	73 11/19	
18	4½	48 12/16	77 14/16	77 2/3	
17	4¼	53 11/16	82 12/16	82 4/17	
16	4	58 2/16	87 14/16	87 3/8	
15	3¾	63 15/16	93 1/16	93 1/5	
14	3½	71 5/16	100 7/16	99 6/7	
13	3¼	78 11/16	107 13/16	107 7/13	
12	3	88 7/16	117 9/16	116 4/8	

(In column C, written vertically: Added to 29 1/8 makes)

*See footnote to later table.

AA. The number of equal spaces in the shorter leg, that contained the same parcel of air diversely extended.

B. The height of the mercurial cylinder in the longer leg, that compressed the air into those dimensions.

C. The height of the mercurial cylinder, that counterbalanced the pressure of the atmosphere.

D. The aggregate of the two last columns, B and C, exhibiting the pressure sustained by the included air.

E. What the pressure should be according to the hypothesis, that supposes that pressures and expansions to be in reciprocal proportion.

leg was perpendicular, and the other, that contained the air, parallel to the horizon, we at last procured a tube of the figure expressed in the scheme; which tube, though of a pretty bigness, was so long, that the cylinder, whereof the shorter leg of it consisted, admitted a list of paper, which had before been divided into 12 inches and their quarters, and the longer leg admitted another list of paper of divers feet in length, and divided after the same manner. Then quicksilver being poured in to fill up the bended part of the glass, that the surface of it in either leg might rest in the same horizontal line, as we lately taught, there was more and more quicksilver poured into the longer tube; and notice being watchfully taken how far the mercury was risen in that longer tube, when it appeared to have ascended to any of the divisions in the shorter tube, the several observations that were thus successively made, and as they were made set down, afforded us the foregoing table. . . .

And to let you see, that we did not (as a little above) in-

A TABLE OF THE RAREFACTION OF THE AIR*

	A	B	C	D	E
A. The number of equal spaces at the top of the tube, that contained the same parcel of air.	1	00		$29^3/_4$	$29 \ ^3/_4$
	$1 \ ^1/_2$	$10^5/_8$		$19^1/_8$	$19 \ ^5/_6$
	2	$15^3/_8$		$14^3/_8$	$14 \ ^7/_8$
	3	$20^2/_8$		$9^4/_8$	$9^{15}/_{12}$
	4	$22^5/_8$		$7^1/_8$	$7 \ ^7/_{16}$
B. The height of the mercurial cylinder, that together with the spring of the included air counterbalanced the pressure of the atmosphere.	5	$24^1/_8$	Subtracted from $29^3/_4$ leaves	$5^5/_8$	$5^{19}/_{20}$
	6	$24^7/_8$		$4^7/_8$	$4^{23}/_{24}$
	7	$25^4/_8$		$4^2/_8$	$4 \ ^1/_4$
	8	26		$3^6/_8$	$3^{23}/_{32}$
	9	$26^3/_8$		$3^3/_8$	$3^{11}/_{36}$
C. The pressure of the atmosphere.	10	$26^6/_8$		3	$2^{39}/_{40}$
	12	$27^1/_8$		$2^5/_8$	$2^{23}/_{48}$
	14	$27^4/_8$		$2^2/_8$	$2 \ ^1/_8$
D. The complement of B to C, exhibiting the pressure sustained by the included air.	16	$27^6/_8$		2	$1^{55}/_{64}$
	18	$27^7/_8$		$1^7/_8$	$1^{47}/_{72}$
	20	28		$1^6/_8$	$1^9/_{80}$
	24	$28^2/_8$		$1^4/_8$	$1^{23}/_{96}$
E. What that pressure should be according to the hypothesis.	28	$28^3/_8$		$1^3/_8$	$1 \ ^1/_{16}$
	32	$28^4/_8$		$1^2/_8$	$0^{911}/_{128}$

*Column E of each table contains figures which are clearly erroneous but which are to be found in the second (corrected) edition of Boyle's works, dated 1738. – J.J.K.

considerately mention the weight of the incumbent atmospherical cylinder as a part of the weight resisted by the imprisoned air, we will here annex, that we took care, when the mercurial cylinder in the longer leg of the pipe was about an hundred inches high, to cause one to suck at the open orifice; whereupon (as we expected) the mercury in the tube did notably ascend. ... And therefore we shall render this reason of it that the pressure of the incumbent air being in part taken off by its expanding itself into the sucker's dilated chest, the imprisoned air was thereby enabled to dilate itself manifestly, and repel the mercury, that compressed it, till there was an equality of force betwixt the strong spring of the compressed air on the one part, and the tall mercurial cylinder, together with the contiguous dilated air, on the other part.

Now, if to what we have thus delivered concerning the compression of the air, we add some observations concerning its spontaneous expansion, it will the better appear, how much the phenomena of these mercurial experiments depend upon the differing measures of strength to be met with in the air's spring, according to its various degrees of compression and laxity.

———

JOSEPH BLACK
1728–99

THE CHEMISTRY OF FIXED AIR (CARBON DIOXIDE) IS STUDIED EXPERIMENTALLY

THERE is no easy explanation of Joseph Black's choice of a subject for his dissertation, submitted in 1754 to the University of Edinburgh. Written in Latin and entitled *De humore acido a cibis orto et magnesia alba*, it might have been left, like many similar documents when they have served their purpose, to moulder in an obscure corner of a library. Fortunately, Black's interests went beyond the mere attainment of a medical degree, and within the year he amplified his studies and presented them, in English, to the Philosophical Society of Edinburgh as *Experiments upon Magnesia Alba* [*Magnesium Carbonate*], *Quicklime and some other Alcaline Substances*. With this 'brilliant model, perhaps the first successful model, of quantitative chemical investigation ... a classic exemplar of experimental science worthy of comparison with Newton's *Optiks*',* Black established the British school of pneumatic chemists and contributed materially, if indirectly, to Lavoisier's achievement.

Black was a Scot born at Bordeaux, France, where his father had established himself as a successful merchant. He was sent, at the age of twelve, to a private school in Ireland and then at sixteen entered the University of Glasgow to study medicine. Here he came under the influence of Dr William Cullen who, at that time, introduced the study of chemistry at the University. These lectures represent the turning-point in Black's career. He became Cullen's assistant, served him at Glasgow, and followed him to Edinburgh, where he received the degree of Doctor of Medicine in 1754.

*Henry Guerlac, 'Joseph Black and Fixed Air', *Isis*, Vol. 48, 1957, p. 125.

Black's paper of 1755 describes the chemical behaviour of some common alkalis (carbonates) such as limestone, chalk, and magnesium carbonate. When such substances are calcined (burned), they give off a gas Black called 'fixed air'.

We now know that the gas observed by Black was carbon dioxide, but Black did not go beyond establishing by intensive and careful experimentation that the gas was a constituent of the compounds from which it was released by heating and roasting and that this gas (which he called *air*) was different from atmospheric air, resembling air which had been vitiated by combustion or by respiration.

Black, who later became Professor of Chemistry at the University of Edinburgh, went on to develop the use of accurate measuring instruments in his studies of heat. He is largely responsible for defining the concepts of specific and latent heat. He is remembered, too, in his association with James Watt, whose experiments with heat arose out of his attempts to improve the Newcomen atmospheric engine and led to the development of the first effective steam engine.

The experiments described in the following extract (from *Experiments upon Magnesia Alba*) exemplify the sort of material which stimulated Black's contemporaries, in particular Priestley and Cavendish. This paper has been reprinted as No. 1 in the series of Alembic Club Reprints.

¶ PART I

... By the following experiments, I proposed to know whether this substance could be reduced to a quick-lime.

An ounce of *magnesia* was exposed in a crucible for about an hour to such a heat as is sufficient to melt copper. When taken out, it weighed three drams and one scruple, or had lost 7/12 of its former weight.

I repeated, with the *magnesia* prepared in this manner, most of those experiments I had already made upon it before calcination, and the result was as follows.

It dissolves in all the acids, and with these composes salts exactly similar to those described in the first set of experiments: but what is particularly to be remarked, it is dissolved without any the least degree of effervescence.

It slowly precipitates the corrosive sublimate of mercury in the form of a black powder.

It separates the volatile alkali in salt ammoniac from the acid, when it is mixed with a warm solution of that salt. But it does not separate an acid from a calcarious earth, nor does it induce the least change upon lime-water.

Lastly, when a dram of it is digested with an ounce of water in a bottle for some hours, it does not make any the least change in the water. The *magnesia*, when dried, is found to have gained ten grains; but it neither effervesces with acids, nor does it sensibly affect lime-water.

Observing *magnesia* to lose such a remarkable proportion of its weight in the fire, my next attempts were directed to the investigation of this volatile part, and among other experiments, the following seemed to throw some light upon it.

Three ounces of *magnesia* were distilled in a glass retort and receiver, the fire being gradually increased until the *magnesia* was obscurely red hot. When all was cool, I found only five drams of a whitish water in the receiver, which had a faint smell of the spirit of hartshorn, gave a green colour to the juice of violets, and rendered the solutions of corrosive sublimate and of silver very slightly turbid. But it did not sensibly effervesce with acids.

The *magnesia*, when taken out of the retort, weighed an ounce, three drams, and thirty grains, or had lost more than half of its weight. It still effervesced pretty briskly with acids, tho' not so strongly as before this operation.

The fire should have been raised here to the degree requisite for the perfect calcination of *magnesia*. But even from this imperfect experiment, it is evident, that of the volatile parts contained in that powder, a small proportion only is water; the rest cannot, it seems, be retained in vessels, under a visible form. Chemists have often observed, in their distillations, that part of a body has vanished from their senses, notwithstanding the utmost care to retain it; and they have always found, upon further inquiry, that subtile part to be air, which having been imprisoned in the body, under a solid form, was set free and rendered fluid and elastic by the fire. We may therefore safely conclude, that the volatile matter, lost in the calcination of *magnesia*, is mostly air; and hence the calcined *magnesia* does not emit air, or make an effervescence when mixed with acids.

The water, from its properties, seems to contain a small portion of volatile alkali, which was probably formed from the earth, air, and water, or from some of these combined together; and perhaps also from a small quantity of inflammable matter which adhered accidentally to the *magnesia*. Whenever Chemists meet with this salt, they are inclined to ascribe its origin to some animal, or putrid vegetable, substance; and this they have always done, when they obtained it from the calcarious earths, all of which afford a small quantity of it. There is, however, no doubt that it can sometimes be produced independently of any such mixture, since many fresh vegetables and tartar afford a considerable quantity of it. And how can it, in the present instance, be supposed, that any animal or vegetable matter adhered to the *magnesia*, while it was dissolved by an acid, separated from this by an alkali, and washed with so much water?

Two drams of *magnesia* were calcined in a crucible, in the manner described above, and thus reduced to two scruples and twelve grains. This calcined *magnesia* was dissolved in a sufficient quantity of spirit of vitriol, and then again separated from the acid by the addition of an alkali, of which a large quantity is necessary for this purpose. The *magnesia*, being very well washed and dried, weighed one dram and fifty grains. It effervesced violently, or emitted a large quantity of air, when thrown into acids, formed a red powder when mixed with a solution of sublimate, separated the calcarious earths from an acid, and sweetened limewater: and had thus recovered all those properties which it had but just now lost by calcination: nor had it only recovered its original properties, but acquired besides an addition of weight nearly equal to what had been lost in the fire; and, as it is found to effervesce with acids, part of the addition must certainly be air.

This air seems to have been furnished by the alkali from which it was separated by the acid; for Dr Hales has clearly proved, that alkaline salts contain a large quantity of fixed air, which they emit in great abundance when joined to a pure acid. In the present case, the alkali is really joined to an acid, but without any visible emission of air; and yet the air is not retained in it: for the neutral salt, into which it is converted, is the same in quantity, and in every other respect, as if the acid employed had not been previously saturated with *magnesia*, but offered to the alkali in its pure state, and had driven the air out of it in their conflict. It seems therefore evident, that the air was forced from the alkali by the acid, and lodged itself in the *magnesia*.

These considerations led me to try a few experiments, whereby I might know what quantity of air is expelled from an alkali, or from *magnesia*, by acids.

Two drams of a pure fixed alkaline salt, and an ounce of water, were put into a Florentine flask, which, together with its contents, weighed two ounces and two drams. Some oil of vitriol diluted with water was dropt in, until the salt was exactly saturated; which it was found to be, when two drams, two scruples, and three grains of this acid had been added. The vial with its contents now weighed two ounces, four drams, and fifteen grains. One scruple, therefore, and eight grains were lost during the ebullition, of which a trifling portion may be water, or something of the same kind. The rest is air.

The celebrated *Homberg* has attempted to estimate the quantity of solid salt contained in a determined portion of the several acids. He saturated equal quantities of an alkali with each of them; and, observing the weight which the alkali had gained, after being perfectly dried, took this for the quantity of solid salt contained in that share of the acid which performed the saturation. But we learn from the above experiment, that his estimate was not accurate, because the alkali loses weight as well as gains it.

Two drams of *magnesia*, treated exactly as the alkali in the last experiment, were just dissolved by four drams, one scruple, and seven grains of the same acid liquor, and lost one scruple and sixteen grains by the ebullition.

Two drams of *magnesia* were reduced, by the action of a violent fire, to two scruples and twelve grains, with which the same process was repeated, as in the two last experiments; four drams, one scruple, and two grains of the same acid, were required to compleat the solution, and no weight was lost in the experiment.

As in the separation of the volatile from the fixed parts of bodies, by means of heat, a small quantity of the latter is generally raised with the former; so the air and water, originally contained in the *magnesia*, and afterwards dissipated by the fire, seem to have carried off a small part of the fixed earth of this substance. This is probably the reason, why calcined *magnesia* is saturated with a quantity of acid, somewhat less than what is required to dissolve it before calcination: and the same may be assigned as one cause which hinders us from restoring the whole of its original weight, by solution and precipitation.

I took care to dilute the vitriolic acid, in order to avoid the heat and ebullition which it would otherwise have excited in the water; and I chose a Florentine flask, on account of its lightness, capacity, and shape, which is peculiarly adapted to the experiment; for the vapours raised by the ebullition circulated for a short time, thro' the wide cavity of the vial, but were soon collected upon its sides, like dew, and none of them seemed to reach the neck, which continued perfectly dry to the end of the experiment.

We now perceive the reason why crude and calcined *magnesia*, which differ in many respects from one another, agree however in composing the same kind of salt, when dissolved in any particular acid; for the crude *magnesia* seems to differ from the calcined chiefly by containing a considerable quantity of air, which air is unavoidably dissipated and lost during the dissolution.

From our experiments, it seems probable, that the increase of weight which some metals acquire, by being first dissolved in acids, and then separated from them again by alkalis, proceeds from air furnished by the alkalis. And that in the *aurum fulminans,* which is prepared by the same means, this air adheres to the gold in such a peculiar manner, that, in a moderate degree of heat, the whole of it recovers its elasticity in the same instant of time; and thus, by the violent shock which it gives to the air around, produces the loud crack or fulmination of this powder. Those who will imagine the explosion of such a minute portion of fixed air, as can reside in the *aurum fulminans,* to be insufficient for the excessive loudness of the noise, will consider, that it is not a large quantity of motion communicated to the air, but rather a smart stroke which produces sound, and that the explosion of but a few particles of fixed air may be capable of causing a loud noise, provided they all recover their spring suddenly, and in the same instant.

The above experiments lead us also to conclude, that volatile alkalis, and the common absorbent earths, which lose their air by being joined to acids, but shew evident signs of their having recovered it, when separated from them by alkalis, received it from these alkalis which lost it in the instant of their joining with the acid.

The following are a few experiments upon three of the absorbent earths, made in order to compare them with one another, and with *magnesia.*

Suspecting that *magnesia* might possibly be no other than a common calcarious earth, which had changed its nature by having been previously combined with an acid, I saturated a small quantity of chalk with the muriatic acid, separated the acid from it again by means of a fixed alkali, and carefully washed away the whole of the salt.

The chalk when dried was not found to have suffered any alteration; for it effervesced with the vitriolic acid, but did not dissolve in it; and when exposed to a violent fire, was converted into a quick-lime, in all respects similar to that obtained from common chalk.

In another experiment of the same kind, I used the vitriolic acid with the same event.

Any calcarious matter reduced to a fine powder, and thrown into a warm solution of alum, immediately raises a brisk effervescence. But the powder is not dissolved; it is rather increased in bulk: and if the addition be repeated until it is no longer accompanied with effervescence, the liquor loses all taste of the alum, and yields only a very light cloud upon the admixture of an alkali.

From this experiment we learn, that acids attract the calcarious earths more strongly than they do the earth of alum; and as the acid in this salt is exactly the same with the vitriolic, it composes with the calcarious earth a neutral substance, which is very difficultly soluble in water, and therefore falls down to the bottom of the vessel along with the earth of alum, which is deprived of its acid. The light cloud formed by the alkali proceeds from the minute portion of the calcarious compound which saturates the water.

The earth of animal bones, when reduced to a fine powder and thrown into a diluted vitriolic acid, gradually absorbs the acid in the same manner as the calcarious earths, but without any remarkable effervescence. When it is added to the nitrous or to the muriatic acid, it is slowly dissolved. The compound liquor thence produced is extremely acrid, and still changes the colour of the juice of violets to a red, even after it is fully saturated with the absorbent. Distilled vinegar has little or no effect upon this earth; for after a long digestion it still retains its sour taste, and gives only a light cloud upon the addition of an alkali.

By dropping a dissolved fixed alkali into a warm solution of alum, I obtained the earth of this salt, which, after being well washed and dryed, was found to have the following properties.

It is dissolved in every acid but very slowly, unless assisted by heat. The several solutions, when thoroughly saturated, are all astringent with a slight degree of an acid taste, and they also agree with a solution of alum in this, that they give a red colour to the infusion of turnsol.

Neither this earth, nor that of animal bones, can be converted into quick-lime by the strongest fire, nor do they suffer any change worth notice. Both of them seem to attract acids but weakly, and to alter their properties less when united to them than the other absorbents.

¶ PART II

In reflecting afterwards upon these experiments, an explication of the nature of lime offered itself, which seemed to account, in an easy manner, for most of the properties of that substance.

It is sufficiently clear, that the calcarious earths in their native state, and that the alkalis and *magnesia* in their ordinary condition, contain a large quantity of fixed air, and this air certainly adheres to them with considerable force, since a strong fire is necessary to separate it from *magnesia,* and the strongest is not sufficient to expel it entirely from fixed alkalis, or take away their power of effervescing with acid salts.

These considerations led me to conclude, that the relation between fixed air and alkaline substances was somewhat similar to the relation between these and acids; that as the calcarious earths and alkalis attract acids strongly and can be saturated with them, so they also attract fixed air, and are in their ordinary state saturated with it: and when we mix an acid with an alkali or with an absorbent earth, that the air is then set at liberty, and breaks out with violence; because the alkaline body attracts it more weakly than it does the acid, and because the acid and air cannot both be joined to the same body at the same time.

I also imagined that, when the calcarious earths are exposed to the action of a violent fire, and are thereby converted into quick-lime, they suffer no other change in their composition than the loss of a small quantity of water and of their fixed air. The remarkable acrimony which we perceive in them after this process, was not supposed to proceed from any additional matter received in the fire, but seemed to be an essential property of the pure earth, depending on an attraction for those several substances which it then became capable of corroding or dissolving, which attraction had been insensible as long as the air adhered to the earth, but discovered itself upon the separation.

This supposition was founded upon an observation of the most frequent consequences of combining bodies in chemistry. Commonly when we join two bodies together, their acrimony or attraction for other substances becomes immediately either less perceivable or entirely insensible; altho' it was sufficiently strong and remarkable before their union, and may be rendered evident again by disjoining them. A neutral salt, which is composed of an acid and alkali, does not possess the acrimony of either of its constituent parts. It can easily be separated from water, has little or no effect upon metals, is incapable of being joined to inflammable bodies, and of corroding and dissolving animals and vegetables; so that the attraction both of the acid and alkali for these several substances seems to be suspended till they are again separated from one another.

Crude lime was therefore considered as a peculiar acrid earth rendered mild by its union with fixed air: and quicklime as the same earth, in which, by having separated the air, we discover that acrimony or attraction for water, for animal, vegetable, and for inflammable substances.

That the calcarious earths really lose a large quantity of air when they are burnt to quick-lime, seems sufficiently proved by an experiment of Mr *Margraaf*, an exceedingly accurate and judicious Chemist. He subjected eight ounces of *osteocolla* to distillation in an earthen retort, finishing his process with the most violent fire of a reverberatory, and caught in the receiver only two drams of water, which by its smell and properties shewed itself to be slightly alkaline. He does not tell us the weight of the *osteocolla* remaining in the retort, and only says, that it was converted into quick-lime; but as no calcarious earth can, be converted into quick-lime, or bear the heat which he applied without losing above a third of its weight, we may safely conclude, that the loss in his experiment was proportional, and proceeded chiefly from the dissipation of fixed air.

According to our theory, the relation of the calcarious earth to air and water appeared to agree with the relation of the same earth to the vitriolic and vegetable acids. As chalk for instance has a stronger attraction for the vitriolic than for the vegetable acid, and is dissolved with more difficulty when combined with the first, than when joined to the second: so it also attracts air more strongly than water, and is dissolved with more difficulty when saturated with air than when compounded with water only.

A calcarious earth deprived of its air, or in the state of quick-lime, greedily absorbs a considerable quantity of water, becomes soluble in that fluid, and is then said to be slaked; but as soon as it meets with fixed air, it is supposed to quit the water and join itself to the air, for which it has a superior attraction, and is therefore restored to its first state of mildness and insolubility in water.

When slaked lime is mixed with water, the fixed air in the water is attracted by the lime, and saturates a small portion of it, which then becomes again incapable of dissolution, but part of the remaining slaked lime is dissolved and composes lime-water.

If this fluid be exposed to the open air, the particles of quick-lime which are nearest the surface gradually attract the particles of fixed air which float in the atmosphere. But at the same time that a particle of lime is thus saturated with air, it is also restored to its native state of mildness and insolubility; and as the whole of this change must happen at the surface, the whole of the lime is successively collected there under its original form of an insipid calcarious earth, called the cream or crusts of lime-water.

When quick-lime itself is exposed to the open air, it absorbs the particles of water and of fixed air which come within its sphere of attraction, as it meets with the first of these in greatest plenty, the greatest part of it assumes the form of slaked lime; the rest is restored to its original state; and if it be exposed for a sufficient length of time, the whole of it is gradually saturated with air, to which the water as gradually yields its place.

We have already shown by experiment, that *magnesia alba* is a compound of a peculiar earth and fixed air. When this substance is mixed with lime-water, the lime shows a stronger attraction for fixed air than that of the earth of *magnesia*; the air leaves this powder to join itself to the lime. And as neither the lime when saturated with air, nor the *magnesia* when deprived of it, are soluble in water, the lime-water becomes perfectly pure and insipid, the lime which it contained being mixed with the *magnesia*. But if the *magnesia* be deprived of air by calcination before it is mixed with the lime-water, this fluid suffers no alteration.

If quick-lime be mixed with a dissolved alkali, it likeways shows an attraction for fixed air superior to that of the alkali. It robs this salt of its air, and thereby becomes mild itself, while the alkali is consequently rendered more corrosive, or discovers its natural degree of acrimony or strong attraction for water, and for bodies of the inflammable, and of the animal and vegetable kind; which attraction was less perceivable as long as it was saturated with air. And the volatile alkali when deprived of its air, besides this attraction for various bodies, discovers likeways its natural degree of volatility, which was formerly somewhat repressed by the air adhering to it, in the same manner as it is repressed by the addition of an acid.

This account of lime and alkalis recommended itself by its simplicity, and by affording an easy solution of many *phaenomena*, but appeared upon a nearer view to be attended with consequences that were so very new and extraordinary, as to render suspicious the principles from which they were drawn.

I resolved however to examine, in a particular manner, such of these consequences as were the most unavoidable, and found the greatest number of them might be reduced to the following propositions:

I. If we only separate a quantity of air from lime and alkalis, when we render them caustic they will be found to lose part of their weight in the operation, but will saturate the same quantity of acid as before, and the saturation will be performed without effervescence.

II. If quick-lime be no other than a calcarious earth deprived of its air, and whose attraction for fixed air is stronger than that of alkalis, it follows, that, by adding to it a sufficient quantity of alkali saturated with air, the lime will recover the whole of its air, and be entirely restored to its original weight and condition: and it also follows, that the earth separated from lime-water by an alkali, is the lime which was dissolved in the water now restored to its original mild and insoluble state.

III. If it be supposed that slaked lime does not contain any parts which are more fiery, active, or subtile than others, and by which chiefly it communicates its virtues to water; but that it is an uniform compound of lime and water: it follows, that, as part of it can be dissolved in water, the whole of it is also capable of being dissolved.

IV. If the acrimony of the caustic alkali does not depend on any part of the lime adhering to it, a caustic or soap-ley will consequently be found to contain no lime, unless the quantity of lime employed in making it were greater than what is just sufficient to extract the whole air of the alkali; for then as much of the superfluous quick-lime might possibly be dissolved by the ley as would be dissolved by pure water, or the ley would contain as much lime as lime-water does.

V. We have shown in the former experiments, that absorbent earths lose their air when they are joined to an acid; but recover it, if separated again from that acid, by means of an ordinary alkali: the air passing from the alkali to the earth, at the same time that the acid passes from the earth to the alkali.

If the caustic alkali therefore be destitute of air, it will separate *magnesia* from an acid under the form of a *magnesia* free of air, or which will not effervesce with acids; and the same caustic alkali will also separate a calcarious earth from acids under the form of a calcarious earth destitute of air, but saturated with water, or under the form of slaked lime.

These were all necessary conclusions from the above suppositions. Many of them appeared too improbable to deserve any further attention; some however, I found upon reflection, were already seconded by experience. Thus *Hoffman* has observed, that quick-lime does not effervesce with spirit of vitriol; and it is well known that the caustic spirit of urine, or of salt ammoniac, does not emit air, when mixed with acids. This consideration excited my curiosity, and determined me to inquire into the truth of them all by way of experiment. I therefore engaged myself in a set of trials; the history of which is here subjoined. Some new facts are likeways occasionally mentioned; and here it will be proper to inform the reader, that I have never mentioned any, without satisfying myself of their truth by experiment, tho' I have sometimes taken the liberty to neglect describing the experiments when they seemed sufficiently obvious.

Desiring to know how much of an acid a calcarious earth will absorb, and what quantity of air is expelled during the dissolution, I saturated two drams of chalk with diluted spirit of salt, and used the Florentine flask, as related in a similar experiment upon *magnesia*. Seven drams and one grain of the acid finished the dissolution, and the chalk lost two scruples and eight grains of air.

This experiment was necessary before the following, by which I proposed to inquire into the truth of the first proposition so far as it relates to quick-lime.

Two drams of chalk were converted into a perfect quick-lime, and lost two scruples and twelve grains in the fire. This quick-lime was slaked or reduced to a milky liquor with an ounce of water, and then dissolved in the same manner, and with the same acid, as the two drams of chalk in the preceding experiment. Six drams, two scruples and fourteen grains of the acid finished the saturation without any sensible effervescence or loss of weight.

It therefore appears from these experiments, that no air is separated from quick-lime by an acid, and that chalk saturates nearly the same quantity of acid after it is converted into quick-lime as before.

With respect to the second proposition, I tried the following experiments.

A piece of perfect quick-lime made from two drams of chalk, and which weighed one dram and eight grains, was reduced to a very fine powder, and thrown into a filtrated mixture of an ounce of a fixed alkaline salt and two ounces of water. After a slight digestion, the powder being well washed and dried, weighed one dram and fifty eight grains. It was similar in every trial to a fine powder of ordinary chalk, and was therefore saturated with air which must have been furnished by the alkali.

A dram of pure salt of tartar was dissolved in fourteen pounds of lime-water, and the powder thereby precipitated, being carefully collected and dried, weighed one and fifty grains. When exposed to a violent fire, it was converted into a true quick-lime, and had every other quality of a calcarious earth.

This experiment was repeated with the volatile alkali, and also with the fossil or alkali of sea-salt, and exactly with the same event.

The third proposition had less appearance of probability than the foregoing; but, as an accurate experiment was the only test of its truth, I reduced eight grains of perfect quick-lime made of chalk, to an exceedingly subtile powder, by slaking it in two drams of distilled water boiling hot and immediately threw the mixture into eighteen ounces of distilled water in a flask. After shaking it, a light sediment, which floated thro' the liquor, was allowed to subside; and this, when collected with the greatest care, and dried, weighed, as near as I could guess, one third of a grain. The water tasted strongly of the lime, had all the qualities of lime-water and yielded twelve grains of precipitate, upon the addition of salt of tartar. In repeating this experiment, the quantity of sediment was sometimes less than the above, and sometimes amounted to half a grain. It consisted partly of an earth which effervesced violently with *aqua fortis,* and partly of an ochry powder, which would not dissolve in that acid. The ochry powder, as it usually appears in chalk to the eye, in the form of veins running thro' its substance, must be considered only as an accidental or foreign admixture; and, with respect to the minute portion of alkaline earth which composed the remainder of the sediment, it cannot be supposed to have been originally different from the rest, and incapable, from its nature, of being converted into quick-lime, or of being dissolved in water; it seems rather to have consisted of a small part of the chalk in its mild state, or saturated with air, which had either remained, for want of a sufficient fire to drive it out entirely, or had been furnished by the distilled water.

I indeed expected to see a much larger quantity of sediment produced from the lime, on account of the air which water constantly contains, and with a view to know whether water retains its air when fully saturated with lime, a lime-water was made as strong as possible; four ounces of which were placed under the receiver of an air-pump, together with four ounces of common water in a vial of the same size; and, upon exhausting the receiver, without heating the vials, the air arose from each, in nearly the same quantity: from whence it is evident, that the air, which quick-lime attracts, is of a different kind from that which is mixed with water. And that it is also different from common elastic air, is sufficiently proved by daily experience; for lime-water, which soon attracts air, and forms a crust when exposed in open and shallow vessels, may be preserved, for any time, in bottles which are but slightly corked, or closed in such a manner as would allow free access to elastic air, were a vacuum formed in the bottle. Quick-lime therefore does not attract air when in its most ordinary form, but is capable of being joined to one particular species only, which is dispersed thro' the atmosphere, either in the shape of an exceedingly subtile powder, or more probably in that of an elastic fluid. To this I have given the name of fixed air, and perhaps very improperly; but I thought it better to use a word already familiar in philosophy, than to invent a new name, before we be more fully acquainted with the nature and properties of this substance, which will probably be the subject of my further inquiry. . . .

———

JOSEPH PRIESTLEY
1733–1804

THE PREPARATION OF DEPHLOGISTICATED
AIR (OXYGEN) AND ITS RÔLE IN
COMBUSTION

PRIESTLEY differs from many of his immediate predecessors in not approaching chemistry from a background of medicine; he became a scientist almost by chance. In more than his science, however, his life demonstrated vividly how far freedom of thought had been carried since the breakdown of the authority of scholasticism. He was a radical in politics, sympathizing with the French and American Revolutions, and a Dissenter in religion. For much of his life he worked in cities which were growing under the influence of the Industrial Revolution, and his interests lay there rather than in London. While in Birmingham, he was a member of a provincial academy, the Lunar Society, a philosophical group which met once a month near to full moon 'so as to have the benefit of the light on returning home'. Here he met James Watt and Mathew Boulton, Erasmus Darwin the grandfather of Charles, Wedgwood the potter, Galton the manufacturer, Baskerville who improved printing type.*

Priestley was born at Fieldhead, near Leeds, into a staunch Calvinist family, and was intended to enter the ministry. His unorthodox views on original sin and eternal damnation led him, however, to the Unitarian ministry. He later taught at Warrington Academy and heard a few lectures in elementary chemistry, but his interest in science was roused by meeting Benjamin Franklin, and discussing electricity with him.

Some of his early chemical experiments were done in a brewery near his home after he moved to a ministry in

*This book is set in Baskerville type.

Leeds. Here he identified the carbon dioxide produced by fermentation with Black's 'fixed air', and showed that, dissolved merely in water, it made an acceptable drink, soda-water.

Historically, Priestley's most important discovery was that of oxygen, which he named according to its properties, 'dephlogisticated air'. He made it by heating mercuric oxide (red oxide of mercury), *mercurius calcinatus per se*, in a closed glass container; this was achieved by focusing the sun's rays on to the oxide by means of a large burning glass. Oxygen had been discovered by Scheele (by a different method) a little earlier, but Priestley's results were the first to be published.

Priestley examined the effects of the new air on combustion and respiration. He showed that burning candles and breathing animals used up this air when in a closed container, but that it was regenerated by growing green plants. After breathing it himself, he wrote: 'Who can tell but that in time this pure air may become a fashionable article in luxury. Hitherto only my mice and myself have had the breathing of it.' But he also added 'as a candle burns out much faster in this air than in common air, so we might live out too fast. A moralist at least may say that the air which nature has provided for us is as good as we deserve.'

In 1791 Priestley's house, library, and laboratory in Birmingham were destroyed by fire at the hands of a mob who feared that those who opposed Church and King might start in England a revolution like that which was taking place in France. Three years later he left England for the United States where he remained for the rest of his life. He was offered a Chair of Chemistry and a Unitarian ministry. He chose, however, to set up his own laboratory in Northumberland, Pennsylvania, and to continue his experiments. During this period he prepared carbon monoxide.

His chemical discoveries were interpreted entirely in terms of the phlogiston theory, which he championed until his death, but he was able to share his advanced political and religious ideas in comfort with men like Washington, Jefferson, and John Adams.

The two readings are taken from the six-volume *Experiments and Observations on Different Kinds of Air* published in 1775. The first reading will be found in Alembic Club Reprints No. 7.

¶ SECTION III *Of Dephlogisticated Air, and the Constitution of the Atmosphere*

The contents of this section will furnish a very striking illustration of the truth of a remark, which I have more than once made in my philosophical writings, and which can hardly be too often repeated, as it tends greatly to encourage philosophical investigations; viz. that more is owing to what we call *chance*, that is, philosophically speaking, to the observation of *events arising from unknown causes*, than to any proper *design*, or pre-conceived *theory* in this business. This does not appear in the works of those who write *synthetically* upon these subjects; but would, I doubt not, appear very strikingly in those who are the most celebrated for their philosophical acumen, did they write *analytically* and ingenuously.

For my own part, I will frankly acknowledge, that, at the commencement of the experiments recited in this section, I was so far from having formed any hypothesis that led to the discoveries I made in pursuing them, that they would have appeared very improbable to me had I been told of them; and when the decisive facts did at length obtrude themselves upon my notice, it was very slowly, and with great hesitation, that I yielded to the evidence of my senses. And yet, when I re-consider the matter, and compare my last discoveries relating to the constitution of the atmosphere with the first, I see the closest and the easiest connexion in the world between them, so as to wonder that I should not have been led immediately from the one to the other. That this was not the case, I attribute to the force of prejudice, which, unknown to ourselves, biasses not only our *judgments*, properly so called, but even the perceptions of our senses: for we may take a maxim so strongly for granted, that the plainest evidence of sense will not intirely change, and often hardly modify our persuasions; and the more ingenious a man is, the more effectually he is entangled in his errors; his ingenuity only helping him to deceive himself, by evading the force of truth.

There are, I believe, very few maxims in philosophy that have laid firmer hold upon the mind, than that air, meaning atmospherical air (free from various foreign matters, which were always supposed to be dissolved, and intermixed with it) is a *simple elementary substance*, indestructible, and unalterable, at least as much so as water is supposed to be. In the course of my inquiries, I was, however, soon satisfied that atmospherical air is not an unalterable thing; for that the phlogiston with which it becomes loaded from bodies burning in it, and animals breathing it, and various other chemical processes, so far alters and depraves it, as to render it altogether unfit for inflammation, respiration, and other purposes to which it is subservient; and I had discovered that agitation in water, the process of vegetation, and probably other natural processes, by taking out the superfluous phlogiston, restore it to its original purity. But I own I had no idea of the possibility of going any farther in this way, and thereby procuring air purer than the best common air. I might, indeed, have naturally imagined that such would be air that should contain less phlogiston than the air of the atmosphere; but I had no idea that such a composition was possible.

It will be seen in my last publication, that, from the experiments which I made on the marine acid air, I was led to conclude that common air consisted of some acid (and I naturally inclined to the acid that I was then operating upon) and phlogiston; because the union of this acid vapour and phlogiston made inflammable air; and inflammable air, by agitation in water, ceases to be inflammable, and becomes respirable. And though I could never make it quite so good as common air, I thought it very probable that vegetation, in more favourable circumstances than any in which I could apply it, or some other natural process, might render it more pure.

Upon this, which no person can say was an improbable supposition, was founded my conjecture, of volcanos having given birth to the atmosphere of this planet, supplying it with a permanent air, first inflammable, then deprived of its inflammability by agitation in water, and farther purified by vegetation.

Several of the known phenomena of the *nitrous acid* might have led me to think, that this was more proper for the constitution of the atmosphere than the marine acid: but my thoughts had got into a different train, and nothing but a series of observations, which I shall now distinctly relate, compelled me to adopt another hypothesis, and brought me, in a way of which I had then no idea, to the solution of the great problem, which my reader will perceive I have had in view ever since my discovery that the atmospherical air is alterable, and therefore that it is not an elementary substance, but a *composition*, viz. what this composition is, or *what is the thing that we breathe*, and how is it to be made from its constituent principles.

At the time of my former publication, I was not possessed of a *burning lens* of any considerable force; and for want of one, I could not possibly make many of the experiments that I had projected, and which, in theory, appeared very promising. I had, indeed, a *mirror* of force sufficient for my purpose. But the nature of this instrument is such, that it cannot be applied, with effect, except upon substances that are capable of being suspended, or resting on a very slender support. It cannot be directed at all upon any substance in the form of *powder*, nor hardly upon any thing that requires to be put into a vessel of quicksilver; which appears to me to be the most accurate method of extracting air from a great variety of substances, as was explained in the Introduction to this volume. But having afterwards procured a lens of twelve inches diameter, and twenty inches focal distance, I proceeded with great alacrity to examine, by the help of it, what kind of air a great variety of substances, natural and factitious, would yield, putting them into the vessels represented fig. *a*,* which I filled with quicksilver, and kept inverted in a bason of the same. Mr Warltire, a good chymist, and lecturer in natural philosophy, happening to be at that time in Calne, I explained my views to him, and was furnished by him with many substances, which I could not otherwise have procured.

With this apparatus, after a variety of other experiments, an account of which will be found in its proper place, on the first of August, 1774, I endeavoured to extract air from *mercurius calcinatus per se;* and I presently found that, by means of this lens, air was expelled from it very readily. Having got about three or four times as much as the bulk of my materials, I admitted water to it, and found that it was not imbibed by it. But what surprized me more than I can well express, was, that a candle burned in this air with a remarkably vigorous flame, very much like that enlarged flame with which a candle burns in nitrous air, exposed to iron or liver of sulphur; but as I had got nothing like this remarkable appearance from any kind of air besides this particular modification of nitrous air, and I knew no nitrous acid was used in the preparation of *mercurius calcinatus*, I was utterly at a loss how to account for it.

In this case, also, though I did not give sufficient attention to the circumstance at that time, the flame of the candle, besides being larger, burned with more splendor and heat than in that species of nitrous air; and a piece of red-hot wood sparkled in it, exactly like paper dipped in a solution of nitre, and it consumed very fast; an experiment which I had never thought of trying with nitrous air.

At the same time that I made the above mentioned experiment, I extracted a quantity of air, with the very same property, from the common *red precipitate*, which being produced by a solution of mercury in spirit of nitre, made me conclude that this peculiar property, being similar to that of the modification of nitrous air above mentioned,

*See Plate 7.

depended upon something being communicated to it by the nitrous acid; and since the *mercurius calcinatus* is produced by exposing mercury to a certain degree of heat, where common air has access to it, I likewise concluded that this substance had collected something of *nitre*, in that state of heat, from the atmosphere.

This, however, appearing to me much more extraordinary than it ought to have done, I entertained some suspicion that the *mercurius calcinatus*, on which I had made my experiments, being bought at a common apothecary's, might, in fact, be nothing more than red precipitate; though, had I been any thing of a practical chymist, I could not have entertained any such suspicion. However, mentioning this suspicion to Mr Warltire, he furnished me with some that he had kept for a specimen of the preparation, and which, he told me, he could warrant to be genuine. This being treated in the same manner as the former, only by a longer continuance of heat, I extracted much more air from it than from the other.

This experiment might have satisfied any moderate sceptic: but, however, being at Paris in the October following, and knowing that there were several very eminent chymists in that place, I did not omit the opportunity, by means of my friend Mr Magellan, to get an ounce of *mercurius calcinatus* prepared by Mr Cadet, of the genuineness of which there could not possibly be any suspicion; and at the same time, I frequently mentioned my surprize at the kind of air which I had got from this preparation to Mr Lavoisier, Mr le Roy, and several other philosophers, who honoured me with their notice in that city; and who, I dare say, cannot fail to recollect the circumstance.

At the same time, I had no suspicion that the air which I had got from the *mercurius calcinatus* was even wholesome, so far was I from knowing what it was that I had really found; taking it for granted, that it was nothing more than such kind of air as I had brought nitrous air to be by the processes above mentioned; and in this air I have observed that a candle would burn sometimes quite naturally, and sometimes with a beautiful enlarged flame, and yet remain perfectly noxious.

At the same time that I had got the air above mentioned from *mercurius calcinatus* and the red precipitate, I had got the same kind from *red lead* or *minium*. In this process, that part of the minium on which the focus of the lens had fallen, turned yellow. One third of the air, in this experiment, was readily absorbed by water, but, in the remainder, a candle burned very strongly, and with a crackling noise.

That fixed air is contained in red lead I had observed before; for I had expelled it by the heat of a candle, and had found it to be very pure. I imagine it requires more heat than I then used to expel any of the other kind of air.

This experiment with *red lead* confirmed me more in my suspicion, that the *mercurius calcinatus* must get the property of yielding this kind of air from the atmosphere, the process by which that preparation, and this of red lead is made, being similar. As I never make the least secret of any thing that I observe, I mentioned this experiment also, as well as those with the *mercurius calcinatus*, and the red precipitate, to all my philosophical acquaintance at Paris, and elsewhere; having no idea, at that time, to what these remarkable facts would lead.

Presently after my return from abroad, I went to work upon the *mercurius calcinatus*, which I had procured from Mr Cadet; and, with a very moderate degree of heat, I got from about one fourth of an ounce of it, an ounce-measure of air, which I observed to be not readily imbibed, either by the substance itself from which it had been expelled (for I suffered them to continue a long time together before I transferred the air to any other place) or by water, in which I suffered this air to stand a considerable time before I made any experiment upon it.

In this air, as I had expected, a candle burned with a vivid flame; but what I observed new at this time (Nov. 19), and which surprized me no less than the fact I had discovered before, was, that, whereas a few moments agitation in water will deprive the modified nitrous air of its property of admitting a candle to burn in it; yet, after more than ten times as much agitation as would be sufficient to produce this alteration in the nitrous air, no sensible change was produced in this. A candle still burned in it with a strong flame; and it did not, in the least, diminish common air, which I have observed that nitrous air, in this state, in some measure, does.

But I was much more surprized, when, after two days, in which this air had continued in contact with water (by which it was diminished about one twentieth of its bulk) I agitated it violently in water about five minutes, and found that a candle still burned in it as well as in common air. The same degree of agitation would have made phlogisticated nitrous air fit for respiration indeed, but it would certainly have extinguished a candle.

These facts fully convinced me, that there must be a very material difference between the constitution of the air from *mercurius calcinatus*, and that of phlogisticated nitrous air, notwithstanding their resemblance in some particulars. But though I did not doubt that the air from *mercurius calcinatus* was fit for respiration, after being agitated in water, as every kind of air without exception, on which I had tried the experiment, had been, I still did not suspect that it was respirable in the first instance; so far was I from having any idea of this air being, what it really was, much superior, in this respect, to the air of the atmosphere.

In this ignorance of the real nature of this kind of air, I continued from this time (November) to the first of March following; having, in the mean time, been intent upon my experiments on the vitriolic acid air above recited, and the various modifications of air produced by spirit of nitre, an account of which will follow. But in the course of this month, I not only ascertained the nature of this kind of air, though very gradually, but was led by it to the complete discovery of the constitution of the air we breathe.

Till this first of March, 1775, I had so little suspicion of the air from *mercurius calcinatus,* etc. being wholesome, that I had not even thought of applying to it the test of nitrous air; but thinking (as my reader must imagine I frequently must have done) on the candle burning in it after long agitation in water, it occurred to me at last to make the experiment; and putting one measure of nitrous air to two measures of this air, I found, not only that it was diminished, but that it was diminished quite as much as common air, and that the redness of the mixture was likewise equal to that of a similar mixture of nitrous and common air.

After this I had no doubt but that the air from *mercurius calcinatus* was fit for respiration, and that it had all the other properties of genuine common air. But I did not take notice of what I might have observed, if I had not been so fully possessed by the notion of there being no air better than common air, that the redness was really deeper, and the diminution something greater than common air would have admitted.

Moreover, this advance in the way of truth, in reality, threw me back into error, making me give up the hypothesis I had first formed, viz. that the *mercurius calcinatus* had extracted spirit of nitre from the air; for I now concluded that all the constituent parts of the air were equally, and in their proper proportion, imbibed in the preparation of this substance, and also in the process of making red lead. For at the same time that I made the above-mentioned experiment on the air from *mercurius calcinatus*, I likewise observed that the air which I had extracted from red lead, after the fixed air was washed out of it, was of the same nature, being diminished by nitrous air like common air: but, at the same time, I was puzzled to find that air from the red precipitate was diminished in the same manner, though the process for making this substance is quite different from that of making the two others. But to this circumstance I happened not to give much attention.

I wish my reader be not quite tired with the frequent repetition of the word *surprize*, and others of similar import; but I must go on in that style a little longer. For the next day I was more surprised than ever I had been before, with finding that, after the above-mentioned mixture of nitrous air and the air from *mercurius calcinatus*, had stood all night, (in which time the whole diminution must have taken place; and, consequently, had it been common air, it must have been made perfectly noxious, and intirely unfit for respiration or inflammation) a candle burned in it, and even better than in common air.

I cannot, at this distance of time, recollect what it was that I had in view in making this experiment; but I know I had no expectation of the real issue of it. Having acquired a considerable degree of readiness in making experiments of this kind, a very slight and evanescent motive would be sufficient to induce me to do it. If, however, I had not happened, for some other purpose, to have had a lighted candle before me, I should probably never have made the trial; and the whole train of my future experiments relating to this kind of air might have been prevented.

Still, however, having no conception of the real cause of this phenomenon, I considered it as something very extraordinary; but as a property that was peculiar to air extracted from these substances, and *adventitious;* and I always spoke of the air to my acquaintance as being substantially the same thing with common air. I particularly remember my telling Dr Price, that I was myself perfectly satisfied of its being common air, as it appeared to be so by the test of nitrous air; though, for the satisfaction of others, I wanted a mouse to make proof quite complete.

On the eighth of this month I procured a mouse, and put it into a glass vessel, containing two ounce-measures of the air from *mercurius calcinatus*. Had it been common air, a full-grown mouse, as this was, would have lived in it about a quarter of an hour. In this air, however, my mouse lived a full half hour; and though it was taken out seemingly dead, it appeared to have been only exceedingly chilled; for, upon being held to the fire, it presently revived, and appeared not to have received any harm from the experiment.

By this I was confirmed in my conclusion, that the air extracted from *mercurius calcinatus*, etc. was, *at least, as good* as common air; but I did not certainly conclude that it was any *better;* because, though one mouse would live only a quarter of an hour in a given quantity of air, I knew it was not impossible but that another mouse might have lived in it half an hour; so little accuracy is there in this method of ascertaining the goodness of air: and indeed I have never had recourse to it for my own satisfaction, since the discovery of that most ready, accurate, and elegant test that nitrous air furnishes. But in this case I had a view to publishing the most generally-satisfactory account of my experiments that the nature of the thing would admit of.

This experiment with the mouse, when I had reflected upon it some time, gave me so much suspicion that the air into which I had put it was better than common air, that I was induced, the day after, to apply the test of nitrous air to a small part of that very quantity of air which the mouse had breathed so long; so that, had it been common air, I was satisfied it must have been very nearly, if not altogether, as noxious as possible, so as not to be affected by nitrous air; when, to my surprize again, I found that though it had been breathed so long, it was still better than common air. For after mixing it with nitrous air, in the usual proportion of two to one, it was diminished in the proportion of $4\frac{1}{2}$ to $3\frac{1}{2}$; that is, the nitrous air had made it two ninths less than before, and this in a very short space of time; whereas I had never found that, in the longest time, any common air was reduced more than one fifth of its bulk by any proportion of nitrous air, nor more than one fourth by any phlogistic process whatever. Thinking of this extraordinary fact upon my pillow, the next morning I put another measure of nitrous air to the same mixture, and, to my utter astonishment, found that it was farther diminished to almost one half of its original quantity. I then put a third measure to it; but this did not diminish it any farther: but, however, left it one measure less than it was even after the mouse had been taken out of it.

Being now fully satisfied that this air, even after the mouse had breathed it half an hour, was much better than common air; and having a quantity of it still left, sufficient for the experiment, viz. an ounce-measure and a half, I put the mouse into it; when I observed that it seemed to feel no shock upon being put into it, evident signs of which would have been visible, if the air had not been very wholesome; but that it remained perfectly at its ease another full half hour, when I took it out quite lively and vigorous. Measuring the air next day, I found it to be reduced from $1\frac{1}{2}$ to $\frac{2}{3}$ of an ounce-measure. And after this, if I remember well (for in my *register* of the day I only find it noted, that it was *considerably diminished* by nitrous air) it was nearly as good as common air. It was evident, indeed, from the mouse having been taken out quite vigorous, that the air could not have been rendered very noxious.

For my farther satisfaction I procured another mouse, and putting it into less than two ounce-measures of air extracted from *mercurius calcinatus* and air from red precipitate (which, having found them to be of the same quality, I had mixed together) it lived three quarters of an hour. But not having had the precaution to set the vessel in a warm place, I suspect that the mouse died of cold. However, as it had lived three times as long as it could probably have lived in the same quantity of common air, and I did not expect much accuracy from this kind of test, I did not think it necessary to make any more experiments with mice.

Being now fully satisfied of the superior goodness of this kind of air, I proceeded to measure that degree of purity, with as much accuracy as I could, by the test of nitrous air; and I began with putting one measure of nitrous air to two measures of this air, as if I had been examining common air; and now I observed that the diminution was evidently greater than common air would have suffered by the same treatment. A second measure of nitrous air reduced it to two thirds of its original quantity, and a third measure to one half. Suspecting that the diminution could not proceed much farther, I then added only half a measure of nitrous air, by which it was diminished still more; but not much, and another half measure made it more than half of its original quantity; so that, in this case, two measures of this air took more than two measures of nitrous air, and yet remained less than half of what it was. Five measures brought it pretty exactly to its original dimensions.

At the same time, air from the *red precipitate* was diminished in the same proportion as that from *mercurius calcinatus*, five measures of nitrous air being received by two measures of this without any increase of dimensions. Now as common air takes about one half of its bulk of nitrous air, before it begins to receive any addition to its dimensions from more nitrous air, and this air took more than four half-measures before it ceased to be diminished by more nitrous air, and even five half-measures made no addition to its original dimensions, I conclude that it was between four and five times as good as common air. It will be seen that I have since procured air better than this, even between five and six times as good as the best common air that I have ever met with. . . .

¶ SECTION VII *Of the Purification of Air by Plants and the Influence of Light on that Process*

One of my earliest observations on the subject of air, but made casually, when, in fact, I expected a contrary result from the process, was the purification of air injured by respiration or putrefaction, by the vegetation of plants. But at that time I was altogether ignorant of the part that *light* had to act in the business. At the publication of the experiments recited in the last section, I had fully ascertained the influence of light in the production of dephlogisticated air in water by means of a *green substance*, which I at first supposed to be a plant, but not being able to discover the form of one, I contended myself with calling it simply *green matter*.

Several of my friends, however, better skilled in botany than myself, never entertained any doubt of its being a plant; and I had afterwards the fullest conviction that it must be one. Mr Bewly has lately observed the regular form of it by a microscope. My own eyes having always been weak, I have, as much as possible, avoided the use of a microscope.

The principal reason that made me question whether this green matter was a plant, besides my not being able to discover the form of it, was its being produced, as I then thought, in a phial close stopped. But this being only with a common cork, the seeds of this plant, which must float invisibly in the air, might have insinuated themselves through some unperceived fracture in it; or the seeds might have been contained in the water previous to its being put into the phial. Both Mr Bewly and myself found, in the course of the last summer, that when distilled water was exposed to the sun, in phials filled in part with quicksilver, and in part with distilled water, and inverted in basons of quicksilver, none of this green matter was ever produced; no seed of this plant having been able to penetrate through the mercury, to reach the water incumbent upon it, though, in several cases, it will be seen, that these seeds diffuse and insinuate themselves, in a manner that is truly wonderful.

Without light, it is well known, that no plant can thrive; and if it do grow at all in the dark, it is always white, and is, in all other respects, in a weak and sickly state. Healthy plants are probably in a state similar to that of *sleep* in the absence of light, and do not resume their proper functions, but by the influence of light, and especially the action of the rays of the sun. This was the reason why no green matter was ever produced by means of mere *warmth* in my former experiments, and that in jars standing in the same exposure, but covered so that the light had no access to them, no pure air was collected, none of the green matter being then found in them.

This I verified most completely by covering the greatest part of a glass jar with black sealing-wax, which made it thoroughly opaque; and besides answering that purpose better than brown paper, as I made the experiment before mentioned, did not imbibe any of the water, and therefore did not promote the evaporation of it. To be able to observe whether any air was collected in these jars, or not, the upper part of them was not coated with sealing-wax, but had a thick moveable cap of paper, which I could easily take off, and then inspect the surface of the water.

In order to satisfy myself as fully as possible with respect to this remarkable circumstance, I also made the following experiments, the results of which are, indeed, very decisive in favour of the influence of *light* in this case.

Having a large trough of water, full of recent green matter, giving air very copiously, so that all the surface of it was covered with froth, and jars filled with it, and inverted, collected great quantities of it, and very fast; I filled a jar with it, and, inverting it in a bason of the same, I placed it in a dark room. From that instant no more air was yielded by it, and in a few days it had a very offensive smell, the green vegetable matter with which it abounded being then all dead, and putrid.

Again, having filled a receiver with fresh pump water, and having waited till it was in a state of giving air copiously, I removed it into a dark room; and from that time the production of air from it intirely ceased. When I placed it again in the sun, it gave no air till about ten days after, when it had more green matter, the former plants being probably all dead; and no air could be produced till new ones were formed. . . .

It appears from these experiments, that air combined with water is liable to be phlogisticated by respiration, and to be dephlogisticated by vegetation, as much as air in an elastic state, out of water. For fishes, as I shall observe, foul the air contained in the water in which they are confined, and water plants now appear to purify it. This is no doubt one of the great uses of weeds, and other aquatic plants, with which fresh water lakes, and even seas abound, as well as their serving for food to a great number of fishes.

———

CARL WILHELM SCHEELE
1742–86

THE ISOLATION OF OXYGEN AND THE
COMPOSITION OF THE ATMOSPHERE

IN 1774 Scheele wrote a letter of thanks to Lavoisier for a copy of one of Lavoisier's works and suggested an experiment in which dry silver carbonate is heated with a burning glass and the gas given off is collected. 'You will see,' he wrote, 'how much air is produced in which a candle will burn and an animal will live.' This letter leaves no doubt that Scheele had prepared oxygen and observed some of its properties before Priestley's independent discovery. In his experiments Scheele had isolated oxygen by the action of heat on silver carbonate, mercuric carbonate, mercuric oxide, manganese dioxide, and other substances.

The life of Scheele was a perpetual struggle against poverty and ill health, but this failed to restrain a man possessed of unusual powers of observation. Scheele was born at Stralsund, Pomerania, a Swedish province at the time of his birth. His formal schooling was brief, and at the age of fourteen he was apprenticed to an apothecary. In the eight years of his service, his master encouraged him to study chemistry and pharmacy and to experiment with the many substances to be found in the stock-in-trade of the pharmacist. Having served his apprenticeship, Scheele worked for the next ten years for two other apothecaries and finally in 1775 he purchased his own business. His entire life was devoted to the study of chemistry, and his discoveries earned for him the title of the greatest experimental chemist of the eighteenth century.

Scheele was remote from the circles of Edinburgh, London, Paris, and Northern Italy whose members freely communicated their discoveries. The absence of regular scientific periodicals left him uninformed about the work of other scientists in the field. Like many other experimenters, he accumulated his data until he had enough material for a book; hence, although he had actually isolated what he called 'fire-air', the discovery was not known, except perhaps to Lavoisier, until Scheele's great *Chemical Treatise on Air and Fire* was published in 1777. It is certain that Scheele had not seen Priestley's book and was not aware of his discoveries.

The *Chemical Treatise on Air and Fire* (translated by Leonard Dobbin in 1931) is the source of the selections chosen* to illustrate Scheele's work. They reveal quite clearly the correctness of Scheele's methods. He was able to account for the phenomena he observed in phlogistic terms. In addition to the detailed study of oxygen and its chemical behaviour he described his discovery of the composition of the atmosphere and a host of other new observations, in which he probably again anticipated Priestley. One of the most notable of these was his recognition of the chemical effect of light upon compounds of silver, in which, in effect, he provided a basis for the invention of photography. His other great discoveries included chlorine, arsenic, tartaric, citric, benzoic and lactic acids, glycerine, and prussic acid. He recognized manganese as a metal and studied the chemical properties of silica, magnesia, oxalic acid, and fluorspar as well as molybdic and tungstic acids.

Scheele was made a Fellow of the Swedish Royal Academy of Sciences two years before his *Treatise* was published, an honour never before or since bestowed upon a pharmacist. He poured his life's blood into his chemical experiments, exposing himself to all types of chemicals and fumes, unquestionably undermining his health in his burning zeal for science. He died in his forty-fifth year, a victim, in a sense, of his own inner fire.

⁋ *On Air and Fire*

1. It is the object and chief business of chemistry to skilfully

*See also Alembic Club Reprints No. 8.

separate substances into their constituents, to discover their properties, and to compound them in different ways.

How difficult it is, however, to carry out such operations with the greatest accuracy, can only be unknown to one who either has never undertaken this occupation, or at least has not done so with sufficient attention.

2. Hitherto chemical investigators are not agreed as to how many elements or fundamental materials compose all substances. In fact this is one of the most difficult problems; some indeed hold that there remains no further hope of searching out the elements of substances. Poor comfort for those who feel their greatest pleasure in the investigation of natural things! Far is he mistaken, who endeavours to confine chemistry, this noble science, within such narrow bounds! Others believe that earth and phlogiston are the things from which all material nature has derived its origin. The majority seem completely attached to the peripatetic elements.

3. I must admit that I have bestowed no little trouble upon this matter in order to obtain a clear conception of it. One may reasonably be amazed at the numerous ideas and conjectures which authors have recorded on the subject, especially when they give a decision respecting the fiery phenomenon; and this very matter was of the greatest importance to me. I perceived the necessity of a knowledge of fire, because without this it is not possible to make any experiment; and without fire and heat it is not possible to make use of the action of any solvent. I began accordingly to put aside all explanations of fire; I undertook a multitude of experiments in order to fathom this beautiful phenomenon as fully as possible. I soon found, however, that one could not form any true judgement regarding the phenomena which fire presents, without a knowledge of the air. I saw, after carrying out a series of experiments, that air really enters into the mixture of fire, and with it forms a constituent of flame and of sparks. I learned accordingly that a treatise like this, on fire, could not be drawn up with proper completeness without taking the air also into consideration.

4. Air is that fluid invisible substance which we continually breathe, which surrounds the whole surface of the earth, is very elastic, and possesses weight. It is always filled with an astonishing quantity of all kinds of exhalations, which are so finely subdivided in it that they are scarcely visible even in the sun's rays. Water vapours always have the preponderance amongst these foreign particles. The air, however, is also mixed with another elastic substance resembling air, which differs from it in numerous properties, and is, with good reason, called aerial acid by Professor Bergman. It owes its presence to organized bodies, destroyed by putrefaction or combustion.

5. Nothing has given philosophers more trouble for some years than just this delicate acid or so-called fixed air. Indeed it is not surprising that the conclusions which one draws from the properties of this elastic acid are not favourable to all who are prejudiced by previously conceived opinions. These defenders of the Paracelsian doctrine believe that the air is in itself unalterable; and, with Hales, that it really unites with substances thereby losing its elasticity; but that it regains its original nature as soon as it is driven out of these by fire or fermentation. But since they see that the air so produced is endowed with properties quite different from common air, they conclude, without experiment proofs, that this air has united with foreign materials, and that it must be purified from these admixed foreign particles by agitation and filtration with various liquids. I believe that there would be no hesitation in accepting this opinion, if one could only demonstrate clearly by experiments that a given quantity of air is capable of being completely converted into fixed or other kind of air by the admixture of foreign materials; but since this has not been done, I hope I do not err if I assume as many kinds of air as experiment reveals to me. For when I have collected an elastic fluid, and observe concerning it that its expansive power is increased by heat and diminished by cold, while it still uniformly retains its elastic fluidity, but also discover in it properties and behaviour different from those of common air, then I consider myself justified in believing that this is a peculiar kind of air. I say that air thus collected must retain its elasticity even in the greatest cold, because otherwise an innumerable multitude of varieties of air would have to be assumed, since it is very probable that all substances can be converted by excessive heat into a vapour resembling air.

6. Substances which are subjected to putrefaction or to destruction by means of fire diminish, and at the same time consume, a part of the air; sometimes it happens that they perceptibly increase the bulk of the air, and sometimes finally that they neither increase nor diminish a given quantity of air – phenomena which are certainly remarkable. Conjectures can here determine nothing with certainty, at least they can only bring small satisfaction to a chemical philosopher, who must have his proofs in his hands. Who does not see the necessity of making experiments in this case, in order to obtain light concerning this secret of nature?

7. *General properties of ordinary air.*

(1) Fire must burn for a certain time in a given quantity of air. (2) If, so far as can be seen, this fire does not produce during combustion any fluid resembling air, then, after the fire has gone out of itself, the quantity of air must be diminished between a third and a fourth part. (3) It must not unite with common water. (4) All kinds of animals must live for a certain time in a confined quantity of air. (5) Seeds, as for example peas, in a given quantity of similarly confined air, must strike roots and attain a certain height with the aid of some water and of a moderate heat.

Consequently, when I have a fluid resembling air in its external appearance, and find that it has not the properties mentioned, even when only one of them is wanting, I feel convinced that it is not ordinary air.

8. *Air must be composed of elastic fluids of two kinds.*

First Experiment. I dissolved one ounce of alkaline liver of sulphur in eight ounces of water; I poured 4 ounces of this solution into an empty bottle capable of holding 24 ounces of water, and closed it most securely with a cork; I then inverted the bottle and placed the neck in a small vessel with water; in this position I allowed it to stand for 14 days. During this time the solution had lost a part of its red colour and had also deposited some sulphur: afterwards I took the bottle and held it in the same position in a larger vessel with water, so that the mouth was under and the bottom above the water-level, and withdrew the cork under the water; immediately water rose with violence into the bottle. I closed the bottle again, removed it from the water, and weighed the fluid which it contained. There were 10 ounces. After subtracting from this the 4 ounces of solution of sulphur there remain 6 ounces, consequently it is apparent from this experiment that of 20 parts of air 6 parts have been lost in 14 days.

9. *Second Experiment*. (*a*) I repeated the preceding experiment with the same quantity of liver of sulphur, but with this difference that I only allowed the bottle to stand a week, tightly closed. I then found that of 20 parts of air only 4 had been lost. (*b*) On another occasion I allowed the very same bottle to stand 4 months; the solution still possessed a somewhat dark yellow colour. But no more air had been lost than in the first experiment, that is to say 6 parts.

10. *Third Experiment*. I mixed 2 ounces of caustic ley, which was prepared from alkali of tartar and unslaked lime and did not precipitate lime water, with half an ounce of the preceding solution of sulphur which likewise did not precipitate lime water. This mixture had a yellow colour. I poured it into the same bottle, and after this had stood 14 days, well closed, I found the mixture entirely without colour and also without precipitate. I was enabled to conclude that the air in this bottle had likewise diminished, from the fact that air rushed into the bottle with a hissing sound after I had made a small hole in the cork.

11. *Fourth Experiment*. (*a*) I took 4 ounces of a solution of sulphur in lime water; I poured this solution into a bottle and closed it tightly. After 14 days the yellow colour had disappeared, and of 20 parts of air 4 parts had been lost. The solution contained no sulphur, but had allowed a precipitate to fall which was chiefly gypsum. (*b*) Volatile liver of

sulphur likewise diminishes the bulk of air. (c) Sulphur, however, and volatile spirit of sulphur, undergo no alteration in
it.

12. Fifth Experiment. I hung up over burning sulphur, linen
rags which were dipped in a solution of alkali of tartar. After
the alkali was saturated with the volatile acid, I placed the
rags in a flask, and closed the mouth most carefully with a
wet bladder. After 3 weeks had elapsed I found the bladder
strongly pressed down; I inverted the flask, held its mouth
in water, and made a hole in the bladder; thereupon water
rose with violence into the flask and filled the fourth part.

13. Sixth Experiment. I collected in a bladder the nitrous air
which arises on the dissolution of the metals in nitrous acid,
and after I had tied the bladder tightly I laid it in a flask and
secured the mouth very carefully with a wet bladder. The
nitrous air gradually lost its elasticity, the bladder collapsed,
and became yellow as if corroded by *aqua fortis*. After 14 days
I made a hole in the bladder tied over the flask, having previously held it, inverted, under water; the water rose rapidly
into the flask, and it remained only $\frac{2}{3}$ empty.

14. Seventh Experiment. (a) I immersed the mouth of a flask
in a vessel with oil of turpentine. The oil rose in the flask a
few lines every day. After the lapse of 14 days the fourth part
of the flask was filled with it; I allowed it to stand for 3 weeks
longer, but the oil did not rise higher. All those oils which
dry in the air, and become converted into resinous substances, possess this property. Oil of turpentine, however,
and linseed oil rise up sooner if the flask is previously rinsed
out with a concentrated sharp ley. (b) I poured 2 ounces of
colourless and transparent animal oil of Dippel into a bottle
and closed it very tightly; after the expiry of two months the
oil was thick and black. I then held the bottle, inverted,
under water and drew out the cork; the bottle immediately
became $\frac{1}{4}$ filled with water.

15. Eighth Experiment. (a) I dissolved 2 ounces of vitriol of
iron in 32 ounces of water, and precipitated this solution
with a caustic ley. After the precipitate had settled, I poured
away the clear fluid and put the dark green precipitate of

iron so obtained, together with the remaining water, into the before-mentioned bottle (§8), and closed it tightly. After 14 days (during which time I shook the bottle frequently), this green calx of iron had acquired the colour of crocus of iron, and of 40 parts of air 12 had been lost. (*b*) When iron filings are moistened with some water and preserved for a few weeks in a well closed bottle, a portion of the air is likewise lost. (*c*) The solution of iron in vinegar has the same effect upon air. In this case the vinegar permits the dissolved iron to fall out in the form of a yellow crocus, and becomes completely deprived of this metal. (*d*) The solution of copper prepared in closed vessels with spirit of salt likewise diminishes air. In none of the foregoing kinds of air can either a candle burn or the smallest spark glow.

16. It is seen from these experiments that phlogiston, the simple inflammable principle, is present in each of them. It is known that the air strongly attracts to itself the inflammable part of substances and deprives them of it: not only this may be seen from the experiments cited, but it is at the same time evident that on the transference of the inflammable substance to the air a considerable part of the air is lost. But that the inflammable substance alone is the cause of this action, is plain from this, that, according to the 10th paragraph, not the least trace of sulphur remains over, since, according to my experiments this colourless ley contains only some vitriolated tartar. The 11th paragraph likewise shows this. But since sulphur alone, and also the volatile spirit of sulphur, have no effect upon the air (§ 11 *c*), it is clear that the decomposition of liver of sulphur takes place according to the laws of double affinity – that is to say, that the alkalies and lime attract the vitriolic acid, and the air attracts the phlogiston.

It may also be seen from the above experiments, that a given quantity of air can only unite with, and at the same time saturate, a certain quantity of the inflammable substance: this is evident from the 9th paragraph, *letter b*. But whether the phlogiston which was lost by the substances was still present in the air left behind in the bottle, or whether the air which was lost had united and fixed itself with the materials such as liver of sulphur, oils, etc., are questions of importance.

From the first view, it would necessarily follow that the inflammable substance possessed the property of depriving the air of part of its elasticity, and that in consequence of this it becomes more closely compressed by the external air. In order now to help myself out of these uncertainties, I formed the opinion that any such air must be specifically heavier than ordinary air, both on account of its containing phlogiston and also of its greater condensation. But how perplexed was I when I saw that a very thin flask which was filled with this air, and most accurately weighed, not only did not counterpoise an equal quantity of ordinary air, but was even somewhat lighter. I then thought that the latter view might be admissible; but in that case it would necessarily follow also that the lost air could be separated again from the materials employed. None of the experiments cited seemed to me capable of showing this more clearly than that according to the 10th paragraph, because this residuum, as already mentioned, consists of vitriolated tartar and alkali. In order therefore to see whether the lost air had been converted into fixed air, I tried whether the latter showed itself when some of the caustic ley was poured into lime water; but in vain – no precipitation took place. Indeed, I tried in several ways to obtain the lost air from this alkaline mixture, but as the results were similar to the foregoing, in order to avoid prolixity I shall not cite these experiments. Thus much I see from the experiments mentioned, that the air consists of two fluids, differing from each other, the one of which does not manifest in the least the property of attracting phlogiston, while the other, which composes between the third and the fourth part of the whole mass of the air, is peculiarly disposed to such attraction. But where this latter kind of air has gone to after it has united with the inflammable substance, is a question which must be decided by further experiments, and not by conjectures.

We shall now see how the air behaves towards inflammable substances when they get into fiery motion. We shall first consider that kind of fire which does not give out during the combustion any fluid resembling air.

17. First Experiment. I placed 9 grains of phosphorus from urine in a thin flask, which was capable of holding 30 ounces of water, and closed its mouth very tightly. I then heated, with a burning candle, the part of the flask where the phosphorus lay; the phosphorus began to melt, and immediately afterwards took fire; the flask became filled with a white cloud, which attached itself to the sides like white flowers; this was the dry acid of phosphorus. After the flask had become cold again, I held it, inverted, under water and opened it; scarcely had this been done when the external air pressed water into the flask; this water amounted to 9 ounces.

18. Second Experiment. When I placed pieces of phosphorus in the same flask and allowed it to stand, closed, for 6 weeks, or until it no longer glowed, I found that $\frac{1}{3}$ of the air had been lost.

19. Third Experiment. I placed 3 teaspoonfuls of iron filings in a bottle capable of holding 2 ounces of water; to this I added an ounce of water, and gradually mixed with them half an ounce of oil of vitriol. A violent heating and fermentation took place. When the froth had somewhat subsided, I fixed into the bottle an accurately fitting cork, through which I had previously fixed a glass tube A (Fig. 1).* I placed this bottle in a vessel filled with hot water, *B B* (cold water would greatly retard the solution). I then approached a burning candle to the orifice of the tube, whereupon the inflammable air took fire and burned with a small yellowish-green flame. As soon as this had taken place, I took a small flask *C*, which was capable of holding 20 ounces of water, and held it so deep in the water that the little flame stood in the middle of the flask. The water at once began to rise gradually into the flask, and when the level had reached the point *D* the flame went out. Immediately afterwards the water began to sink again, and was entirely driven out of the flask. The space in the flask up to *D* contained 4 ounces, therefore

*See Plate 5.

the fifth part of the air had been lost. I poured a few ounces of lime water into the flask in order to see whether any aerial acid had also been produced during the combustion, but I did not find any. I made the same experiment with zinc filings, and it proceeded in every way similarly to that just mentioned. I shall demonstrate the constituents of this inflammable air further on; for, although it seems to follow from these experiments that it is only phlogiston, still other experiments are contrary to this.

We shall now see the behaviour of air towards that kind of fire which gives off, during the combustion, a fluid resembling air.

20. *Fourth Experiment.* It is well known that the flame of a candle absorbs air; but as it is very difficult, and, indeed, scarcely possible, to light a candle in a closed flask, the following experiment was made in the first place: I set a burning candle in a dish full of water; I then placed an inverted flask over this candle; at once there arose from the water large air bubbles, which were caused by the expansion, by heat, of the air in the flask. When the flame became somewhat smaller, the water began to rise in the flask; after it had gone out and the flask had become cold, I found the fourth part filled with water. This experiment was very undecisive to me, because I was not assured whether this fourth part of the air had not been driven out by the heat of the flame; since necessarily in that case the external air resting upon the water seeks equilibrium again after the flask has become cold, and presses the same measure of water into the flask as of air had been previously driven out by the heat. Accordingly, I made the following experiment:

21. *Fifth Experiment.* (a) I pressed upon the bottom of the dish A (Fig. 2)* a tough mass, of the thickness of two fingers, made of wax, resin, and turpentine melted together; in the middle I fastened a thick iron wire which reached to the middle of the flask B; upon the point of this wire C, I stuck a small wax candle, whose wick I had twisted together out of three slender threads. I then lighted the candle, and at the

*See Plate 5.

same time placed over it the inverted flask *B*, which I then pressed very deep into the mass. As soon as this was done, I filled the dish with water. After the flame was extinguished and everything had become quite cold, I opened the flask in the same position under the water, when 2 ounces of water entered; the flask held 160 ounces of water. Accordingly, there is wanting here so much air as occupies the space of 2 ounces of water. Has this air been absorbed by the inflammable substance, or has the heat of the small flame driven it out even before I could press the flask into the tough mass? The latter seems to have taken place in this case, as I conclude from the following: I took a small flask capable of holding 20 ounces of water; in this I caused a candle to burn as in the preceding; after everything had become cold, I opened this flask likewise under water, whereupon similarly nearly 2 ounces entered. Had the former 2 ounces measure of air been absorbed, then there should have been only 2 drachms measure absorbed in this experiment.

(*b*) I repeated the preceding experiment with the large flask in exactly the same way, except that I employed spirit of wine in place of the candle. I fastened three iron wires, which were of equal length and reached up to the middle of the flask, into the tough mass which was firmly pressed on to the bottom of the dish. Upon these wires I laid a four-cornered plate of metal, and upon this I placed a small vessel into which spirit of wine was poured. I set fire to this and placed the flask over it. After cooling, I observed that 3 ounces measure of air had been driven out by the heat of the flame.

(*c*) Upon the same stand I placed a few small glowing coals, and allowed them to go out in the same way under the flask. I found after cooling that the heat of the coals had driven out three and a half ounces measure of air.

These experiments seem to prove that the transference of phlogiston to the air does not always diminish its bulk, which, however, the experiments mentioned in §§ 8–16 show distinctly. But the following will show that that portion of the air which unites with the inflammable substances, and is

at the same time absorbed by it, is replaced by the newly
formed aerial acid.

*

24. *Experiments which prove that ordinary air, consisting of two
kinds of elastic fluids, can be compounded again after these have been
separated from each other by means of phlogiston.*

I have already stated in § 16 that I was not able to find
again the lost air. One might indeed object, that the lost air
still remains in the residual air which can no more unite
with phlogiston; for, since I have found that it is lighter than
ordinary air, it might be believed that the phlogiston united
with this air makes it lighter, as appears to be known already
from other experiments. But since phlogiston is a substance,
which always presupposes some weight, I much doubt whether such hypothesis has any foundation.

*

42. *First Experiment.* I filled a bottle which was capable of
holding 16 ounces of water with pure fire-air. ... I placed
the bottle, inverted, in a glass which was filled with a solution of liver of sulphur. The solution rose a little into the
bottle hour by hour, and after the lapse of 2 days the bottle
was filled with it.

43. *Second Experiment.* I mixed in a bottle 14 parts of that
air from which the fire-air had been removed by liver of
sulphur (§ 8), and which I have called vitiated air (§ 29),
with 4 parts of our fire-air, and placed the bottle, inverted
and open, in a vessel which was also filled with a solution of
liver of sulphur. After 14 days the 4 parts of fire-air were lost,
and the solution had risen into their place.

44. *Third Experiment.* After I had filled a bottle with our
air, I poured some colourless animal oil into it and closed it
tightly. After a few hours it had already become brown, and
by the next day black. It is no small inconvenience to preserve this oil white in apothecaries' shops. It is found necessary to pour this oil into small phials, and to preserve it most
carefully from the access of air. When such a colourless oil is
mixed with any acid, the acid, as well as the oil, becomes

black even in an hour, although it has been diluted with water. Even vinegar has the same effect. There is no other reason, therefore, why the oil becomes at once black in the air, than that the fire-air present in the air deprives it of its phlogiston, and thereby develops a subtle acid, previously united with this phlogiston, which produces the blackness.

45. *Fourth Experiment.* (a) Into a bottle of 7 ounces, which was filled with fire-air, I put a piece of phosphorus from urine and closed it with a cork. I then heated, by means of a burning candle, the place where the phosphorus lay; the phosphorus took fire with very great brilliancy. As soon as the flame had gone out, the bottle broke into fragments.

(b) As the bottle in the foregoing experiment was very thin, I repeated it with a somewhat thicker bottle, and after everything had become cold I wanted to take the cork out of the bottle under water. It was not possible for me to do this, however, so tightly did the external air press the cork into the bottle. Accordingly I forced it inside the bottle; thereupon water entered the bottle and filled it almost completely. Since the first bottle was only very thin, the reason that it was crushed must be ascribed to the external air.

(c) When I mixed vitiated air with one third of fire-air, and burned a piece of phosphorus in the mixture, only one third of it was absorbed.

*

49. I have mentioned (§ 16) that I found vitiated air lighter than ordinary air. Must it not follow from this that the fire-air is heavier than our air? As a matter of fact, I actually found, when I accurately weighed as much fire-air as occupied the space of 20 ounces of water, that this was almost 2 grains heavier than the same bulk of common air.

50. These experiments show, therefore, that this fire-air is just that air by means of which fire burns in common air; only it is there mixed with a kind of air which seems to possess no attraction at all for the inflammable substance, and this it is which places some hindrance in the way of the otherwise rapid and violent inflammation. And in fact, if air consisted of nothing but fire-air, water would surely ren-

der small service in extinguishing outbreaks of fire. Aerial acid mixed with this fire-air, has the same effect as vitiated air. I mixed one part of fire-air with four parts of aerial acid; in this mixture a candle still burned moderately well. The heat which lurks in the small interstices of the inflammable substance cannot possibly make up so much heat as is felt in fire; and I think I am not mistaken when I conclude from my experiments that the heat is really brought forth and produced in the first place from fire-air and the phlogiston of the inflammable substance. . . .

HENRY CAVENDISH
1731–1810

WATER IS SHOWN TO BE A COMPOUND
OF TWO GASES

ECCENTRICITY is often the hallmark of genius, for intense concentration is not always conducive to correct social behaviour. In modern scientific circles it is less easy to ignore public opinion and even the most brilliant of our scientists manage to accommodate themselves to the exigencies of community life, but the eighteenth and nineteenth centuries produced a number of men whose escapades enliven their biographies. Among these, Henry Cavendish is a notable example; a wealthy bachelor, consumed with scientific curiosity, he lived in the heart of London society but went to extreme and often absurd lengths to avoid the crowd. Shy of women especially (his female servants were required to keep out of his sight), he spent a lifetime in the laboratory and the library. One of his retreats was a house built into the branches of a tree in the square which now bears his name.

Out of this solitude came contributions to science which put Cavendish into the same rank as his great contemporaries, Black, Priestley, Scheele, and Lavoisier.

Cavendish was a most versatile investigator. Many of his researches were not revealed in his lifetime. His notes on some pioneer work in electricity, in which he anticipated Faraday, were found and published by Clerk Maxwell only in 1879. A detailed study of the chemistry of arsenic, made available in 1921, shows his priority over Scheele. His ingenious experiment to measure the density of the earth with the use of a torsion balance achieved such a remarkably precise result that it has not been appreciably improved upon since.

Our immediate interest is in Cavendish's studies of

carbon dioxide and hydrogen, which were published as researches on 'factitious air'. These works of first importance represented the last of the contributions to pneumatic chemistry which, begun by Black and continued by Scheele and Priestley, served as the experimental basis from which Lavoisier established the general structure of modern chemistry.

In his experiments on hydrogen, which he called 'inflammable air', Cavendish found that he could produce this gas by the action of metals such as zinc, iron, and tin on dilute acids, particularly hydrochloric and sulphuric. He used precise methods for collecting the gas over water and for measuring it, and he discovered that equal weights of the same metal yielded the same amount of gas whichever acid was used. His conclusions were not always accurate. Like many of his contemporaries, Cavendish assumed that the gas came from the metal and was either phlogiston or a compound of phlogiston with water.

In the selection which we have chosen to illustrate his experimental methods, Cavendish describes a repetition of an experiment of Priestley in which an explosion of inflammable air with common air produced a dew which lined the walls of the vessel. Priestley reported that a loss of weight occurred in this chemical reaction. Cavendish's experiment showed no loss of weight; the common air lost one-fifth of its volume, whereas all the inflammable air disappeared in giving rise to the dew. By burning hydrogen in air and collecting the resulting dew, Cavendish found in it the properties of water. He had, in fact, established that water is a compound, but he, like Priestley, did not realize the significance of his observation.

Cavendish's accurate quantitative studies entitle him to share the credit for the discovery with Lavoisier, who recognized its significance. Moreover, Cavendish, by further experiments along similar lines, was able to detect the existence of an unexplained residue which, a century later, was discovered to be the element *argon*. Cavendish measured this minute unknown as constituting 0·80 per cent of common air. Actually argon constitutes 0·94 per cent – a remarkable tribute to Càvendish's accurate researches.

The selection that follows is taken from 'Experiments on Air', published in *Philosophical Transactions*, Vol. 74 (1784), and can be found in Alembic Club Reprints No. 3.

¶ *Experiments on Air*

The following experiments were made principally with a view to find out the cause of the diminution which common air is well known to suffer by all the various ways in which it is phlogisticated, and to discover what becomes of the air thus lost or condensed; and as they seem not only to determine this point, but also to throw great light on the constitution and manner of production of dephlogisticated air, I hope they may be not unworthy the acceptance of this society.

Many gentlemen have supposed that fixed air is either generated or separated from atmospheric air by phlogistication, and that the observed diminution is owing to this cause; my first experiments therefore were made in order to ascertain whether any fixed air is really produced thereby. Now, it must be observed, that as all animal and vegetable substances contain fixed air, and yield it by burning, distillation, or putrefaction, nothing can be concluded from experiments in which the air is phlogisticated by them. The only methods I know, which are not liable to objection, are by the calcination of metals, the burning of sulphur or phosphorus, the mixture of nitrous air, and the explosion of inflammable air. Perhaps it may be supposed, that I ought to add to these the electric spark; but I think it much most likely, that the phlogistication of the air, and production of fixed air, in this process, is owing to the burning of some inflammable matter in the apparatus. When the spark is taken from a solution of tournsol, the burning of the tournsol may produce this effect; when it is taken from lime-water, the burning of some foulness adhering to the tube, or perhaps of some inflammable matter contained in the lime, may have the same effect; and when quicksilver or metallic knobs are used, the calcination of them may contribute to the phlogistication of the air, though not to the production of fixed air.

There is no reason to think that any fixed air is produced by the first method of phlogistication. Dr Priestley never found lime-water to become turbid by the calcination of metals over it: Mr Lavoisier also found only a very slight and scarce perceptible turbid appearance, without any precipitation, to take place when lime-water was shaken in a glass vessel full of the air in which lead had been calcined; and even this small diminution of transparency in the lime-water might very likely arise, not from fixed air, but only from its being fouled by particles of the calcined metal, which we are told adhered in some places to the glass. This want of turbidity has been attributed to the fixed air uniting to the metallic calx, in preference to the lime; but there is no reason for supposing that the calx contained any fixed air; for I do not know that any one has extracted it from calces prepared in this manner; and though most metallic calces prepared over the fire, or by long exposure to the atmosphere, where they are in contact with fixed air, contain that substance, it by no means follows that they must do so when prepared by methods in which they are not in contact with it.

Dr Priestley also observed, that quicksilver, fouled by the addition of lead or tin, deposits a powder by agitation and exposure to the air, which consists in great measure of the calx of the imperfect metal. He found, too, some powder of this kind to contain fixed air; but it is by no means clear that this air was produced by the phlogistication of the air in which the quicksilver was shaken; as the powder was not prepared on purpose, but was procured from quicksilver fouled by having been used in various experiments, and may therefore have contained other impurities besides the metallic calces.

I never heard of any fixed air being produced by the burning of sulphur or phosphorus; but it has been asserted, and commonly believed, that lime-water is rendered cloudy by a mixture of common and nitrous air; which, if true, would be a convincing proof that on mixing those two substances some fixed air is either generated or separated; I therefore examined this carefully. Now it must be observed, that as common air usually contains a little fixed air, which is no essential part of it, but is easily separated by lime-water; and as nitrous air may also contain fixed air, either if the metal from which it is procured be rusty, or if the water of the vessel in which it is caught contain calcareous earth, suspended by fixed air, as most waters do, it is proper first to free both airs from it by previously washing them with lime-water.* Now I found, by repeated experiments, that if the lime-water was clean, and the two airs were previously washed with that substance, not the least cloud was produced, either immediately on mixing them, or on suffering them to stand upwards of an hour, though it appeared by the thick clouds which were produced in the lime-water, by breathing through it after the experiment was finished, that it was more than sufficient to saturate the acid formed by the decomposition of the nitrous air, and consequently that if any fixed air had been produced, it must have become visible. Once indeed I found a small cloud to be formed on the surface, after the mixture had stood a few minutes. In this experiment the lime-water was not quite clean; but whether the cloud was owing to this circumstance, or to the air's having not been properly washed, I cannot pretend to say.

Neither does any fixed air seem to be produced by the explosion of the inflammable air obtained from metals, with either common or dephlogisticated air. This I tried by put-

*Though fixed air is absorbed in considerable quantity by water, as I shewed in *Phil. Trans.*, vol. LVI. yet it is not easy to deprive common air of all the fixed air contained in it by means of water. On shaking a mixture of ten parts of common air, and one of fixed air, with more than an equal bulk of distilled water, not more than half of the fixed air was absorbed, and on transferring the air into fresh distilled water only half the remainder was absorbed, as appeared by the diminution which it still suffered on adding lime-water.

ting a little lime-water into a glass globe fitted with a brass cock, so as to make it air tight, and an apparatus for firing air by electricity. This globe was exhausted by an air-pump, and the two airs, which had been previously washed with lime-water, let in, and suffered to remain some time, to shew whether they would affect the lime-water, and then fired by electricity. The event was, that not the least cloud was produced in the lime-water, when the inflammable air was mixed with common air, and only a very slight one, or rather diminution of transparency, when it was combined with dephlogisticated air. This, however, seemed not to be produced by fixed air; as it appeared instantly after the explosion, and did not increase on standing, and was spread uniformly through the liquor; whereas if it had been owing to fixed air, it would have taken up some short time before it appeared, and would have begun first at the surface, as was the case in the above-mentioned experiment with nitrous air. What it was really owing to I cannot pretend to say; but if it did proceed from fixed air it would shew that only an excessively minute quantity was produced.* On the whole, though it is not improbable that fixed air may be generated in some chymical processes, yet it seems certain that it is not the general effect of phlogisticating air, and that the diminution of common air is by no means owing to the generation or separation of fixed air from it.

As there seemed great reason to think, from Dr Priestley's experiments, that the nitrous and vitriolic acids were convertible into dephlogisticated air, I tried whether the dephlogisticated part of common air might not, by phlogistication, be changed into nitrous or vitriolic acid. For this purpose I impregnated some milk of lime with the fumes of burning sulphur, by putting a little of it into a large glass receiver, and burning sulphur therein, taking care to keep the mouth of the receiver stopt till the fumes were all absorbed; after which the air of the receiver was changed, and more sulphur burnt in it as before, and the process

*Dr Priestley also found no fixed air to be produced by the explosion of inflammable and common air. Vol. V. p. 124.

repeated till 122 grains of sulphur were consumed. The milk of lime was then filtered and evaporated, but it yielded no nitrous salt, nor any other substance except selenite; so that no sensible quantity of the air was changed into nitrous acid. It must be observed, that as the vitriolic acid produced by the burning sulphur is changed by its union with the lime into selenite, which is very little soluble in water, a very small quantity of nitrous salt, or any other substance which is soluble in water, would have been perceived.

*

In Dr Priestley's last volume of experiments is related an experiment of Mr Warltire's, in which it is said that, on firing a mixture of common and inflammable air by electricity in a close copper vessel holding about three pints, a loss of weight was always perceived, on an average about two grains, though the vessel was stopped in such a manner that no air could escape by the explosion. It is also related, that on repeating the experiment in glass vessels, the inside of the glass, though clean and dry before, immediately became dewy; which confirmed an opinion he had long entertained, that common air deposits its moisture by phlogistication. As the latter experiment seemed likely to throw great light on the subject I had in view, I thought it well worth examining more closely. The first experiment also, if there was no mistake in it, would be very extraordinary and curious; but it did not succeed with me; for though the vessel I used held more than Mr Warltire's, namely, 24,000 grains of water, and though the experiment was repeated several times with different proportions of common and inflammable air, I could never perceive a loss of weight of more than one-fifth of a grain, and commonly none at all. It must be observed, however, that though there were some of the experiments in which it seemed to diminish a little in weight, there were none in which it increased. *

In all the experiments, the inside of the glass globe be-

*Dr Priestley, I am informed, has since found the experiment not to succeed.

came dewy, as observed by Mr Warltire; but not the least sooty matter could be perceived. Care was taken in all of them to find how much the air was diminished by the explosion, and to observe its test. The result is as follows: the bulk of the inflammable air being expressed in decimals of the common air,

Common air	Inflammable air	Diminution	Air remaining after the explosion	Test of this air in first method	Standard
1	1,241	,686	1,555	,055	,0
	1,055	,642	1,413	,063	,0
	,706	,647	1,059	,066	,0
	,423	,612	,811	,097	,03
	,331	,476	,855	,339	,27
	,206	,294	,912	,648	,58

In these experiments the inflammable air was procured from zinc, as it was in all my experiments, except where otherwise expressed: but I made two more experiments, to try whether there was any difference between the air from zinc and that from iron, the quantity of inflammable air being the same in both, namely, 0,331 of the common; but I could not find any difference to be depended on between the two kinds of air, either in the diminution which they suffered by the explosion, or the test of the burnt air.

From the fourth experiment it appears, that 423 measures of inflammable air are nearly sufficient to completely phlogisticate 1000 of common air; and that the bulk of the air remaining after the explosion is then very little more than four-fifths of the common air employed; so that as common air cannot be reduced to a much less bulk than that by any method of phlogistication, we may safely conclude, that when they are mixed in this proportion, and exploded, almost all the inflammable air, and about one-fifth part of the common air, lose their elasticity, and are condensed into the dew which lines the glass.

The better to examine the nature of this dew, 500,000

grain measures of inflammable air were burnt with about
two and a half times that quantity of common air, and the
burnt air made to pass through a glass cylinder eight feet
long and three-quarters of an inch in diameter, in order to
deposit the dew. The two airs were conveyed slowly into
this cylinder by separate copper pipes, passing through a
brass plate which stopped up the end of the cylinder; and
as neither inflammable nor common air can burn by themselves, there was no danger of the flame spreading into the
magazines from which they were conveyed. Each of these
magazines consisted of a large tin vessel, inverted into another vessel just big enough to receive it. The inner vessel
communicated with the copper pipe, and the air was forced
out of it by pouring water into the outer vessel; and in order
that the quantity of common air expelled should be two and
a half times that of the inflammable, the water was let into
the outer vessels by two holes in the bottom of the same tin
pan, the hole which conveyed the water into that vessel in
which the common air was confined being two and a half
times as big as the other.

In trying the experiment, the magazines being first filled
with their respective airs, the glass cylinder was taken off,
and water let, by the two holes, into the outer vessels, till
the airs began to issue from the ends of the copper pipes;
they were then set on fire by a candle, and the cylinder put
on again in its place. By this means upwards of 135 grains
of water were condensed in the cylinder, which had no
taste nor smell, and which left no sensible sediment when
evaporated to dryness; neither did it yield any pungent
smell during the evaporation; in short, it seemed pure water.

In my first experiment, the cylinder near that part where
the air was fired was a little tinged with sooty matter, but
very slightly so; and that little seemed to proceed from the
putty with which the apparatus was luted, and which was
heated by the flame; for in another experiment, in which it
was contrived so that the luting should not be much
heated, scarce any sooty tinge could be perceived.

By the experiments with the globe it appeared, that when

inflammable and common air are exploded in a proper proportion, almost all the inflammable air, and near one-fifth of the common air, lose their elasticity, and are condensed into dew. And by this experiment it appears, that this dew is plain water, and consequently that almost all the inflammable air, and about one-fifth of the common air, are turned into pure water.

In order to examine the nature of the matter condensed on firing a mixture of dephlogisticated and inflammable air, I took a glass globe, holding 8800 grain measures, furnished with a brass cock and an apparatus for firing air by electricity. This globe was well exhausted by an air-pump, and then filled with a mixture of inflammable and dephlogisticated air, by shutting the cock, fastening a bent glass tube to its mouth, and letting up the end of it into a glass jar inverted into water, and containing a mixture of 19500 grain measures of dephlogisticated air, and 37000 of inflammable; so that, upon opening the cock, some of this mixed air rushed through the bent tube, and filled the globe.* The cock was then shut, and the included air fired by electricity, by which means almost all of it lost its elasticity. The cock was then again opened, so as to let in more of the same air, to supply the place of that destroyed by the explosion, which was again fired, and the operation continued till almost the whole of the mixture was let into the globe and exploded. By this means, though the globe held not more than the sixth part of the mixture, almost the whole of it was exploded therein, without any fresh exhaustion of the globe.

As I was desirous to try the quantity and test of this burnt air, without letting any water into the globe, which would have prevented my examining the nature of the condensed matter, I took a larger globe, furnished also with a stop cock, exhausted it by an air-pump, and screwed it on upon the cock of the former globe; upon which, by opening both

*In order to prevent any water from getting into this tube, while dipped under water to let it up into the glass jar, a bit of wax was stuck upon the end of it, which was rubbed off when raised above the surface of the water.

cocks, the air rushed out of the smaller globe into the larger, till it became of equal density in both; then, by shutting the cock of the larger globe, unscrewing it again from the former, and opening it under water, I was enabled to find the quantity of the burnt air in it; and consequently, as the proportion which the contents of the two globes bore to each other was known, could tell the quantity of burnt air in the small globe before the communication was made between them. By this means the whole quantity of the burnt air was found to be 2950 grain measures; its standard was 1,85.

The liquor condensed in the globe, in weight about thirty grains, was sensibly acid to the taste, and by saturation with fixed alkali, and evaporation, yielded near two grains of nitre; so that it consisted of water united to a small quantity of nitrous acid. No sooty matter was deposited in the globe. The dephlogisticated air used in this experiment was procured from red precipitate, that is, from a solution of quicksilver in spirit of nitre distilled till it acquires a red colour.

ANTOINE LAURENT LAVOISIER
1743-94

OXYGEN AS THE KEY TO THE THEORY
OF COMBUSTION

LAVOISIER was the son of a wealthy Parisian, and was intended to study law. He became interested in science, however, won a government prize at the age of twenty and was elected to the Academy of Sciences at twenty-five. He was then appointed a member of the Fermes Générales, a group of aristocrats who paid the government a fixed sum for the privilege of collecting and retaining taxes. This provided an income which Lavoisier used for his scientific pursuits.

In 1772 his interest in Boyle's experiments led him to investigate combustion and calcination for himself. Combustion of sulphur and of phosphorus was accompanied by a gain in weight. In some experiments with closed vessels, combustion ceased when the air (or some part of it) was consumed. The container then showed no gain in weight; when it was opened to the atmosphere, however, air rushed in and a gain in weight was then recorded.

In 1774 Priestley visited Lavoisier in Paris and described his experiments on dephlogisticated air prepared from mercuric oxide. Lavoisier at once undertook the experiment described in the accompanying passage, showing that mercury burned in air to form red calx (mercuric oxide) leaving a residual gas which extinguished lighted candles and asphyxiated animals. Strong heating subsequently decomposed the calx and produced an 'air' which, mixed with the residual air from the first experiment, resumed the nature of the 'common air' with which he had started. On such experiments he based his theory of combustion as the combination of the burning substance with oxygen.

Lavoisier considerably assisted the subsequent use of his theory by initiating a reform in the language of chemistry, which he thought cumbersome, awkward, and inconsistent. He helped to draw up the first table of nomenclature for chemical substances, making it correspond with their chemical composition. Thus Cavendish's 'inflammable air' was renamed hydrogen, meaning water-former. He published a *Traité élémentaire de chimie,* which had a great influence on the development of modern chemistry. The extract below is from the English translation made by Robert Kerr in 1790.

Lavoisier had many interests outside his own experiments. As director of the government factories, he improved the manufacture of saltpetre and gunpowder, so helping the military development of France. He devised a system of streetlighting, assisted in drawing up the first geological maps of France, and by applying scientific methods, greatly increased the yields of farms on his own estates.

Mme Lavoisier became a partner in his scientific work, learning Latin and English in order to translate scientific works for his use. She made the plates and engravings for his books, one example of which is reproduced here. She was several years younger than Lavoisier, and eleven years after his death married the physicist Benjamin Thompson (Count Rumford).

Lavoisier's life was cut short by the French Revolution. He was summoned from a scientific experiment on respiration to appear before the Revolutionary Tribunal and was executed, a month after Priestley had left England for the United States. He suffered for his association with the aristocrats who had abused their positions, although he took a great deal of interest in social problems, especially education and prison reform. Appeals from his friends, based on his greatness as a scientist, were rejected by his judges. 'The Republic has no need of savants.' This view, which some are perpetually tempted to utter, did not prevent the spreading of Lavoisier's influence, though it could be claimed that for some time the savants flourished more noticeably in other countries than in France.

ANTOINE LAURENT LAVOISIER

¶ CHAPTER III *Analysis of Atmospheric Air, and its Division into two Elastic Fluids; the one fit for Respiration, the other* incapable *of being respired.*

From what has been premised, it appears, that our atmosphere is composed of a mixture of every substance capable of retaining the gasseous or aëriform state in the common temperature, and under the usual degrees of pressure which it experiences. These fluids constitute a mass, in some measure homogeneous, extending from the surface of the earth to the greatest height hitherto attained, of which the density continually decreases in the inverse ratio of the superincumbent weight. But, as I have before observed, it is possible that this first stratum may be surmounted by several others consisting of very different fluids.

Our business, in this place, is to endeavour to determine, by experiments, the nature of the elastic fluids which compose the inferior stratum of air which we inhabit. Modern chemistry has made great advances in this research, and it will appear by the following details that the analysis of atmospherical air has been more rigorously determined than that of any other substance of the class. Chemistry affords two general methods of determining the constituent principles of bodies, the method of analysis, and that of synthesis. When, for instance, by combining water with alcohol, we form the species of liquor called, in commercial language, brandy or spirit of wine, we certainly have a right to conclude, that brandy, or spirit of wine, is composed of alcohol combined with water. We can produce the same result by the analytical method; and in general it ought to be considered as a principle in chemical science, never to rest satisfied without both these species of proofs.

We have this advantage in the analysis of atmospherical air, being able both to decompound it, and to form it anew in the most satisfactory manner. I shall, however, at present confine myself to recount such experiments as are most conclusive upon this head; and I may consider most of these as my own, having either first invented them, or having repeated those of others, with the intention of analysing atmospherical air, in perfectly new points of view.

I took a matrass (*A*, fig. 14. plate II)* of about 36 cubical inches capacity, having a long neck *B C D E*, of six or seven lines internal diameter, and having bent the neck as in Plate IV,† Fig. 2 so as to allow of its being placed in the furnace *M M N N*, in such a manner that the extremity of its neck *E* might be inserted under a bell-glass *F G*, placed in a trough of quicksilver *R R S S*; I introduced four ounces of pure mercury into the matrass, and, by means of a syphon, exhausted the air in the receiver *F G*, so as to raise the quicksilver to *L L*, and I carefully marked the height at which it stood by pasting on a slip of paper. Having accurately noted the height of the thermometer and barometer, I lighted a fire in the furnace *M M N N*, which I kept up almost continually during twelve days, so as to keep the quicksilver always very near its boiling-point. Nothing remarkable took place during the first day: The mercury, though not boiling, was continually evaporating, and covered the interior surface of the vessel with small drops, which gradually augmenting to a sufficient size, fell back into the mass at the bottom of the vessel. On the second day, small red particles began to appear on the surface of the mercury, these, during the four or five following days, gradually increased in size and number; after which they ceased to increase in either respect. At the end of twelve days, seeing that the calcination of the mercury did not at all increase, I extinguished the fire, and allowed the vessels to cool. The bulk of air in the body and neck of the matrass, and in the bell-glass, reduced to a medium of 28 inches of the barometer and 54·5° of the thermometer, at the commencement of the experiment was about 50 cubical inches. At the end of the experiment the remaining air, reduced to the same medium pressure and temperature, was only between 42 and 43 cubical inches; consequently it had lost about ⅙ of its bulk. Afterwards, having collected all the red particles,

*Not reproduced.
†See Plate 8.

formed during the experiment, from the running mercury in which they floated, I found these to amount to 45 grains.

I was obliged to repeat this experiment several times, as it is difficult in one experiment both to preserve the whole air upon which we operate, and to collect the whole of the red particles, or calx of mercury, which is formed during the calcination. It will often happen in the sequel, that I shall, in this manner, give in one detail the results of two or three experiments of the same nature.

The air which remained after the calcination of the mercury in this experiment, and which was reduced to $\frac{5}{6}$ of its former bulk, was no longer fit either for respiration or for combustion; animals being introduced into it were suffocated in a few seconds, and when a taper was plunged into it, it was extinguished as if it had been immersed in water.

In the next place, I took the 45 grains of red matter formed during this experiment, which I put into a small glass retort, having a proper apparatus for receiving such liquid, or gasseous product, as might be extracted: Having applied a fire to the retort in a furnace, I observed that, in proportion as the red matter became heated, the intensity of its colour augmented. When the retort was almost red hot, the red matter began gradually to decrease in bulk, and in a few minutes after it disappeared altogether; at the same time $41\frac{1}{2}$ grains of running mercury were collected in the recipient, and 7 or 8 cubical inches of elastic fluid, greatly more capable of supporting both respiration and combustion than atmospherical air, were collected in the bell-glass.

A part of this air being put into a glass tube of about an inch diameter, showed the following properties: A taper burned in it with a dazzling splendour, and charcoal, instead of consuming quietly as it does in common air, burnt with a flame, attended with a decrepitating noise, like phosphorus, and threw out such a brilliant light that the eyes could hardly endure it. This species of air was discovered almost at the same time by Dr Priestley, Mr Scheele, and myself. Dr Priestley gave it the name of *dephlogisticated air*, Mr Scheele called it *empyreal air*. At first I named it *highly respirable air*, to which has since been substituted the term of *vital air*. We shall presently see what we ought to think of these denominations.

In reflecting upon the circumstances of this experiment, we readily perceive; that the mercury, during its calcination, absorbs the salubrious and respirable part of the air, or, to speak more strictly, the base of this respirable part; that the remaining air is a species of mephitis, incapable of supporting combustion or respiration; and consequently that atmospheric air is composed of two elastic fluids of different and opposite qualities. As a proof of this important truth, if we recombine these two elastic fluids, which we have separately obtained in the above experiment, viz., the 42 cubical inches of mephitis, with the 8 cubical inches of highly respirable air, we reproduce an air precisely similar to that of the atmosphere, and possessing nearly the same power of supporting combustion and respiration, and of contributing to the calcination of metals.

Although this experiment furnishes us with a very simple means of obtaining the two principal elastic fluids which compose our atmosphere, separate from each other, yet it does not give us an exact idea of the proportion in which these two enter into its composition: For the attraction of mercury to the respirable part of the air, or rather to its base, is not sufficiently strong to overcome all the circumstances which oppose this union. These obstacles are the mutual adhesion of the two constituent parts of the atmosphere for each other, and the elective attraction which unites the base of vital air with caloric; in consequence of these, when the calcination ends, or is at least carried as far as is possible, in a determinate quantity of atmospheric air, there still remains a portion of respirable air united to the mephitis, which the mercury cannot separate. I shall afterwards show, that at least in our climate, the atmospheric air is composed of respirable and mephitic airs, in the proportion of 27 and 73; and I shall then discuss the causes of the uncertainty which still exists with respect to the exactness of that proportion.

Since, during the calcination of mercury, air is decomposed, and the base of its respirable part is fixed and combined with the mercury, it follows, from the principles already established, that caloric and light must be disengaged during the process. But the two following causes prevent us from being sensible of this taking place; as the calcination lasts during several days, the disengagement of caloric and light, spread out in a considerable space of time, becomes extremely small for each particular moment of the time, so as not to be perceptible; and, the operation being carried on by means of fire in a furnace, the heat produced by the calcination itself becomes confounded with that proceeding from the furnace. I might add that, the respirable part of the air, or rather its base, in entering into combination with the mercury, does not part with all the caloric which it contained, but still retains a part of it in the new compound; but the discussion of this point, and its proofs from experiment, do not belong to this part of our subject.

It is, however, easy to render this disengagement of caloric and light evident to the senses, by causing the decomposition of air to take place in a more rapid manner. And for this purpose, iron is excellently adapted, as it possesses a much stronger affinity for the base of respirable air than mercury. The following elegant experiment of Mr Ingenhouz, upon the combustion of iron, is well known. Take a piece of fine iron wire, twisted into a spiral, (*BC*, Plate IV, Fig. 17) fix one of its extremities *B* into the cork *A*, adapted to the neck of the bottle *DEFG*, and fix to the other extremity of the wire *C*, a small morsel of tinder. Matters being thus prepared, fill the bottle *DEFG* with air deprived of its mephitic part; then light the tinder, and introduce it quickly with the wire upon which it is fixed, into the bottle which you stop up with the cork *A*, as is shown in the figure (17 Plate IV). The instant the tinder comes into contact with the vital air it begins to burn with great intensity; and, communicating the inflammation to the iron wire, it likewise takes fire, and burns rapidly, throwing out brilliant sparks; these fall to the bottom of the vessel in rounded globules, which become black in cooling, but retain a degree of metallic splendour. The iron thus burnt is more brittle even than glass, and is easily reduced into powder, and is still attractable by the magnet, though not so powerfully as it was before combustion. As Mr Ingenhouz has neither examined the change produced on the iron, nor upon the air by this operation, I have repeated the experiment under different circumstances, in an apparatus adapted to answer my particular views, as follows.

Having filled a bell-glass (A, Plate IV, Fig. 3) of about six pints measure, with pure air, or the highly respirable part of air, I transported this jar by means of a very flat vessel, into a quicksilver bath in the bason, BC, taking care to render the surface of the mercury perfectly dry both within and without the jar with blotting paper. I then provided a small cup of china-ware D, very flat and open, in which I placed some small pieces of iron, turned spirally, and arranged in such a way as seemed most favourable for the combustion being communicated to every part. To the end of one of these pieces of iron was fixed a small morsel of tinder, to which was added about the sixteenth part of a grain of phosphorus, and, by raising the bell-glass a little, the china cup, with its contents, were introduced into the pure air. I know that, by this means some common air must mix with the pure air in the glass; but this, when it is done dexterously, is so very trifling, as not to injure the success of the experiment. This being done, a part of the air is sucked out from the bell-glass, by means of a syphon GHI, so as to raise the mercury within the glass to EF; and, to prevent the mercury from getting into the syphon, a small piece of paper is twisted round its extremity. In sucking out the air, if the motion of the lungs only be used, we cannot make the mercury rise above an inch or an inch and a half; but, by properly using the muscles of the mouth, we can, without difficulty, cause it to rise six or seven inches.

I next took an iron wire, properly bent for the purpose, and making it red hot in the fire, passed it through the mercury into the receiver, and brought it in contact with the small piece of phosphorus attached to the tinder. The phosphorus instantly took fire, which communicated to the tinder, and from that to the iron. When the pieces have been properly arranged, the whole iron burns, even to the last particle, throwing out a white brilliant light similar to that of Chinese fireworks. The great heat produced by this combustion melts the iron into round globules of different sizes, most of which fall into the China cup; but some are thrown out of it, and swim upon the surface of the mercury. At the beginning of the combustion, there is a slight augmentation in the volume of the air in the bell-glass, from the dilatation caused by the heat; but, presently afterwards, a rapid diminution of the air takes place, and the mercury rises in the glass, insomuch that, when the quantity of iron is sufficient, and the air operated upon is very pure, almost the whole air employed is absorbed.

It is proper to remark in this place, that, unless in making experiments for the purpose of discovery, it is better to be contented with burning a moderate quantity of iron; for, when this experiment is pushed too far, so as to absorb much of the air, the cup D, which floats upon the quicksilver, approaches too near the bottom of the bell-glass; and the great heat produced, which is followed by a very sudden cooling, occasioned by the contact of the cold mercury, is apt to break the glass. In which case, the sudden fall of the column of mercury, which happens the moment the least flaw is produced in the glass, causes such a wave, as throws a great part of the quicksilver from the bason. To avoid this inconvenience, and to ensure success to the experiment, one dram and a half of iron is sufficient to burn in a bell-glass, which holds about eight pints of air. The glass ought likewise to be strong, that it may be able to bear the weight of the column of mercury which it has to support.

By this experiment, it is not possible to determine, at one time, both the additional weight acquired by the iron, and the changes which have taken place in the air. If it is wished to ascertain what additional weight has been gained by the iron, and the proportion between that and the air absorbed, we must carefully mark upon the bell-glass, with a diamond, the height of the mercury, both before and after the experiment.* After this, the syphon (*GH*, Pl. IV, fig. 3) guarded, as before, with a bit of paper, to prevent its filling with mercury, is to be introduced under the bell-glass, having the thumb placed upon the extremity, *G*, of the syphon, to regulate the passage of the air; and by this means the air is gradually admitted, so as to let the mercury fall to its level. This being done, the bell-glass is to be carefully removed, the globules of melted iron contained in the cup, and those which have been scattered about, and swim upon the mercury, are to be accurately collected, and the whole is to be weighed. The iron will be found in that state called *martial ethiops* by the old chemists, possessing a degree of metallic brilliancy, very friable, and readily reducible into powder, under the hammer, or with a pestle and mortar. If the experiment has succeeded well, from 100 grains of iron will be obtained 135 or 136 grains of ethiops, which is an augmentation of 35 per cent.

If all the attention has been paid to this experiment which it deserves, the air will be found diminished in weight exactly equal to what the iron has gained. Having therefore burnt 100 grains of iron, which has acquired an additional weight of 35 grains, the diminution of air will be found exactly 70 cubical inches; and it will be shewn, in the sequel, that the weight of vital air is pretty nearly half a grain for each cubical inch; so that, in effect, the augmentation of weight in the one exactly coincides with the loss of it in the other.

I shall observe here, once for all, that, in every experiment of this kind, the pressure and temperature of the air, both before and after the experiment, must be reduced, by calculation, to a common standard of 54·5° of the thermometer, and 28 inches of the barometer....

If it be required to examine the nature of the air which

*It will likewise be necessary to take care that the air contained in the glass, both before and after the experiment, be reduced to a common temperature and pressure, otherwise the results of the following calculations will be fallacious. [Trans. note.]

remains after this experiment, we must operate in a somewhat different manner. After the combustion is finished, and the vessels have cooled, we first take out the cup, and the burnt iron, by introducing the hand through the quicksilver, under the bell-glass; we next introduce some solution of potash, or caustic alkali, or of the sulphuret of potash, or such other substances as are judged proper for examining their action upon the residuum of air. I shall, in the sequel, give an account of these methods of analysing air, when I have explained the nature of these different substances, which are only here in a manner incidentally mentioned. After this examination, so much water must be let into the glass as will displace the quicksilver, and then, by means of a shallow dish placed below the bell-glass, it is to be removed into the common water pneumato-chemical apparatus, where the air remaining may be examined at large, and with great facility.

When very soft and very pure iron has been employed in this experiment, and, when the combustion has been performed in the purest respirable or vital air, free from all admixture of the noxious or mephitic part, the air which remains after the combustion will be found as pure as it was before; but it is difficult to find iron entirely free from a small portion of charry matter, which is chiefly abundant in steel. It is likewise exceedingly difficult to procure pure air perfectly free from some admixture of mephitis, with which it is almost always contaminated: that species of noxious air does not, in the smallest degree, disturb the result of the experiment, as it is always found at the end exactly in the same quantity as at the beginning.

I mentioned before, that we have two ways of determining the constituent parts of atmospheric air, the method of analysis, and that by synthesis. The calcination of mercury has furnished us with an example of each of these methods, since, after having deprived it of the respirable part, by means of the mercury, we have restored it again, so as to recompose an air precisely similar to that of the atmosphere. But we can equally accomplish this synthetic composition of atmospheric air, by borrowing the materials of which it is formed from different kingdoms of nature. We shall see hereafter that, when animal substances are dissolved in the nitric acid, a great quantity of gas is disengaged, which extinguishes light, and is unfit for animal respiration, being exactly similar to the noxious or mephitic part of atmospheric air. And, if we take 73 parts, by weight, of this elastic fluid, and mix it with 27 parts of highly respirable air, procured from calcined mercury, we shall form an elastic fluid precisely similar to atmospheric air in all its properties.

There are many other methods of separating the respirable from the noxious part of the atmospheric air, which cannot be taken notice of in this place, without anticipating information, which properly belongs to the subsequent chapters. The experiments already adduced may suffice for an elementary treatise; and, in matters of this nature, the choice of our evidences is of far greater consequence than their number.

I shall close this article, by pointing out the property possessed by atmospheric air, and all the known gasses, of dissolving water; which circumstance it is of great consequence to attend to in all experiments of this nature. Mr Saussure found, by experiment, that a cubical foot of atmospheric air is capable of holding 12 grains of water in solution. Other gasses, as the carbonic acid, appear capable of dissolving a greater quantity; but experiments are still wanting by which to determine their several proportions. This water, held in solution by gasses, gives rise to particular phenomena, which require great attention in many experiments, and which has frequently proved the source of great errors to chemists in determining the results of their experiments.

INDEX

INDEX

*A selection of Pelican Books
is described on the
following pages*

THE SCIENCE OF ANIMAL BEHAVIOUR

P. L. Broadhurst

For generations men have employed dogs and hawks to hunt, cormorants to fish, and performing animals for entertainment. Modern research, on scientific lines, may greatly widen the use of animals in human society. In this brief and fascinating study the director of the animal psychology laboratory at London University's Institute of Psychiatry recounts how, with the use of test apparatus, monkeys can learn to work for wages paid in token coins; how white rats can be trained to thread their way through a maze or taught specific drills in such devices as the 'shuttle box'. He describes, too, the scientific observations which have been made on the behaviour in the wild of, for instance, penguins and crabs, and the questions that these raise.

Such experimentation and observation, under approved conditions, can be shown to advance the treatment of human mental disorders and to help in the study of such difficult problems as pre-natal influences. The study of animal behaviour may also, as the author suggests, lead to such extraordinary developments as the training of chimpanzees as engine-drivers or the employment of pigeons as production-line inspectors.

This authoritative book explains very clearly the meaning and purpose of modern research into animal behaviour.

SCIENCE AND HUMAN VALUES

J. Bronowski

Dr Bronowski, as all those who have watched his stimulating programmes on television will have noticed, is equally at home in the world of science and of the arts. In these essays he describes the essence of the creative process – that leap of the imagination which distinguishes the mathematician as much as the poet – and develops an ethic for science, which he describes as a human progress and no mere mechanism. Among the propositions he puts forward are that the concept is more profound than its laws and the act of judging more critical than the judgement.

'A remarkable book, and the affirmation of a remarkable man. If I were trying to select six works, in order to explain to an intelligent non-scientist something of the deepest meaning of science, Bronowski's would be one of them. ... Bronowski has built a structure of values, built them with what he himself has called the ethical enthusiasm of his rabbinical ancestors, but also with poetic feeling and a passionate identification with the human future' – Sir Charles Snow in the *New Statesman*

EXPERIMENTAL PSYCHICAL RESEARCH

Robert H. Thouless

'To examine without prejudice or prepossession and in a scientific spirit those faculties of man, real or supposed, which appear to be inexplicable on any generally recognized hypothesis.'

So runs an official description of the object of the Society for Psychical Research, and it is with the same object in view that Dr R. H. Thouless takes the reader over the experimental research in parapsychology.

Dr Thouless examines meticulously the aims, methods, and results of a wide range of fascinating work: the classic experiments in reproducing drawings, guessing cards, and throwing dice are rigorously analysed, and research work on gifted stage performers is looked at with a fresh, critical eye. Dr Thouless also has much to say on method. He examines the control of possible fraud in both subject and experimenter and, in answering the crucial question 'Can the apparent successes be explained by chance?' leads the reader to a balanced judgement on the significance of laboratory results. A final chapter suggests some useful lines for future research.

Here is a classic account of the main evidence for 'those faculties of man, real or supposed, which appear to be inexplicable'.

THE FABRIC OF THE HEAVENS

Stephen Toulmin and June Goodfield

Stars, planets, meteors, thunderbolts, earthquakes, hailstorms, and plagues of locusts – all these phenomena which we so carefully distinguish and classify must have seemed to primitive man to be tokens of a largely hostile Nature. Why should he have thought otherwise? For between him and us lie millennia of accumulating knowledge.

Spanning these millennia – and spanning too the notorious gulf between science and the humanities – Stephen Toulmin and June Goodfield show how soothsayers, philosophers, and mathematicians have all contributed to man's evolving view of the universe. They trace the crucial stages of 2,500 years of arguments and experiments which led from the theories of the early Babylonian astronomers by way of Pythagoras and Aristotle, Galileo, and Newton, to the modern view of the solar system.

'A dashing and brilliant book. . . . The authors have the splendid gift of communicating intellectual excitement. If this doesn't rub off on to a reader, he must be as nearly intellectually dead as doesn't matter' – Sir Charles Snow in the *Observer*

THE WESTERN INTELLECTUAL TRADITION

J. Bronowski and Bruce Mazlish

'The steam engine helped to shape the modern world at least as much as Napoleon and Adam Smith' – Sir Charles Snow
In this study of the development of ideas from the Renaissance to the opening of the nineteenth century Dr Bronowski, who is as well known as Sir Charles Snow as an integrator of science and the humanities, has collaborated with a distinguished American historian and philosopher. They have tried to see all history, and certainly all intellectual history, as a unity, with religion influencing government, science affecting religion, technology shaping society, philosophy changing the arts, and each playing on all the others in a complex and evolving pattern in which the mind of man has been supreme. This volume realizes their aim with impressive thoroughness and success, and it is notable for its excellent accounts of the lives and thoughts of the most influential European minds – from Leonardo to Galileo, from Cromwell to Rousseau, and from Adam Smith to Hegel.

'A splendid book ... Their method is that of the intellectual biography ... the emphasis is on inter-relationship, especially that of science and the humanities' – *Guardian*

'Written with clarity, modesty, and force, all rare qualities in such literature' – *Sunday Times*

'A history of ideas with a rare comprehensiveness' – *Observer*

CAREERS IN TECHNOLOGY

Maurice Goldsmith

The flesh and bones of life in a modern society demand more and more scientists, mathematicians, engineers, and technologists. Of these Britain is renownedly short, and the plan to double our output of qualified men in ten years is not going to be easy to complete.

Here is a book to engage the interest of young men and women in scientific and technological careers. In it the director of Science Information Service presents these careers in an attractive and original way by linking them with current technological developments. Detailing the kind of work done in various fields he explains what educational standards, qualifications, and training are required of entrants.

In a practical 'handbook' section the author gives a full list (with their addresses) for the whole United Kingdom of the universities, colleges, training establishments, professional associations, official bodies, and companies which operate training schemes. He also provides information about grants and awards, together with a list of books, pamphlets, and films which can serve the would-be technologist.

For a complete list of books available please write to Penguin Books whose address can be found on the back of the title page